MODERN LANGUAGES
IN THE UNIVERSITIES

MODERN LANGUAGES

IN THE UNIVERSITIES

A Guide to Courses of Study
in Five European Languages
at Universities in the
United Kingdom

EDITED BY H. H. STERN, M.A., PH.D.

LONDON
MACMILLAN & CO LTD
NEW YORK · ST MARTIN'S PRESS
1965

First Edition 1961 (published by The Modern Language Association)
Second Edition 1965
This Edition is based on information received in 1963 and 1964

MACMILLAN AND COMPANY LIMITED
St Martin's Street London WC 2
also Bombay Calcutta Madras Melbourne

THE MACMILLAN COMPANY OF CANADA LIMITED
70 Bond Street Toronto 2

ST MARTIN'S PRESS INC
175 Fifth Avenue New York 10010 NY

PREFACE TO THE FIRST EDITION

Education in Great Britain is characterized by the large measure of freedom enjoyed by the Principals and Heads of Department of its schools, colleges and universities, and by the liberty of the individual pupil or student to choose which centre of advanced learning he would like to attend. It is obvious, therefore, that the more fully informed a student can be about the nature of the courses offered by a particular institution, the better will he be able to make his choice in accordance with his own aptitudes and interests.

This became abundantly apparent at a conference of the Modern Language Association held at New College, Oxford, in January 1960, when the main subject of discussion was what the universities look for in the potential student of modern languages. It was eventually resolved that the Association should invite, from Heads of all univer-- sity departments of French, German, Spanish, Italian and Russian, a personal description of the various courses they offer. Their response to this invitation has provided by far the major part of the content of this book. The Association gratefully acknowledges their invaluable help and co-operation.

The object of this book is to help sixth-formers who are interested in modern language studies at universities in the choice of university courses. It is hoped that it will also be of use to careers advisers and finally, that teachers of modern languages in schools, colleges and universities may find some food for thought in these descriptions of modern language studies in British universities.

We believe that it is the first time a book of this kind has been published. If it is found to be of value, we shall hope, from time to time, to publish revised editions. In that event, all the contributors will have had an opportunity to see the book as a whole, which should enable us to reach a greater measure of similarity in the method of presentation of the various courses. In the meantime, we would warn the reader that the absence of reference to a particular feature in any one course does not necessarily mean that it is not to be found there; some departments may have mentioned activities which others have taken for granted. In any event, the Modern Language Association will welcome constructive criticism of this publication.

The book is a *guide* and an *introduction*. It does not pretend to replace any official university prospectuses or regulations, which the potential student must not fail to study and observe in making application for admission or in taking any other decision affecting his university studies.

The first part (pp. 3-13) is addressed to the future student but we hope that teachers will read it too. It contains advice, especially on combinations of subjects, which the sixth-former may feel he has met too late. He will be grateful to discover that his teachers have

v

taken these matters into account in advising him at an earlier stage of his career.

Nor is our aim to be of service merely to the future specialist in modern languages. These studies may form a part of a degree course in other subjects. Information on this point has been included.

The work of compiling and editing the book has been in the hands of a small committee consisting of the officers of the Modern Language Association and three of its members. Miss W. A. Matthews, of Fylde Lodge High School, Stockport, was Chairman of the Association at the time when the project was first undertaken, and other members of the committee have been: Dr. Constance Davies, of the Department of Education, University College of North Wales, Bangor; Mr. D. Grey of the West Leeds High School; and Dr. H. H. Stern, of the Education Department of the University of Hull. Whilst the whole committee has been consulted and has collaborated at every stage in the preparation of the book, by far the greater part of the work has been undertaken by Dr. Stern. The Association gratefully acknowledges the care, thought, time and energy that he has devoted to the task.

N. G. OSBORNE
Chairman, 1960–61
W. L. PRESSWOOD
Honorary Secretary

PREFACE TO THE SECOND EDITION

The publication of a second edition of this book only four years after the appearance of the first is primarily an indication of the rapid changes and developments currently taking place in British universities. This trend will no doubt continue, and it may well be that within a similar interval of time a third edition may be necessary.

But both the Council of the Modern Language Association and many Heads of Language Departments in the universities have considered it desirable to offer a new and complete edition now, rather than wait for further changes. This decision is based on the fact that the first edition clearly met a very definite need. Not only was it found useful by applicants for university entrance; the universities themselves have appreciated having candidates attending for interview who were informed in advance about the courses they hoped to follow. Fluid, therefore, as the situation still is, we have decided to make available information which is as complete and up to date as possible.

Like the first, this second edition has been prepared by Dr. H. H. Stern; and although, with him, we gratefully acknowledge the help given both by the universities and by members and staff of the M.L.A., it is to Dr. Stern that our thanks are mainly due and very gladly given.

K. S. WHITTON
Chairman, 1963–64
W. L. PRESSWOOD
Honorary Secretary

CONTENTS

PLAN OF THE GUIDE

This guide gives details of university courses in five major modern languages: French, German, Spanish, Russian and Italian.[1] The universities offering courses in these languages are listed in alphabetical order and (following the arrangement of universities in the *Commonwealth Universities Yearbook*[2]) English universities are listed first, the university colleges in the University of Wales second, Scottish universities third, and lastly the Queen's University, Belfast, Northern Ireland. Since language studies in certain universities do not quite fit into the plan of this book, their general schemes of study with modern languages are set out in the last chapter. This applies to Cambridge, East Anglia, Essex, Oxford, Sussex and York.

The information on each language department is classified under two main heads: I. *Courses of Study*, and II. *Admission to Courses*. It is further subdivided as follows:

I. COURSES OF STUDY

1. TYPES OF COURSES

The principal courses in which a modern language can be studied in the department are named and briefly described.

2. CHARACTERISTICS OF COURSES

Any marked features of the courses provided which have not already been described under 1 will be indicated in this section.

3. COMBINATION OF COURSES

This section is intended to help the future student to consider other subjects with which he can combine the study in the department.

4. RESIDENCE ABROAD

This section describes the current policy of the department concerning residence abroad.

5. METHODS OF STUDY

In this section information will be found on distinctive teaching methods to which the department attributes importance.

6. OTHER ACTIVITIES

This section gives information on modern language societies, play productions and similar additional activities.

[1] For a list of other languages that can be studied in British universities see Appendix, p. 357.
[2] Published annually by the Association of Universities of the British Commonwealth, 36 Gordon Square, London, W.C.1.

II. ADMISSION TO COURSES

1. QUALIFICATIONS REQUIRED

This section gives information on the requirements for entrance to the faculty or departments in operation at present. It includes, in particular, requirements in Latin and qualifications looked for above the general requirement ('matriculation'). If a study of a language can be started at the university (normally Italian or Russian, sometimes Spanish, but usually not German or French) this will also be indicated in this section.

2. SELECTION OF STUDENTS

The selection procedure of the department for applicants satisfying the rules under 1 is described in this section. It will also give candidates some idea of the qualities modern language departments look for in their choice of students.

3. TRANSFER

It is sometimes difficult for a future student to decide whether he should apply for a Special or General degree course of studies. It is, therefore, of some importance for him to know at what point in his career this decision has to be taken. Some universities distinguish between Special and General degree students from the beginning; others do so only after the completion of an initial course. Transfer from General to Special courses or vice versa is sometimes hard and sometimes easy. Information on these questions can be found in this section.

4. NUMBERS

University departments of languages have usually no fixed number of entrants year by year. But it is possible to indicate approximately the annual intake. The number of entrants will give an idea of the size of a department, a factor which may influence one's preference.

SOME HINTS
FOR FUTURE STUDENTS OF
MODERN LANGUAGES

WHO SHOULD STUDY MODERN LANGUAGES AT A UNIVERSITY?

To begin with, you should search your heart and ask yourself very seriously whether language studies at a university are really right for you. A flair for languages is a valuable asset but by itself it is not enough. A glance at the *Courses of Study* in the subsequent pages will show that the programme for practically any language at any of the universities—up to whatever level it will be taken—will demand some or all of the following:

(1) a thorough study of the modern language, including translation from and into English, essays, oral practice and phonetics;

(2) a study of the evolution of the language from its early beginnings to the present day, combined with the reading of texts illustrating some earlier phases of development;

(3) an intensive and critical study of literary texts, and wide reading of the literature of the language in question, covering all periods of its history;

(4) some acquaintance with the history and institutions of the country, and also with its art and music;

(5) willingness on your part to spend some time—ranging from one month to a full year—in the country concerned.

As will be explained below (see p. 5), university language courses vary in length from one to four years, and in the intensity and range of the demands they make upon language students, but the majority can be described as *academic courses of study in language and literature.* An interest in language *and* literature is, therefore, almost essential. One may, perhaps, regret that there are few opportunities for a study of languages which allow for other combinations of interests, but it is as well to know that by and large modern language studies are based on the conviction—and with good reason—that a study of a language should be coupled with a study of its literary masterpieces.[1] If you look carefully at the parts of the handbook entitled *Courses of Study*, you will discern certain differences in bias from one university to another, or from department to department. Some tend to be traditionalist, others strike out in new directions; some lay more stress on language, others on literature; some place great emphasis on historical

---

[1] It should be noted that in a number of universities today there are some language courses which can be combined with studies in history, politics, area studies, government, drama or philosophy. See on this point also p. 8 below, where suggestions are offered as to how languages can be combined with non-linguistic or non-literary studies.

developments, others on the modern period in language and literature. There are departments with a bias towards 'life, thought and institutions', towards the arts or towards 'general linguistics'. But even if we make allowance for these distinctions, the fact remains that the studies consist mainly of language and literature and you should not lightly enter upon such a course unless you are convinced that you can work with reasonable satisfaction in both these fields.

University teachers often complain that too many of their students lack an interest in and understanding for literature and therefore fail to benefit from what they consider to be educationally the most valuable aspect of the course. The person who takes little interest in the literature of his own country is not likely to approach with the right kind of interest and background the literature of other nations. Departments, therefore, particularly like those students who have shown *interest in English literature*; and we would suggest to you that, if you want to take up languages at a university, you do not neglect your English. Remember also that a linguist is almost invariably for a time a teacher of English abroad. But it is not only for this utilitarian reason that we suggest continued English studies; the wider a student's acquaintance with English life, language and letters, the more fruitful will be his foreign language studies.

Another subject which can be of considerable value in the study of a modern language and its literature is *Latin*, and it is for this reason that many university departments like undergraduates to come up with a knowledge of Latin, particularly if the student intends to read French, Spanish or Italian. There is no doubt that a student who has Latin to 'O' or, preferably, 'A' Level, has a far wider choice of departments to which he can apply than one who has no Latin. Nevertheless, schools, in advising their pupils, often tend to assume too readily that the classical (Latin or Greek) requirement is universal for modern linguists. This is by no means so. A careful reading of Sections II.1 and II.2, which deal with qualifications for admission and selection of students, will show that it is possible to find a considerable number of departments in which less importance is attributed to Latin, or even those which have no Latin rule of admission at all.

All university studies are more or less specialized. They demand concentrated attention for a long time: for one, two, three or even four years, you will be working in a comparatively restricted field of study and activity. In the case of modern languages it means that you must be prepared to devote yourself for months or years to one or two languages, to one or two countries, their literature and culture. Although superficially this seems narrow, there is there a wealth of knowledge, experience and interest to fill a lifetime of study. When university or college tutors choose their language students, they like to know whether the applicant has the stamina for this whole-hearted attention and concentration that is needed, and at the same time, whether he or she has at least an inkling of the range of possibilities that these studies open up. You should, therefore, ask yourself two questions: (*a*) is your interest in languages sustained enough and (*b*) which aspects of the work that you have done so far attract you particularly? Obviously you cannot be expected to give a final and clear-cut answer to such questions. But there are certain indications. Your success and interest in sixth-form studies can serve as an obvious guide. But beyond that there are other clues. The pupil who, at least once in his life, has already taken the plunge and has lived in a foreign country for a time, e.g. youth hostelling, at a holiday course, or on an exchange visit, has a more realistic knowledge of that country than one who has never ventured abroad. On the other hand, the boy or girl who has never troubled to make contact with the country itself or to find out about its politics, life and thought has not—perhaps not yet—grasped what language studies really involve. If you would like to know more about the qualities modern language departments look for in their future students glance at some of the entries under II.2 and see also page 12.

WHICH KIND OF COURSE SHOULD YOU CHOOSE?

Many young people faced with the problem we have just discussed fail to realize that the answer required is not one demanding a choice between strict alternatives, either 'Yes, I am going to be a linguist', or 'No, I am not'. It is important for you to understand that most university subjects, including modern languages, can be taken to various levels. The first thing, then, for you to decide is whether you want a language or languages to play a part in your university studies at all. Having come to the conclusion that they should, you can then go on and ask yourself whether you want them to play a major or minor part in the work you are proposing to do at university in the coming three or four years. Of course, the decision on this question does not depend entirely on you. For example, you may opt for a Special degree course in French at the University of X, you may even be offered a place in this course, but your tutors may come to the conclusion that your work is not of the right calibre for it and suggest to you that you should take a less specialized course of studies. Although, then, the final decision is not entirely yours, you ought to be clear in your own mind what you would like to do, assuming that you qualify. This guide is intended to help you to make your choice intelligently. Often sixth-formers—in ignorance of the large number of varied possibilities that are open to them—timidly follow in what seem to them the safe-footsteps of others from their school, choose the same university and the same combination of subjects, or are obsessed with questions of the prestige of this or that university, instead of weighing up various possibilities and trying to find the university, the course of study and combination of subjects which are most suitable for *themselves*. In trying to make up your mind you are bound to need the help and advice of persons who have had experience of university studies in languages, especially your sixth-form teachers.

If we now take a brief glance at the various types of courses available (they are listed in the *Guide* under I.1 and further described under I.2) you will soon see that the degree structure and the types of courses offered vary from one university to another. Not only are degree courses given different names, but there are often marked differences in the way the studies are organized. Broadly speaking, however, languages can be studied at a university in five types of courses, though all are not necessarily offered at every university.

(*a*) The *Honours* or *Special degree* is a three- or four-year course in a single subject. Sometimes (usually in English universities) the specialization is there from the beginning of the course, mitigated somewhat by certain additional ('subsidiary', 'supplementary', 'ancillary' and 'accessory') subjects; in other universities (e.g. in Wales or Scotland and in some English universities) the work for the Honours degree begins only after a common broader course lasting one or two years has been successfully completed.

Honours or Special degree courses[1] attempt a study in depth of one language as the student's principal subject. The concentration of purpose that the one-language degree course demands is usually greatly valued by university teachers, because in these courses they can work without reservation to the highest standards of undergraduate studies. They try to attract their best students to the Honours or Special School. To be admitted to it and to retain one's place in it is in itself an achievement. The single-subject Honours degree, therefore, often commands high prestige inside and outside the university. Yet it would be unwise for a future student to go in for this degree if the thought of spending all his time on *one* language is distasteful.

Since the work of the Honours course is so specialized the future Honours student must choose his subsidiary subjects wisely. Usually a wide range of these is open to him; Section I.3 *Combination of Subjects* should help him in his choice. Moreover, in the course of his studies he must come to a decision on any options that may be open to him within the Honours course. This second decision may as yet be far off. Still, it is not unimportant for you to know that there is frequently in the final year, or the final two years, the possibility of choosing some limited field of interest for deeper study. Often the work that is nearest to a student's heart will be done then. Details are indicated under the descriptions of courses (I.1 and I.2).

You should also keep in mind that the one-language Special degree student frequently spends a year abroad, so that his course is likely to last altogether four years. (See Section I.4 on *Residence Abroad*.) Many students go abroad for one year as English assistants to a foreign school or training college. These visits are arranged, on behalf of the Department of Education and Science, by the Central Bureau of Educational Visits and Exchanges, 55a Duke Street,

[1] They are usually described under such names as 'B.A. Special Degree in French', 'B.A. Honours Degree in German Studies', or 'B.A. Honours in Italian'. They are also referred to as 'Single Honours' or 'one-language' degrees.

Grosvenor Square, London, W.1. Throughout the book this scheme will be referred to as *the official scheme.*

(*b*) Instead of taking a one-language Honours degree a student may—in an increasing number of universities—work for a two-subject *Combined, Joint, Double* or *Dual Honours* course.[1] In some universities the Joint degree implies a distinction between a first subject which is taken to a more advanced level and a second subject; in others both subjects are considered equal. In any case the standard usually demanded in these two-subject degrees is very high indeed, and it can only be achieved by a slight reduction in content as compared to the single-language Honours degree and a drastic reduction in, or complete exclusion of, additional or subsidiary subjects. In some universities the two-subject degree course takes four instead of three years. Some students find it frustrating to study more than one subject intensively; for them the choice will no doubt fall on a one-subject degree, but among future linguists there are probably quite a number who would like to be able to offer two languages at equal level. There are good reasons for choosing two kindred languages, e.g. French and Spanish. But it is equally justifiable to combine two languages from two different groups of the European family, e.g. German and Spanish, or Russian and French. Moreover the combination need not necessarily be between two languages. Some universities offer interesting combinations of subjects of which only one is a language, with the object in view that the two subjects chosen should not be merely two separate fields of study which are explored simultaneously; they are offered as related fields, the studies of which are intended (and the courses are often designed with that intention in mind) to support each other. Thus it is possible to combine languages, for example, with Philosophy or Drama or Music and also with Classical Studies, English or Economics. The undergraduate opting for a two-subject degree must consider very carefully which of the combinations is likely to suit him best. If the student studies two languages for a Combined Honours degree he must expect to spend two shorter periods of residence in each of the two countries (see again entries under I.4 on *Residence Abroad*).

(*c*) Next, a modern language can be taken as part of a *General* (or *Ordinary*) degree. Here the language is studied alongside two or, in some places, more than two subjects which may, or may not, be languages. As this type of course advances on a broader front, it is suitable for students who do not wish to commit themselves to the more highly specialized and often more arduous one- or two-subject degree course. In the past the General degree course tended to be a dumping ground for less able students and was often regarded as the Cinderella of the university courses. In recent years it has, however, been recognized that there can be good educational reasons for *not* specializing either too early or too much. Therefore some universities

---

[1] These courses are described under such names as 'Special Degree Joint Schools of Latin and French', 'Joint Honours in Spanish and German', etc.

make a deliberate effort to attract to their General courses those students who come to the more broadly designed General degree out of choice, and not because they cannot be admitted to a Special degree course. The General degree is in some universities a very flexible degree in which subjects can be taken for one, two or three years. If advantage is taken of the many possibilities of combining subjects (see I.3 in the *Guide*) a number of varied interests supporting one another can be catered for.

(*d*) Students who propose to take an Honours or Special degree in another (linguistic or non-linguistic) subject may find that a language can be a very suitable *Subsidiary* subject for a one-year or a two-year course. Languages can usefully be the junior partner in degree courses in history, geography, English, classics, economics, philosophy, sociology, psychology, and also the natural sciences where this is possible.[1]

(*e*) Finally, it is important to realize that new universities may depart from the accepted courses and try to cater for students with linguistic inclinations in a variety of new ways. Thus, in two universities a 'School of European Studies' has been set up, with the intention of placing some of the major European languages and literatures in a broader context of European studies. In another university a knowledge of Russian or Spanish may be cultivated in certain courses in the departments of government and literature within a 'School of Comparative Studies'. At present a number of colleges of advanced technology are planning university degree courses of their own offering new forms of modern language studies. Future students who wish to have a complete picture of modern language studies at university level should make the necessary enquiries and consider these courses before making their choice.

To summarize: whatever course of studies you will eventually embark on, you should try to decide for yourself what role you would like languages to play in your university career. Are they necessary but subordinate to other courses of study, e.g. history, English or philosophy? if so, you might opt for a Subsidiary course in a language. If you would like languages to form part of a somewhat broader non-specialized course of varied studies you may be inclined to choose a General degree or its equivalent. If you want the most intensive and concentrated form of language study you can find, you will presumably try to go in for either the two-subject or the one-subject Honours or Special degree. Finally, if you cannot make up your mind and would like to postpone the decision, you might give preference to one of those universities which do not force you to make this decision at the beginning of the course, but which give you a year or two in which to come to a final decision.

---

[1] Students who have no previous knowledge of a language but would like to start learning one may find that it is often possible to take it as a General or Subsidiary subject (see Section I.1). Usually the rules for residence abroad are more lenient for students taking a language to the Subsidiary or General level.

WHICH LANGUAGES?

Having made up your mind that you want to study languages, you ought to consider which. Those you have studied at school are the obvious choice. But you ought to keep in mind that universities frequently enable undergraduates to start from scratch languages that are not always (or not yet) commonly taught in schools, in particular Spanish, Russian and Italian. Here you may find wonderful opportunities for branching out into new fields. Even if French *or* German, or French *and* German are the subjects which are more or less dictated by your previous studies at school, do not fail to look at those parts of this handbook which are concerned with Spanish, Russian and Italian and ask yourself whether beginning a new language in addition to those you know already, or in place of one of them, might not offer the greatest interest and challenge. Today there is a need in Britain for a much larger number of linguists and other persons who have an intimate knowledge of the languages and civilizations of Spain, Portugal, Latin America, Italy and the Soviet Union.

University departments offering less widely studied languages are usually small. Since they are not so overrun by applicants as, for example, departments of French tend to be, rules for admission may be interpreted less rigidly. Once you are in such a department you may find that you will be given more individual attention than a larger department can give you because the number of students is smaller. It should, however, be pointed out that starting a new language is by no means a soft option. The course is likely to be just as exacting as one that is based on your previous school studies and its educational value is equally high.

As we do not want our *Guide* to become too unwieldy, only passing reference can be made here to other West European languages, in particular the Scandinavian languages and Portuguese, the Slavonic and other East European languages besides Russian, and the African and Oriental languages. But this restriction does not mean that these languages are not regarded as worth studying. How many people in Britain know Chinese, Japanese or another Asian language, or a language of Africa? Very few indeed; the number of languages known and studied in Great Britain is far too restricted.[1] The student who would like to study languages off the beaten track should consult the Appendix at the end of this book, page 357, where most language courses in British universities are tabulated. Among specialized institutions teaching these languages particular mention should be made of

The School of Oriental and African Studies, University of London, W.C.1,

[1] An extension of linguistic studies beyond the most widespread European languages is clearly demanded in all recent official reports on modern languages, in particular the Hayter Report (*Report of the Sub-committee on Oriental, Slavonic, East European and African Studies*, H.M.S.O., 1961); the Annan Report (*The Teaching of Russian*, H.M.S.O., 1962); and the F.B.I. Report (*Foreign Languages in Industry*, published by the Federation of British Industries, 1962).

and of

The School of Slavonic and East European Studies, University of London, W.C.1.

But from the Appendix it will be seen that there are a number of other universities which also offer courses in Oriental, African and Slavonic studies and in which the less widely known European languages can be learnt.

You may wonder about *the vocational value of various languages*. The approach to any language at university level is broad, humane, scholarly, in short, academic in the best sense and not narrow or utilitarian. The object is not to train language teachers, interpreters or commercial correspondents, but to provide through linguistic and literary studies a humane education which may, but does not set out to be, vocationally applicable. If, for the moment, you set aside vocational intentions, it can be argued that any language course could be taken by you with benefit, including those in Scandinavian, Slavonic, Oriental and African languages, provided the course offers the same literary, cultural and linguistic components as you will find in the well-established language courses.

On the other hand, if you want to include in your choice of languages the 'market value' of your studies you ought to bear in mind that teaching in schools, colleges or universities is one of the most common outlets for linguists. Here the greatest demand is obviously for those languages that are widely taught and if you think you might become a teacher of languages you would be well advised to include at least one or two commonly taught languages in your degree course (at present mostly French and German), keeping in mind that there is an increasing demand for teachers of Russian, Spanish or Italian.

Other vocational outlets for language graduates, as for other Arts graduates, are government service, industry and commerce; also libraries and museums. In addition, the linguist, by virtue of his intimate knowledge of a country, its people and language, plays an increasingly important part in many fields of activity as a regional adviser or expert, e.g. in journalism, broadcasting or the British Council. If you have this vocational objective in mind, the range of languages which you might take up is very wide.

As a counsel of perfection one might suggest to you to play safe to begin with by taking a degree in the more conventional languages, such as French, German, Spanish or Russian, partly because they have a safe market value and partly because it will help you to see whether you like languages sufficiently for you to continue still further your study of them. If so, on the basis of this secure foundation, you can then decide whether or not you wish to continue language studies by postgraduate work in less common languages.[1]

---

[1] It should, however, be stressed that institutions such as the School of Oriental and African Studies recruit and accept suitably qualified applicants straight from school.

ADMISSION TO A LANGUAGE DEPARTMENT IN A UNIVERSITY

Before you apply to any university you must obtain the current issue of the handbook *How to apply for admission to a university*, issued by the Universities Central Council on Admissions (UCCA), 29 Tavistock Square, London, W.C.1.

The UCCA handbook lists the names of all courses available in all universities in the United Kingdom and gives instructions on how to apply. Our *Guide* does not replace the UCCA handbook. The two books should be consulted side by side. The *Guide* can help you to find details about many of the courses which are only listed in the UCCA handbook. Therefore, with the help of the two books together, you will be able to find out which universities and which modern language courses are of greatest interest to you.

The handbook will tell you to how many universities you are entitled to apply (at present four) and you will have to arrange your choice in order of preference. It is at this stage that the *Guide* should be of particular assistance to you, in comparing the suitability and preferability of different courses at a number of universities for *your* needs, talents, limitations and inclinations.

Before making your final decision you should narrow down your choice to about half a dozen universities or colleges and, having done so, write to each of these and ask for the prospectus of the course in which you are interested. The prospectus will give you the latest official details about entrance requirements and courses. With our *Guide*, the current UCCA handbook *How to apply for admission to a university*, and the current prospectus of some six or so courses of studies before you, you will have all the necessary information to make your final choice of four and to indicate your order of preference.

Universities are at present in a state of development, and courses of study, as well as conditions of admission, will be modified from time to time. You may, therefore, find that sometimes the information in the UCCA handbook, the university prospectus and our *Guide*, do not completely coincide. If you find such discrepancy you should accept as correct the details given in the current UCCA handbook or the university prospectus, since they are revised annually, whereas this *Guide* can only be brought up to date every few years.

With these general considerations in mind we should now like to explain to you briefly some points in the procedure of admission to courses of study which should help you to understand better the information in this *Guide*. The admission of a student is governed by two factors: (*a*) the applicant must be qualified to enter the department, and (*b*) he must be selected. Accordingly these two points are covered in the *Guide* under the sub-headings II.1 *Qualifications Required*, and II.2 *Selection of Students*.

(*a*) *Qualifications for admission.* All universities have a 'general requirement' for admission. This used to be called (and informally still is) 'matriculation' or 'minimum entrance requirements'. 'Matriculation' originally referred to the act of entering the student's name into the university register. The rules governing this procedure lay down minimum educational standards with which the student has to comply before his admission can be considered. Beyond these rules, which apply to the whole university, each Faculty, College, School or Department of the university may impose its own demands, so as to ensure that students reading for a degree in a given subject have an adequate and more or less uniform background of education. This is the 'course requirement'. For example, most departments of French demand that their applicants have a high standard of attainment in 'A' Level French and, in addition, have 'O' Level Latin.

The student wishing to apply should first find out whether he fulfils the 'general requirement' of the university and, secondly, whether he will be able to meet the demand of the Faculty of Arts or of the Department of Languages. As the 'general requirement' applies to all students, we have omitted it from our *Guide*, unless our informant has specially asked us to include it. Section II.1 will, however, give the 'course requirement' of the department or faculty beyond 'matriculation'. You should consult this section in good time and check the information against the current university prospectus so that you do not find out too late that you are technically excluded from applying to a department to which you would like to go.

(*b*) *Applications and Selection.* The method of application is fully explained in the UCCA handbook. This must be consulted and the procedure explained there strictly followed. The Admissions Officers in the universities study carefully the applications they receive and, on the basis of the information given on the forms, and the report of your referee, may invite you for an interview or offer you a place.

The selection procedure may include written or oral tests besides the interview. Interviews may be entirely in English or partly in English and partly in the foreign language, and may range from personal questions about interests and school activities to questions on literature, the arts and current affairs. The selection procedure and the qualities departments look for are outlined in entries under II.2.

By and large, most departments seem to look for very much the same qualities: they would like students who have lively and open minds, who are interested in the subject of their choice, but also students who, beyond that, have literary or broadly cultural interests. Furthermore, they would like students who, after six to eight years of French, or four to five years of German, have a reasonably good command of the spoken and written language. Finally, they would like the applicant to have thought about the reasons which prompt him to opt for language study.

Read entries under Section II.2 if you want to know in detail what qualities language departments look for in the selection of candidates. Entries in this section may also help you to understand what modern language departments are striving to achieve and what qualities you should try to cultivate if you want to study languages successfully at a university.

H. H. S.

GENERAL REFERENCES

In your choice of courses of study and universities you may also find useful for reference the following publications:

NATIONAL UNION OF TEACHERS. *University and College Entrance: The Basic Facts.* London: N.U.T. (1964). 4s. 6d.

Which University?, with Preface by Sir John Wolfenden. London: Cornmarket Press Ltd. (1963). 15s.

COMMITTEE OF VICE-CHANCELLORS AND PRINCIPALS OF THE UNIVERSITIES OF THE UNITED KINGDOM. *A Compendium of University Entrance Requirements for First Degree Courses in the United Kingdom.* London: Association of Commonwealth Universities (1964). 8s. 6d.

FRENCH STUDIES

UNIVERSITY OF BIRMINGHAM

Department of French

I. COURSES OF STUDY

1. TYPES OF COURSES

(*a*) *B.A. with Honours* includes the language offered as Honours subject, with one Subsidiary subject studied for two years, or two Subsidiary subjects studied for one year each, as approved by the Head of Department. (This latter is an unusual arrangement.) Lasting for four years, this course covers all the usual aspects of French included in such a course, i.e. translation, essay work, close textual study of selected texts in all years, concentrated on 19th- and 20th-century literature in the first year; 16th-18th centuries in the second year; a compulsory course in 16th-century literature, Old French, three optional courses in other periods of literature (including French-Canadian) chosen by the student, and a special course of *lectures expliquées* in the fourth year.

(*b*) French as one subject in degree of *B.A. with Honours in Combined Subjects*. Normally taken as one of two subjects studied concurrently in all three years. Exceptionally a student may be permitted to take in his second and third years a subject which he did not study in his first year. In general, this course follows the pattern of the Honours B.A. course in French only. Courses in philosophy, French social history, Old French and compulsory 16th-century literature taken by students in the Honours School, are not taken by those reading for the degree in Combined Subjects, though the last two may be taken as options. The level of achievement required to gain Honours in this course is high.

(*c*) French as a *Subsidiary* subject: a two-year course similar to that in Honours and Combined subjects, but more restricted in range.

(*d*) A special course in translation from French to English is arranged for students of History.

(*e*) A special *Supplementary* course for students in the Honours School of English.

(*f*) French for Commerce students: a special two-year course, as part of the preparation for the degree of B.Com., can be taken in French as in other modern languages. Attendance at an intensive course and a stay abroad are compulsory. The course aims at equipping students to use the language as an instrument of communication within the field of their main interests, and is open to those who have already reached either Ordinary or Advanced Level French.

Note.—There is now no General degree course.

2. CHARACTERISTICS OF COURSES

(1) The most notable feature of all our first-year work is the concentration upon modern (including contemporary) literature, assisting, as it does, a student's efforts to improve his knowledge of the language as used today. Some stress is also laid on the improvement of spoken French, not only in the first year, but throughout the course.

In all years stress is put upon *close* textual study and much use is made of *explication de texte* and similar techniques, applied in a sensible manner.

In the final year there is a wide range of optional courses to suit all tastes. The object of these courses is to delve really deeply into the chosen subjects under teachers specialized in the particular field. It is in these groups that most of our postgraduate research students first find their real interests.

There is an examinable course in French Philosophy (in the Department of Philosophy) for Honours students in the second year and students are encouraged to attend courses in Fine Arts at the Barber Institute of Fine Arts.

(2) The distinctive feature here is the teaching of literature by an integrated system of formal lectures dealing with selected authors and a system of small tutorial groups (maximum 5-6) dealing with selected works by those authors. With this is linked an essay programme by which each student is seen individually by the tutor to discuss his work, usually twice per term. This combination of methods is at present in use in the first and second year of all departmental courses. The result is that all students are well known to several members of staff before their third year and their abilities and interests can be judged with some accuracy. Such a system must clearly have a limiting influence on expansion of intake. The results, however, would appear to justify this completely.

3. COMBINATION OF SUBJECTS

As Subsidiary subject, a second language is often taken. Spanish, Italian or Russian may be started from scratch. German may not be taken as Subsidiary subject unless the student has passed in German at Advanced Level. English, Latin, Philosophy or History are sometimes also taken.

Subjects from which students reading for the degree in Combined Subjects may choose are found in the printed *Syllabus of the Arts Faculty.*

4. RESIDENCE ABROAD

A year's residence abroad, at present the third year, is required for Honours students in French only. Those reading French as part of a course in Combined Subjects are expected to spend six months in a French-speaking country (if another language is being taken as well then six months will have to be spent in that country as well). A refund of university fees is made for this period.

Our students may go to any university city in France (or sometimes Belgium) except Paris. We have special links with Montpellier and Toulouse and the City of Birmingham has strong links with Lyon. Students are normally required to attend a recognized course at the university of their choice.

5. METHODS OF STUDY

See I.2 above.

6. OTHER ACTIVITIES

The annual French play, entirely produced by the students, reaches a very high standard.

II. ADMISSION TO COURSES

1. QUALIFICATIONS REQUIRED

French Honours: Three subjects passed at Advanced Level which must be 'Arts' subjects (as defined in the Faculty Syllabus, q.v.), one of these being French. This is the formal requirement, in practice a much higher standard than a pass is required in French.

All candidates must have Latin at least at Ordinary Level.

French as part of course leading to B.A. (Honours) in Combined Subjects. Candidates must have passed in French at Advanced Level in G.C.E. There is no formal *Latin* requirement, unless the candidate wishes to read Latin as another of his subjects.

French *cannot* be started from scratch in this Faculty.

2. SELECTION OF STUDENTS

All applications giving evidence that the applicant has fulfilled or is likely to fulfil the requirements detailed above are considered by the joint Admissions Tutors to the French Honours School, those for Combined Subjects by the Admissions Tutor for that degree. A high proportion of candidates is interviewed, normally by the two Admissions Tutors for French acting together. Interviews are arranged as informally as possible and aim at ascertaining the suitability of the candidate for the Honours course, the quality of the candidate's mind, and at discovering whether the candidate has any special qualities which do not come out from a written application form (as well as the unmasking of spurious ones which appear on the form!). It is by no means certain that French will be spoken at the interview.

No certain indication can be given of what will ensure that a candidate will be called for interview since this depends on all the factors which tend to vary from year to year, such as number of applicants, their quality, average age (this last is never decisive but cannot be left out of account) and size of Honours School. (Choice of university, as indicated by candidate, has little effect on whether or not he or she is interviewed, all other things being equal, unless there are special reasons which make this university an obvious or necessary first choice.)

3. TRANSFER

Students are admitted to the Honours course on entrance. Transfers occur but are not actively encouraged.

4. NUMBERS

As a general rule about 40 are admitted annually to the Honours School of French. It may be worth pointing out that only those expected to be able to stay the course are admitted.

Information supplied by Professor F. Mackenzie

UNIVERSITY OF BRISTOL

Department of French

I. COURSES OF STUDY

1. TYPES OF COURSES

French can be studied in the following ways at Bristol:

(*a*) for the *Special degree in French*. This course lasts three years; and students must take a Subsidiary subject during their first two years in the Department, and pass in it before they can be awarded their degree. The Subsidiary subject may be one of the following: Latin, English, German, Spanish, Italian, Art History,[1] Russian or Philosophy.

(*b*) as one of two subjects in the *Special degree* in the following *Joint Schools*: Latin and French, French and German, French and Spanish, Drama and French, and Philosophy and French. French and German, and French and Spanish are now four-year courses; the other Joint School courses take three years.

(*c*) as one of a number of subjects for the *General degree of B.A.* Four subjects have to be taken during the first year, and a free choice is allowed, subject to time-table limitations. Three of these four subjects are studied in the second and third years.

(*d*) *General degree* (*Modern Studies option*). A language is compulsory; at present it may be French, German, Spanish or Russian. The number of subjects to be chosen is the same as for the ordinary General degree, both Economics and Politics being compulsory in the first year.

(*e*) French can be taken as a two-year *Subsidiary* subject to the Special B.A. degree in German, Spanish, Philosophy, Music or Geography. It can also be taken as a one-year *Additional* subject in the Special School of English, and by students in the Faculties of Medicine or Veterinary Science.

All courses in the Arts Faculty, whether Special, Joint Special or General, lead to degrees which can be of either Honours or Pass standard according to the results obtained in the final examinations. Students are classified in the following five ways in the degree examinations: first class, second class (first and second division), third class and pass.

A Special Mention in Oral French may be awarded as a result of the final examinations for the Special, Joint Special and General B.A. degrees. A Commendation on the results of the whole of the final examination may be awarded to a candidate in his Subsidiary subject.

---

[1] Those who choose this subject must pass a departmental qualifying examination in Italian before they enter their second year of study.

2. CHARACTERISTICS OF COURSES

The Special Joint School of Drama and French, which supplies five out of the ten students taking Drama as part of a Special degree course, is worthy of special mention.

For further details on all courses consult the University Arts Faculty prospectus.

3. COMBINATION OF SUBJECTS

See Section I.1 above for Subsidiary and Joint School subjects. Students may also study Additional Spanish (unless they have chosen this already as their Subsidiary subject), or Additional Italian. They must do so if they wish to take 'Romance Philology', or 'France and the Italian Renaissance', as one of the two Special subjects which have to be studied during the third year of the course for the Final degree examination by all students in the Special School of French. (There are nine of these Special subjects in all. The requirements for Joint School students in respect of these vary to some extent. For details, see the Arts Faculty prospectus.)

Spanish and Italian, when taken as Additional subjects for the above purposes, are then studied as languages only, with suitable texts: they are not specifically examination subjects.

4. RESIDENCE ABROAD

Every first-year Special and Joint School degree student must spend six months in France (March to August inclusive); four of these months (March to June) must be spent following the *Cours de Civilisation française* at the Sorbonne, and the end-of-course diploma must be taken and passed in French language and in specified subjects selected from the courses offered. The last two months may be spent anywhere in France or a French-speaking country.

General degree students taking French for three years must, unless exempted by the Arts Board, spend one month in France (or Switzerland or Belgium), following an approved course of study; and students taking the two-year Subsidiary course in French are required to produce evidence of having spent a minimum period of four weeks of supervised study in a French-speaking country.

5. METHODS OF STUDY

The tutorial system is used throughout for oral work in French, and it is also used extensively for work in connection with set books, essays and translations.

6. OTHER ACTIVITIES

Since the War, the French Department has supported the University French Circle in the staging of one major dramatic performance every three years. Racine's *Esther* (1950) and *Athalie* (1956) were staged with the collaboration of the Departments of Drama and Music. Molière's *Les Femmes savantes* (1953) and *Le Misanthrope*

(1959), and the *Électre* of Giraudoux (1962), were staged with the collaboration of the Department of Drama. An individual University Prize, the Racine Prize in French Drama, is awarded annually following a competition, which usually takes the form of dramatic recitation. The University French Circle holds regular meetings; and there is a French Circle Choir.

II. ADMISSION TO COURSES

1. QUALIFICATIONS REQUIRED

The matriculation requirements of the University must be met. A pass at 'O' Level in a classical language is normally required of candidates for the Faculty of Arts; and in the case of candidates for the Special School of French, and the Joint Schools which include French, and for General B.A. candidates (Modern Studies option excepted), this classical language should be Latin. In the case of the Modern Studies option, a pass in French or German or Spanish, *and* in Mathematics *or* a classical language, will be required.

Selections for the General B.A. degree courses are not made by the Department, but a student who has not passed 'A' Level French would not be admitted to the General degree French course.

2. SELECTION OF STUDENTS

For admission to Special degree courses (including Joint Schools), 'A' Level passes in Grade B are required in two subjects, of which French must be one.

Selection is made on (*a*) results at 'O' and 'A' Levels and (*b*) reports from heads of schools; this information may be supplemented by an interview. This will normally include a test in oral French, and some testing of the candidate's general knowledge.

Mature applicants are required to give proof of competence in French if they have not taken 'A' Level or an equivalent examination.

Applicants should note that the competition for admission to the Special School and the Special Joint Schools is very keen. The pressure of applications can be judged from the following figures for the current year (1963). Applications for the Special French School, and the various Special Joint Schools which include French, were made by 1065 candidates for the session 1963–64—nearly twenty times the number of those who could be admitted. Of these, 569 applied for the Special School of French and 496 for the five Joint Schools with French mentioned above.

Special requirements for admission to the Joint Schools. The requirements vary to some extent according to the various combinations of subjects which the candidates wish to study, but applicants should note that the course is an exacting one in all cases. A high standard of attainment will accordingly be expected.

Candidates for admission to the Joint Schools of Latin and French, French and German, and French and Spanish, will be required to have obtained at least a grade B at 'A' Level in each of the two subjects which they propose to study at the University. Candidates for admission to the Joint Schools of Drama and French, or Philosophy and French, will be required to have obtained at least a grade B at 'A' Level in French and in one other subject apart from General Studies. Candidates for the Joint School of Drama and French are expected to have an interest and some experience in the drama field.

Candidates for any of the Joint Schools will normally be required to attend for an interview with representatives of the two departments in question. Those wishing to read French and German, or French and Spanish, should note that the interview will comprise an oral test in both languages concerned.

3. TRANSFER

Students who are admitted to Special degree courses (including Joint Schools) are given a series of linguistic tests in the first fortnight of the session, in order to determine the standard of their French at the time of entry. As a result of these tests, students may be advised to try another subject.

4. NUMBERS

About 40 to 50 candidates have been admitted annually in recent years to the Special School of French and the Joint Schools which include French.

Information supplied by Professor W. McC. Stewart

UNIVERSITY OF DURHAM
Department of French

I. COURSES OF STUDY

1. TYPES OF COURSES

(*a*) *Honours* (with one Subsidiary subject which may be another modern language: German, Russian or Spanish).

(*b*) *Joint Honours* with Spanish or German (this course is intended for students of above-average ability and possessing a good knowledge of *both* languages; French may be combined with other modern languages taken as a Subsidiary subject).

(*c*) *General*, as one of three subjects studied for the B.A. in General Studies, in a preliminary course of one year, followed by a final course of two years.

(*d*) Students in other Honours schools frequently offer French as a *Subsidiary* subject, taking it for two years only, but offering the final course (second and third years) of the B.A. in General Studies.

2. CHARACTERISTICS OF COURSES

An accurate knowledge of modern French, both spoken and written, is the first aim of the Honours course; at the same time the history of the language is studied from the very beginning of the course.

On the foundation of a sound knowledge of the language the syllabus aims to build a good general knowledge of French civilization from the Middle Ages to the present day; while the study of literature is given its proper importance, it is not pursued in a vacuum, but in relation to the history and thought of a given period. The syllabus requires a detailed knowledge of a limited number of works which are studied closely, but wide reading outside this programme is also required. While the student may to some extent follow his own personal interests in the field of literature and ideas, the syllabus demands a general knowledge of the whole sweep of French civilization from the Middle Ages onwards, and does not permit concentration on a few periods chosen at random.

The General course concentrates on the study of the modern language, spoken and written, and on French literature of the more modern periods.

3. COMBINATION OF SUBJECTS

Candidates for Honours in French must offer one Subsidiary subject for two years. They may offer a modern European language (German, Spanish or Russian) or they may offer, with the approval of the Head of the Department, one of the following subjects: Arabic, English, Greek, History, Latin, Music, Philosophy, Religious Knowledge.

4. RESIDENCE ABROAD

Honours students are normally expected to insert, between the second and third year of residence, a year spent as assistant in a French school or training college under the official scheme. Failing this, they are required to spend at least three months in France or a French-speaking country during the period between matriculating and presenting themselves for their final examination.

General students are required to spend at least one month in France or a French-speaking country.

5. METHODS OF STUDY

Lectures, seminars and tutorial methods are used. Considerable emphasis is placed on oral French.

II. ADMISSION TO COURSES

1. QUALIFICATIONS REQUIRED

There are not formally any requirements beyond those for matriculation in the Faculty of Arts in this university. Thus an 'O' Level pass in Latin is accepted even though in fact quite a number of students have an 'A' Level qualification.

French cannot be started from scratch in this university. A candidate for a General degree who offers French must have at least an 'A' Level pass.

2. SELECTION OF STUDENTS

The selection of Honours students is done by a combination of interview plus 'A' Level and 'S' paper results, plus, in the case of the minority of applicants who take it, performance in our own University Scholarship Examination. References from schools are taken into account.

The selection of General students is in the hands of the individual colleges.

3. TRANSFER

(*a*) Students are normally admitted direct to Honours courses on entrance.

(*b*) Transfer to the Honours School is possible at the end of the first year in the General course.

4. NUMBERS

Average number of students admitted to the Honours School in recent years is 40 or so.

Information supplied by Professor J. Lough

UNIVERSITY OF EXETER

Department of French and Italian

I. COURSES OF STUDY

1. TYPES OF COURSES

(a) *B.A. Honours in French.* The course extends over three sessions. In the first two sessions, leading up to the Part I examinations, emphasis is laid on history of literature through the study of prescribed texts, history of language, general studies and practical work. In the third and final session, leading up to the Part II examination, students are invited to specialize in selected fields of literature or language, and to submit a dissertation bearing on one aspect of their special subject. At the same time advanced courses in prose composition and essay-writing are provided, as well as practical classes in oral French and in the writing of commentaries on French literary passages. As an integral part of their Part I examination students are required to take two papers in an Additional subject, which may be English, European History, French History and Civilization, German, Greek, Latin, Music, Philosophy, Spanish, Italian, Russian, or another subject selected with the approval of the Board of the Faculty of Arts.

(b) *B.A. with Combined Honours in French.* Courses in Combined Honours in French and English, French and German, French and Latin, and French and Spanish, are provided. These extend over three years. Students taking the Combined Honours degree are not required to study an Additional subject.

(c) *B.A. General.* Students may read French as one of three subjects for a B.A. General degree in the Faculty of Arts and in the Faculty of Social Studies. The course extends over three years and the examination is taken in two parts. Courses on French history and civilization are a feature of the third-year studies, which of course include literature and thought. Students may obtain a distinction in any of the three subjects studied, but general honours are not awarded.

Background courses in French social and political history are included in the curriculum for both Honours and General students.

2. CHARACTERISTICS OF COURSES

The French studies are organized on traditional lines. They aim at providing a firm grounding in the French language as well as making the student familiar with French literature, life and thought. Emphasis is laid on practical work conducted in tutorial groups. A special feature is the provision of lectures on contemporary French literature. In addition to the courses which appear on the time-table, single lectures or series of lectures by distinguished French and English visitors are arranged each year.

3. COMBINATION OF SUBJECTS

See I.1 above.

4. RESIDENCE ABROAD

Students reading for Honours and General degrees in Modern Languages are required to attend vacation courses abroad or to undertake residence abroad as an integral and essential part of the work for their degree. They nearly all attend vacation courses during their first summer vacation and I like to distribute them throughout France, Switzerland, Belgium and Spain. Over half intercalate a year after Part I to serve as English assistants in French schools, during which time they send in proses and essays, especially in cases where they are unable to attend courses at a French university.

5. METHODS OF STUDY

See I.1 and I.2 above.

II. ADMISSION TO COURSES

1. QUALIFICATIONS REQUIRED

(*a*) 'O' Level pass in Latin is required.

(*b*) At present grade B in French and either grade B in one other subject, or grade C in two other subjects, are deemed sufficient when strong recommendations have been submitted.

In the case of General students grade C at 'A' Level in French is considered adequate where there is no weakness in other subjects.

2. SELECTION OF STUDENTS

The following considerations determine the selection of students:

(*a*) 'A' Level results when known, but provisional acceptances are given early in the year.

(*b*) Much weight is given to interviews. About 150 applicants come up for our interview and are seen by two members of our staff. Questions are of a general character and are often related to the applicant's reading in French, and his other activities. Very great care is given to the consideration of personal references, statements by headmasters and headmistresses, and senior teachers. We look for a good basic knowledge of the language and seek evidence of potential linguistic ability, as well as general intelligence and interest. It would be of assistance if teachers supporting candidates weak on paper would give their reasons in some detail.

(*c*) It is rarely possible to consider candidates who have not given Exeter as their first choice.

3. TRANSFER

(*a*) Students are admitted to Honours courses on entrance.

(*b*) Transfer is possible at the end of the first term, and occasionally at the end of the first session.

4. NUMBERS

The number of students admitted annually to the Honours School is approximately 40.

Information supplied by Professor R. Niklaus

UNIVERSITY OF HULL
Department of French

I. COURSES OF STUDY

1. TYPES OF COURSES

(a) *Special Honours* degree in French: a three-year course; one other subject is studied for five terms.

(b) *Joint Honours* degree: a three-year course; one other subject is studied for three years.

There is no General or Pass degree in Arts in this University.

2. CHARACTERISTICS OF COURSES

All Special Honours students follow basic literary courses throughout their undergraduate career consisting of a series of lectures on Medieval French Literature and Thought, Literature from 1549–1918, and Philosophical and Moral Thought in France (1500–1789). In addition a range of optional subjects, from which students must choose two, allows them to orientate their individual course in the direction of Medieval and Renaissance Studies (optional subjects on History of the French Language, Medieval French Drama) and towards philosophical studies (Selected French Thinkers from the 17th Century to the Present) or towards modern literary studies (optional subjects on the Prose Fiction in the 18th Century, Aesthetics in France, 1715–1815, the Theatre in the 19th and 20th Centuries, and the Novel in the 20th Century). Great attention is paid to practice in the modern language, both written and oral. There are courses in general linguistics and in phonetics.

3. COMBINATION OF SUBJECTS

The most common combinations are with other modern languages (i.e. German, Italian, Spanish or Swedish), Latin, Drama and English.

The University of Hull has instituted the teaching of Russian in 1963.

4. RESIDENCE ABROAD

(1) All Honours students are urged to spend one year (usually the year between the second and third years) in France (or Switzerland) as assistants.

(2) When this is not possible, the summer term of the second year is spent abroad in a French university (Special Honours) or a summer vacation course in France is taken (Joint Honours).

5. METHODS OF STUDY

Tutorial classes are arranged for all Honours students, in groups of four. This enables students to get to know members of staff well and to pursue, in additional, individual work, subjects dealt with in large lectures.

6. OTHER ACTIVITIES

There is an active *Cercle français*, which, in addition to meetings of a widely varied kind, stages a French play annually.

II. ADMISSION TO COURSES

1. QUALIFICATIONS REQUIRED

All students must matriculate in the University. In addition, students reading for a Special or Joint Honours degree in French must have passed French at 'A' Level and Latin at 'O' Level.

A bare pass in 'A' Level French is not sufficient but it is difficult to give a precise grade required (see II.2 below). The usual mark in French of students admitted is either A or B.

2. SELECTION OF STUDENTS

(1) There is no separate entrance examination.

(2) 'A' Level results form an important basis for selection and are used to provide 'conditional marks', on the attainment of which a place is awarded.

(3) Interviews are used on a sample of applicants—usually doubtful cases. I interview about 35 per cent of applicants. The interviews are of 30 minutes and are conducted in English and French by myself and one or two other members of this Department. In these interviews one looks essentially for curiosity of mind and evidence of personal thinking.

(4) Personal references from head teachers and language teachers are important but they vary very much in their objectivity.

3. TRANSFERS

Students are admitted to Honours Schools on entrance.

4. NUMBERS

Thirty-six students are accepted annually for Special Honours courses and 40 for Joint Honours courses.

Information supplied by Professor G. Rees

UNIVERSITY OF KEELE

Department of Modern Languages (French)

I. COURSES OF STUDY

The degree course lasts four years, of which the first, or *Foundation Year*, consists of a compulsory course of lectures designed to introduce the student to some of the methods and information necessary to an estimate of the inheritance, problems and achievements of modern Western European man. This course, identical for students of all subjects, is supplemented by tutorial work adjusted to individual needs. During the last three years, students study two subjects at *Principal* level and two one-year *Subsidiary* subjects: one must be a Science subject; one Subsidiary may be replaced by a course in the Theory and Practice of Education (concurrent with the Principal course) for the Diploma in Education.

1. TYPES OF COURSES

The following courses in French are offered:

(*a*) *French as a Principal subject:* an Honours course lasting three years, which forms, with another Principal course, a Joint Honours degree.

(*b*) *French as a Subsidiary subject:* a one-year course complementary or supplementary to a Joint Honours course in other subjects. This is conceived as an introduction to the literature (some six texts) and civilization and an extension of language work. It operates at either of two levels:

(*i*) post-Ordinary Level (G.C.E.) for scientists, geographers, economists, etc.;

(*ii*) post-Advanced Level (G.C.E.).

(*c*) *Foundation Year Tutorial.* In the Foundation Year there are:

(*i*) one-term tutorial classes in French literature;

(*ii*) one-year tutorial classes in literature for those who have not taken 'A' Level French.

2. CHARACTERISTICS OF COURSES

(1) There are a number of courses in each year (one hour per week each for the whole session), supplemented by the usual composition, translation and oral practice classes.

The present pattern is as follows:

Year 1: (*a*) Classical theatre texts,
       (*b*) Novel (17th–19th-century texts),
       (*c*) Phonetics and *explication*,
       (*d*) Linguistics and history of language.

M.L.—B 2

Year 2: (*a*) 17th- and 18th-century thought,
        (*b*) Renaissance texts,
        (*c*) Either (i) Medieval texts
            or (ii) 19th-century poetry,
        (*d*) Special Subject (begun in third term).

Year 3: (*a*) Modern novel,
        (*b*) Either (i) Medieval texts
            or (ii) Modern theatre,
        (*c*) Special Subject.

(2) Every student has a weekly tutorial throughout the course.

(3) Options for Special Subject study have included: Adam de la Halle, Rutebeuf, Rabelais, Montaigne, Pascal, Corneille, Racine, Rousseau, Diderot, Balzac, Baudelaire, Proust, Sartre, Camus. The option is dealt with tutorially.

3. COMBINATION OF SUBJECTS

In order of frequency, French at Principal level is combined with English, German, History, Latin, Economics, Political Institutions, and Philosophy.

There is no compulsory combination of subjects.

4. RESIDENCE ABROAD

(*a*) A minimum of three months' study in France is required.

(*b*) Over 50 per cent go for a year as assistants. Then they are required to write essays periodically on their Special Subject.

5. METHODS OF STUDY

See I.2 above.

6. OTHER ACTIVITIES

Students' Modern Language Society is active and produces a yearly play.

II. ADMISSION TO COURSES

1. QUALIFICATIONS REQUIRED

Admission is to the University, not to the Department. Normally, however, it is expected that Principal students of French shall have a good 'A' Level pass. It has occurred that students have begun with 'O' Level but this is rare and inadvisable.

No Latin requirement in the University.

2. SELECTION OF STUDENTS

Applications are read by a panel which selects for interview. (All students admitted are interviewed.) The panel of three university teachers has regard to the 'A' Level results, to the head teacher's report and to the results of the interview; understanding of subjects studied, interest in other fields, liveliness of mind, etc.

Candidates suggested as 'suitable for your General course' are not usually successful since the course here is a Joint Honours course with some breadth but is not a General degree course.

3. TRANSFER

(a) Students are admitted to the Department of French after completing the Foundation Year studies.

(b) Transfer is possible. Many who come up to read school subjects change their subjects during the Foundation Year. Transfer during the first term of the first Principal year is also possible.

4. NUMBERS

The number of Honours students fluctuates, according to the make-up of the Foundation Year, between 18 and 25.

Information supplied by Professor R. J. North

UNIVERSITY OF LANCASTER

Department of French Studies

I. COURSES OF STUDY

1. TYPES OF COURSES

Teaching is due to begin in the University of Lancaster in October 1964. The general scheme of studies is as follows:

(*a*) In the first year, students will take three subjects of equal weight, any of which may be studied at a higher level in later years. The final choice need not be made until after the first part of the First Examination, which will take place partly at the end of the second term and partly at the beginning of the second year. The subjects which may be taken with French at this stage are English, Biology, Classical Background, History, Philosophy, Politics and Mathematics.

(*b*) After the First Examination, students will normally take three subjects but these will no longer be of equal weight. One subject will be a *major interest* but the second (*minor*) will be a full part of the course and will be closely linked by content to the 'major' subject. The third will be a deliberately 'distant' subject. Joint 'major' courses will be available in English/French and French/Latin.

Second- and third-year 'minor' options with 'major' French: English or History or Philosophy or Latin. ('Minor' French will be available with any of these subjects when they are taken as 'majors'.)

Second-year 'distant subject' options (two hours per week): Biology or Principles of Science or Mathematics or Operational Research.

(*c*) In the third year the 'minor' subject will be continued with 'major' French.

The results of the first degree will be given by classes, the term *Honours* signifying a level of accomplishment, not a separate type of course.

2. CHARACTERISTICS OF THE COURSE

The course is intended to lead to a degree in the culture of one country while maintaining some pretensions to breadth of education. Details of the first-year syllabus (*Contemporary France and the Human Condition*) may be obtained on request. Applications for registration for the degree of M.A. or Ph.D. may be entertained at any time.

Information supplied by Professor T. E. Lawrenson

UNIVERSITY OF LEEDS
Department of French

I. COURSES OF STUDY

1. TYPES OF COURSES

French may be studied as part of the following courses:

(*a*) *Special Studies in French*, with one Subsidiary subject studied for three years and one for one year;

(*b*) *Special Studies in Modern Languages*, consisting of two of the following: French, Spanish, Italian, German, Russian, or *Special Studies in French and Latin*. These two courses combine two foreign languages of equal weight, with one Subsidiary subject for one year;

(*c*) *General Studies:* French is studied alongside three other subjects in the first year and two in the second and third years;

(*d*) *Subsidiary French:* French is studied for three years as part of a Special Studies course in another foreign language, or as part of Combined Studies in Philosophy and Subsidiary French.

Honours and Pass awards may be obtained in any of these degree courses.

The Special Studies course consists of a qualifying year and normally of three further years, the second of which is spent in France.

2. CHARACTERISTICS OF COURSES

The Special Studies courses are designed to encourage the study not only of the written and spoken language, but of a comprehensive range of 'disciplines', whilst leaving scope for variation by way of 'special subjects'. The range includes the techniques of literature and its historical and aesthetic problems, modern linguistics, stylistics, phonetics, and *explication*, French thought, history and modern institutions.

The General and Subsidiary courses, at Leeds, may be taken to the third year; a good third-year standard makes it possible, with residence abroad, to contemplate teaching.

3. COMBINATION OF SUBJECTS

The Faculty offers a wide range of Subsidiary subjects for Special Studies students, which include subjects already taken at school as well as new ones. The choice is usually arranged to fit the General or Combined Studies schemes, to allow transfer. Latin is not a required subject of study.

4. RESIDENCE ABROAD

Students taking Special Studies in French spend the third term of their second year abroad, most frequently at a university in the country of their three-year Subsidiary subject. The following year is normally spent in France, usually as a paid assistant under the official exchange scheme. Students reading Special Studies in Modern Languages have a period of residence in each country. General Studies students may also spend a year in France; they are required as a minimum to follow a course in France during the summer vacation.

The term abroad and the summer course are facilitated by some supplementation of grant.

5. METHODS OF STUDY

Tutorial work is introduced wherever appropriate, with discussions and papers in advanced groups. Written work is required at all stages. Regular meetings of small groups with native French graduates provide help with spoken French and also with many of the subjects of the course. Individual tutors and group tutors, along with seminar or tutorial teaching, ensure that each student has contact with the staff.

There is a large departmental library and accommodation for study in a specially designed new building.

6. OTHER ACTIVITIES

The French Society arranges concerts, carols, plays, films, etc.; French plays and films are shown by other groups in the University and in the city.

II. ADMISSION TO COURSES

1. QUALIFICATIONS REQUIRED

For Special Studies a good standard in G.C.E. Advanced French is required—normally B—but this must be supported by a good general standard in the 'A' Level examinations. Latin to 'O' Level is also required. For General and Subsidiary French, a reasonable pass in 'A' Level French is necessary.

2. SELECTION OF STUDENTS

There is at present no special entrance examination for Special Studies. Reports and, in selected cases, interviews are taken into account.

3. TRANSFER

Students are admitted to one or other of the types of course (see I.1) in their first year. They may transfer, if this is advisable, early in the first year, or after the June qualifying examination (or after the September re-sit), if sufficiently successful in the examinations, from

Special to General (second year), or from General to Special (first year).

4. NUMBERS

The average intake in October 1961–63 was, in Special Studies, 76; in General and Subsidiary French, 122. These numbers will be considerably increased in the coming years. For most of the work each 'year' of students is divided into smaller classes and groups.

Information supplied by Professor G. T. Clapton

UNIVERSITY OF LEICESTER

Department of French

I. COURSES OF STUDY

1. TYPES OF COURSES

French can be studied in the *B.A. French* and the *B.A. Combined Studies* course.

Attention is drawn to the fact that in the Leicester *B.A. Combined Studies* degree scheme (of which a full description is given in the *University Handbook*) some specialization is possible. One subject, and only one, is studied for three years; and this subject may of course be French. Scores of applications for the B.A. French course are received every year from candidates who would find the B.A. Combined Studies course more appropriate to their intellectual tastes and ambitions. The classification of successful candidates is the same in the B.A. Combined Studies as in the B.A. French course: honours in three classes (the second being divided), and pass.

2. CHARACTERISTICS OF COURSES

The B.A. French course

A fuller description of the B.A. French course than can here be offered is given in a leaflet which is sent to all candidates who are called for interview. On application to the Head of the Department, a copy will gladly be supplied to any teacher of French.

Broadly speaking, this course is designed to introduce students to three different branches of study:

(*i*) Modern (i.e. Renaissance and post-Renaissance) French literature. This is studied throughout the three years of the student's course. It is not an 'outlines-of-literature' course.

It is studied not by 'periods' but by *genres* (poetry, the drama, the novel, and non-fictional prose forms), as exemplified in the work of major authors. Emphasis is placed less on historical considerations than on present significance. Important authors of the 20th century are given their due place. In their final year, students may devote part of their time to a special study of a particular author of their choice. Close analysis of texts is considered indispensable, and classes in literary commentary are held in all years of the course. But wide reading is also expected of students; the comprehensiveness of the list of prescribed and recommended texts is calculated to be a stimulus and a challenge to the ablest.

(*ii*) The history of the French language, with which is combined the study of the literature of the medieval period. This is a compulsory course for first- and second-year students, and adepts may opt to continue with it in their third year. In such cases an adjustment is made in the amount of work required of them in respect of the study of modern French literature.

(*iii*) French history, geography, institutions and achievements in the non-literary arts are studied in the first two years only. Students are encouraged to pursue personal interests in such fields as French painting, architecture and music.

Classes in translation from and into French, and oral classes, are held in all three years.

The B.A. Combined Studies course

The breadth that should be one important characteristic of a university course is supplied for the Combined Studies student by the number and variety of his subjects (in the Leicester scheme at least four, and possibly five). Accordingly, the Combined Studies syllabus in French is much less extensive than the B.A. French degree syllabus. It does not include the history of the language, or any literature earlier than that of the 17th century; and the number of prescribed texts is much smaller. In the third year, students are required to present, as an integral part of their final examination, a dissertation on a topic in the field of French civilization.

3. COMBINATION OF SUBJECTS

Every B.A. French student is required to read during his first five terms one of the following Supplementary subjects: English, Latin, German, History or Philosophy. The choice is made by the student, in consultation with the Head of the Department.

4. RESIDENCE ABROAD

B.A. French students are admitted to the Department on the understanding that they will apply for posts as assistants in French schools. Candidates who would be unlikely to satisfy the requirements of the official scheme are not accepted.

The final-year course of all students is thoroughly discussed with them at the end of their second year, and they are supplied with bibliographies and similar relevant information. During their year in France, they are expected to assume full responsibility for their academic progress, though they are encouraged to maintain contact with members of the staff and to ask for any further advice they need.

B.A. Combined Studies students reading French as their three-year subject are required to spend not less than one month in France.

5. METHODS OF STUDY

Formal lectures have an important part in the Department's work, but so also does tutorial teaching of various kinds; all Special Subject classes, for example, are tutorial classes. The Department has, and intends to preserve, a strong tradition of close and friendly relationships between staff and students.

6. OTHER ACTIVITIES

In addition to activities organized by the French Society, a French play is produced every year.

II. ADMISSION TO COURSES

1. QUALIFICATIONS REQUIRED

Admission to the B.A. French course

Latin at 'O' Level is required.

A good 'A' Level performance is required, including a grade not less than B in French. The requirement for other 'A' Level subjects varies: it is determined in the light of each candidate's academic record and interview performance.

Admission to the B.A. Combined Studies course

Latin is not required.

A good 'A' Level performance is required. Successful candidates are admitted to the Combined Studies course as such: their choice of subjects is not finally determined until they actually register. A student with a grade lower than C in 'A' Level French would be discouraged, though not necessarily prevented, from taking French as his three-year subject.

2. SELECTION OF STUDENTS

B.A. Combined Studies

The selection of Combined Studies students is the responsibility of the Dean of the Faculty.

B.A. French

No candidate is offered a place without an interview.

Candidates are selected for interview on the basis of the head teacher's report, 'O' Level results, 'A' Level results if available, and information supplied by candidates on their application forms.

Reports from heads of schools are often not sufficiently informative. No senior French teacher should hesitate to write to the Head of the Department personally in support of a candidate who can be conscientiously recommended. Much could be done through direct contact of this kind to make selection more efficient.

The quality that the interview is designed chiefly to explore is interest in books and ideas, both in the field of French studies and outside it. Proficiency in the use and understanding of modern French is in itself quite insufficient as a qualification for admission to the course. Candidates are expected to be able to express themselves fluently and accurately in their own language, to show some knowledge of English literature, both classical and contemporary, and to be able to carry on intelligent conversation on general topics. They should be able to show that they have read thoughtfully French texts outside their 'A' Level syllabus. The B.A. French course is too exacting for candidates who have 'not had time' to do this: it is designed for those who are naturally studious, as well as intelligent.

3. TRANSFER

Students are admitted direct to the B.A. French course, in the full expectation that, having been carefully selected for it, they will remain in it—as indeed all but a very small number do. Transfers, either from the B.A. French course to the B.A. Combined Studies course or vice versa, are rare.

4. NUMBERS

Twenty-four students are at present admitted every year to the B.A. French course. The number is expected to rise during the next few years but will never, it is hoped, exceed 30, since it is held that beyond this limit the effectiveness of personal contacts between members of the staff and students, which play an important part in the work of the Department, would be seriously impaired.

Information supplied by Professor L. C. Sykes

UNIVERSITY OF LIVERPOOL

Department of French

I. COURSES OF STUDY

1. TYPES OF COURSES

French can be studied in the following courses:

(*a*) *Honours:* a three- or four-year course, the final year being spent in France. In the first year two additional subjects are read, one for examination, one not for examination. In subsequent years, French alone is studied, save that a second course in a foreign language (without literature) may be prescribed in the second year. Old French is studied throughout the course.

(*b*) *Joint Honours* (French with one other modern language): a four-year course. When French is the principal language, the third year is spent in France (study and thesis, as for Single Honours). When French is the second language, some residence is prescribed during vacations; but French is not studied during the third year.

(*c*) *General*: French may be studied for two or three years as one of a group of subjects. There is no Old French in the two-year course, but the elements of Old French, and an outline of Medieval French literature, are included in the three-year course. Honours may be gained in the General course by students reaching a sufficiently high standard.

2. CHARACTERISTICS OF COURSES

The Honours course and the three-year General course are designed to cover in outline the whole of the history of French literature from the Middle Ages to modern times, and include an intensive study of particular texts chosen from major writers, and of one or more Special Subjects. Also included are courses in modern French language, Old French and phonetics and French institutions. The following options are available:

In *Honours:* (*a*) between Old French and Old Provençal;
(*b*) between three groups of modern writers in the main literary *genres*;

3. COMBINATION OF SUBJECTS

The Joint Honours courses at present authorized are as follows:

French and German	French and Celtic Studies
French and Italian	French and Russian
French and Hispanic Studies	French and English Literature

For Single Honours and the General degree there is no restriction as to what subjects may be combined with French, within the prospectus of the Arts Faculty. The above groupings are here fairly common, together with French and History.

4. RESIDENCE ABROAD

Single Honours students are required to spend the whole of the final academic year in France, during which they follow prescribed study courses at a French university and prepare, in French, a thesis on a reasonably original subject, which may be literary, linguistic or related to some aspect of French life and culture. Students taking Joint Honours with French as the principal component spend the third year in France.

Most Liverpool Honours students go to Paris, where there is a standing arrangement with the *Institut Britannique* to provide a special course consisting of three classes a week concentrated on a single morning. This leaves the students free to pursue their researches the rest of the week.

There is no compulsory residence abroad for other students.

5. METHODS OF STUDY

There is a tutorial system, providing for very small classes in (*a*) oral French practice, (*b*) *explication de texte*.

6. OTHER ACTIVITIES

There is a *Cercle Français*, organized and run mainly by the students and by the French *lecteurs*.

The Department of French produces each year a dramatic performance, usually of a modern French play.

II. ADMISSION TO COURSES

1. QUALIFICATIONS REQUIRED

A pass in Latin at G.C.E. 'O' Level is required for admission to any of the French courses. The other matriculation requirements are

(*i*) at 'O' Level: passes in Mathematics or a science, English language and a modern foreign language;

(*ii*) at 'A' Level: passes in two subjects at least, usually three, with marks substantially above the pass level.

For Honours French (Single or Joint), a mark of at least B in G.C.E. 'A' Level is looked for, supported by good marks in other subjects. For the General course, a pass in French at 'A' Level is expected.

It is not possible to start the study of French in this University.

2. SELECTION OF STUDENTS

For admission to the Honours course in French, candidates should have an average mark at 'A' Level of at least C, with not less than B in French. There is no entrance examination. Most candidates giving Liverpool as their first choice are interviewed, and many, but not all, others.

A candidate who shows evidence of general interest and activities would, other things being equal, be preferred to purely bookish candidates. Some experience of foreign travel and knowledge of foreign literature could be a recommendation.

3. TRANSFER

Students may be admitted direct into the Preliminary Honours course on entry, but students admitted to the General course may transfer to the Honours course, in approved cases, at the end of their first year.

4. NUMBERS

At present about 30 students are admitted to the Preliminary Honours course.

Information supplied by Professor F. T. H. Fletcher

UNIVERSITY OF LONDON: BEDFORD COLLEGE

Department of French Language and Literature

I. COURSES OF STUDY

Bedford College at present admits only women students as undergraduates.

1. TYPES OF COURSES

(a) *Honours*
(b) *General*
(c) *Subsidiary*

2. CHARACTERISTICS OF COURSES

Honours. Courses follow London University regulations. There are three main elements:

(1) the modern language;
(2) the history of the language with early texts;
(3) the history of literature and the study of texts. One author is dealt with as a Special Subject (in small groups — the choice of authors is wide).

Note 1.—The subject is *French Language and Literature.* Courses in French History are available and students may follow them if they so wish.

Note 2.—Non-examination course — a third subject in the first year.

General. The General course is a three-year course of preparation for the University B.A. General degree examination. The course consists of:

(1) the modern language;
(2) French literature (1600 to the present with prescribed books).

Subsidiary. The course consists of the second and third years of the General course taken in the student's first two years. The course in literature is, however, restricted in scope compared with the General course.

3. COMBINATION OF SUBJECTS

(1) Usual Subsidiary subjects for Honours French students are German, Latin, Italian and English but other subjects may be taken. Spanish may be taken by arrangement.

(2) In the first year many students begin Italian as an optional subject.

(3) The General degree permits a wide choice of subjects.

4. RESIDENCE ABROAD

Honours students spend the long vacations (about five months) in France. Students go to holiday courses, take posts in families or at children's camps. Definite work is not prescribed. Permission to intercalate a year, so as to spend it abroad, may also be granted.

5. METHODS OF STUDY

(1) Lectures.
(2) Small discussion groups.
(3) Small groups for oral language work.
(4) Language classes (15 to 20 students).
(5) Individual guidance by tutorial interview.

II. ADMISSION TO COURSES

1. QUALIFICATIONS REQUIRED

Honours

(1) Qualifications as for London minimum entrance (i.e. Latin at 'O' Level).

(2) Pass in College Entrance Examination. (See II.2 below.)

(3) Applicants are advised to take three subjects at 'A' Level.

(4) Students who have taken Latin at 'O' Level only are expected to follow courses in Latin in their first year.

General and Subsidiary

'A' Level in French.

Applicants for admission to the General course take the Entrance Examination. (See II.2 below.)

French cannot be started from scratch.

2. SELECTION OF STUDENTS

College Entrance Examination: one written paper (for French as principal subject: prose, unseen, essay; for French as Subsidiary subject: prose, unseen) and oral examination. Stress is laid on high linguistic attainments.

3. TRANSFER

Students are admitted to the Honours course on entrance. Transfer is possible but rare.

4. NUMBERS

Approximately 20 to 25 students are annually admitted to the Honours School.

Information supplied by Professor J. S. Spink

UNIVERSITY OF LONDON: BIRKBECK COLLEGE

Department of French

I. COURSES OF STUDY

Students are normally admitted to Birkbeck College only if in full-time employment.

1. TYPES OF COURSES

(a) *Honours*
(b) *General*
(c) *Subsidiary*

2. CHARACTERISTICS OF COURSES

Courses of study are governed by the London University regulations, therefore details of courses, given for other Colleges of London University, are applicable.

3. COMBINATION OF SUBJECTS

Students have a wide choice, the commonest chosen being Latin, another modern foreign language, English or History. There are no compulsory combinations.

4. RESIDENCE ABROAD

Students are encouraged to spend time abroad during their course but as ours is a part-time institution this cannot be made compulsory. We do not set them work to do while abroad.

II. ADMISSION TO COURSES

1. QUALIFICATIONS REQUIRED

(a) Advanced Level Latin necessary for Honours.

(b) Both Honours and General must have Advanced Level French. The language cannot be started from scratch.

2. SELECTION OF STUDENTS

There is no entrance examination but there is dictation, a brief test and an interview conducted in French.

Students wishing to do Honours are usually expected to have spent a considerable time in France before entering upon the course. Many of them have spent at least a year there and quite a few have studied French either at a training college or at such places as the French Institute.

3. TRANSFER

(*a*) Students are admitted direct to Honours.

(*b*) Transfer is possible for students found to be unsatisfactory.

4. NUMBERS

Approximately 20 to 25 students are admitted to Honours.

Information supplied by Professor A. Carey Taylor

UNIVERSITY OF LONDON: KING'S COLLEGE

Department of French

I. COURSES OF STUDY

1. TYPES OF COURSES

(*a*) *Honours*; (*b*) *Subsidiary*.

(*a*) *Honours:* a four-year course including a year in France as assistant in a school under the official scheme.

(*b*) *Subsidiary:* a two-year course. The syllabus is part of the London General syllabus and includes the study of the modern language and one of two periods of literature, 17th and 18th centuries with prescribed texts or 19th century with prescribed texts and one 20th-century text.

2. CHARACTERISTICS OF COURSES

Honours

Literature. Lectures spread over the whole field, but students are encouraged to follow their own bent towards some degree of specialization which is made possible by the wide choice of questions in the Finals paper. Our aim is that every student should achieve (1) a general knowledge of who wrote what, when; (2) knowledge of the contents and historical significance of most of the main works, even if some must be at second-hand; (3) first-hand acquaintance with a comparatively limited number of writers.

The London syllabus provides for really close study of a Special Subject, often limited to the outstanding works of a single author. Courses are normally provided in three such subjects from which each student makes his own choice.

Language. We lay special emphasis on an accurate knowledge of the modern language which we want to be both scholarly and up to date. Our students mostly turn out to be fluent and phonetically correct speakers.

All students have to study the history of the language under the following heads:

(1) General history,
(2) Historical phonetics,
(3) Morphology,
(4) Syntax,
(5) Semantics.

Subsidiary

Subsidiary students will not be expected to know much about the general field of French literature, but will attend lectures on the period studied and seminars on the prescribed texts.

3. COMBINATION OF SUBJECTS

Honours

Students read a Subsidiary subject (part of the General course in that subject). Favourite subjects are Latin, English, Spanish, German. Others are possible, e.g. Philosophy, Geography, History.

4. RESIDENCE ABROAD

Honours

Required: the third year to be spent in France as assistant in a school under the official scheme.

5. METHODS OF STUDY

Our method involves a close integration of lectures and seminars (7-10 students) which we find very effective. Students are seen individually as necessary for handing back essays. Seminars involve reading and discussion of papers by students—either on topics or particular literary passages.

6. OTHER ACTIVITIES

We have an active *Cercle Français* which, for example, organizes an annual week-end of readings and discussions at Cumberland Lodge, Windsor Great Park.

II. ADMISSION TO COURSES

1. QUALIFICATIONS REQUIRED

Honours

(*a*) 'O' Level Latin is essential, 'A' Level Latin is strongly preferred.

(*b*) Three 'A' Level subjects are normally required; only in very exceptional cases will applicants with fewer be accepted.

2. SELECTION OF STUDENTS

Entrance test followed by interview. No special preparation is needed for the test, which at present consists of two one-hour papers; (1) translation into French, (2) *précis* in English of a French passage. No official syllabus is published.

Candidates who do well enough in the test are interviewed—usually twice as many as there are places available. Final selection (subject to entrance requirements through G.C.E.) is based on interview and test combined.

3. TRANSFER

(Does not apply.)

4. NUMBERS

About 30 students are admitted to the Honours School each year.

Information supplied by Professor J. M. Cocking

UNIVERSITY OF LONDON:
QUEEN MARY COLLEGE
Department of French[1]

I. COURSES OF STUDY

1. TYPES OF COURSES

(a) *Honours*; (b) *General*; and (c) *Subsidiary*, according to University of London syllabus.

2. CHARACTERISTICS OF COURSES

Lecture courses are given on the history of the language, prescribed medieval and Renaissance texts, and on modern literature.

During their first year students attend introductory lectures on literary criticism, French thought and civilization, the medieval and Renaissance backgrounds.

3. COMBINATION OF SUBJECTS

French Honours is usually taken with German, Spanish, Latin or English as a Subsidiary subject; occasionally History.

The students are free to choose for themselves. They may with special permission begin Spanish from scratch, but require passes at 'A' Level for admission to the other courses.

4. RESIDENCE ABROAD

Students are encouraged to spend a year abroad under the official scheme for assistantships in French schools. Otherwise they are expected to spend one month in France each year during vacation.

While abroad as assistants they are expected to do prose work or essays regularly under the supervision of the Department.

5. METHODS OF STUDY

For their modern literature studies during the whole of their course students work in groups under the supervision of lecturers, with whom they read representative texts month by month. They are directed to prepare essays on questions raised in this work. Throughout their course, during the first two terms of each year, they attend two or three weekly lectures on major authors or on major literary topics, selected according to the special interests and qualifications of

[1] This entry is an unrevised copy of the entry submitted by this Department to the 1961 edition. Applicants are strongly advised to check the information by reference to the current prospectus.

individual members of the staff. The third term in each year is specially devoted to detailed textual analysis.

6. OTHER ACTIVITIES

Other activities are assumed very largely by the French Society, which usually produces a French play during each session.

II. ADMISSION TO COURSES

1. QUALIFICATIONS REQUIRED

Honours

Two subjects at 'A' Level, of which one must be French; 'O' Level Latin accepted, but passes at 'A' Level preferred.

General and Subsidiary

'A' Level G.C.E. in French.

2. SELECTION OF STUDENTS

Selection of students is entirely by interview. The candidate is questioned as to his general intellectual interests as well as on matters of French literature and history. He is asked to read and translate a passage of fairly difficult French, so that his ability to tackle difficulties may be assessed.

Promise of intellectual progress is considered much more important than achievement at school. Candidates whose interest in the subject is merely perfunctory are rejected.

Most candidates are summoned for interview, but candidates living at a considerable distance and whose qualifications do not appear to be outstanding, are warned that they may be unsuccessful and are then summoned only if they insist on being interviewed.

3. TRANSFER

Students are admitted direct to Honours courses. Transfer to General courses during or at the end of the first year is permissible in exceptional circumstances.

4. NUMBERS

Approximately 25 are admitted annually to the Honours School.

Information supplied by Professor J. P. Collas

UNIVERSITY OF LONDON:
ROYAL HOLLOWAY COLLEGE[1]

Department of French

I. COURSES OF STUDY

1. TYPES OF COURSES

French can be studied as follows:[2]

(a) as a subject for an *Honours* degree in French with a Subsidiary subject—a three-year course;

(b) as part of a *General* course with two other subjects. At London it has recently been made a three-year course in the hope of (i) raising its standard as an educational course with a view to making it a reasonable avenue to teaching in grammar or other secondary schools; and (ii) encouraging students to take it who may be of good mental quality, but more apt for a three-subject than a one-subject degree course. There are three divisions in the final result, arrived at by comparison of performance in the three subjects.

(c) as a *Subsidiary* course. This is a two-year course offered by students who are taking an Honours course in another subject— usually German at Royal Holloway College. Qualitatively it is equivalent to the General French course, but quantitatively less.

2. CHARACTERISTICS OF COURSES

The Honours course provides normal training in the language, history of the language, medieval literature and texts; modern literature from 1600 to the present day. Concentration on chosen centuries for modern literature is henceforth allowed, to favour study in depth rather than a superficial or too eclectic overall study. Language training in this course includes conversation and discussion in French. There is also a Special Subject (literary or linguistic); we allow free choice in principle, restricted in fact by the staff problem. In some cases, we send students to other London Colleges for their Special Subjects (e.g. Romance Philology). Free choice is allowed, therefore, (i) in modern literature, and (ii) in Special Subjects.

Students reading the General or Subsidiary course have normal training in the language, and study prescribed modern texts (17th to 20th centuries) with general background. There are no options.

[1] Founded in 1886 as a college for women. In October 1965, 150 men will be admitted, thus doubling the number of first-year students. In three years the college will have a thousand students with a balance between the sexes.

[2] The London syllabus—as regards the Honours and the General courses and also a possible Combined Subject course—is at present under review.

3. COMBINATION OF SUBJECTS

For Honours French see I.1 above.

General students combine French with other Arts subjects.

Under the College's expansion plans for 1965–68 Spanish and Italian will be offered as Subsidiary subjects taught at the College, and it is envisaged that additional Subsidiary subjects, e.g. Russian and Philosophy, may be taught at the College in further phases of expansion.

4. RESIDENCE ABROAD

We have no rule concerning residence but strongly advise such residence in France as the student can undertake. We have, however for the present, an exchange arrangement with the University of Poitiers, by which first-year Honours students spend their first summer term taking courses at Poitiers. We encourage suitable students to interpolate between their second and final year a year in France as assistants.

5. METHODS OF STUDY

We have lecture courses; regular written exercises; proses, translations, philology; general essays in French; essays on the literature in French; partial tutorial system (i.e. essays are returned and discussed individually for about 20 to 30 minutes each); discussions and conversations in French, singly or in small groups. In philology, and also for the study of Special Subjects, some of the instruction is quasi-seminar.

6. OTHER ACTIVITIES

We have special lectures, given at the College by distinguished persons on miscellaneous subjects. We send students to London on occasions to lectures on special or wider interests, e.g. to University special lectures or to lectures at the *Institut Français*. The French Department also has some lectures by visiting lecturers organized in conjunction with students' French Society.

II. ADMISSION TO COURSES

1. QUALIFICATIONS REQUIRED

In the case of Honours students we accept the minimum entrance requirements of London University; but in principle, as regards Latin, we may require students to take a College Latin course in the first year, if they have not obtained 'A' Level Latin, so that they can cope with the history of the language required by the syllabus. In actual fact, we find that these cases seldom arise.

For General students, minimum entrance requirements are sufficient.

Students without previous qualifications in French (normally 'A' Level G.C.E.) are not admitted to these courses.

M.L.—C

2. SELECTION OF STUDENTS

At present there are two methods of application:

(*a*) through the College Scholarship Examination, held in the Michaelmas Term, on which Scholarships and Exhibitions are awarded.

(*b*) through the Universities' Central Council on Admissions. Candidates applying in this way are considered for vacancies and take no written papers, but must be prepared to come to the College for interviews.

Scholarship Examination

This consists of two papers:

(*i*) Composition and unseen translation,

(*ii*) Literature paper, giving candidates the opportunity of treating any three questions on subjects ranging from the 17th to the 20th century.

Candidates who have not obtained 'A' Level Latin and are not proposing to take it in the year of admission are required to take a Latin paper at the Scholarship Examination.

According to performance, a short list is made for interviews. Candidates who have been unsuccessful in obtaining an award may apply for admission, either to the Honours or General course, as under II.2 (*b*) above.

Honours candidates who propose to take Music as a Subsidiary subject are required to take an aural examination if summoned for interview.

Personal references: we welcome references and reports from head teachers and find them helpful, especially reports on candidates' linguistic and literary work, also on their general capabilities.

3. TRANSFER

We select our Honours candidates on the result of these interviews and they begin their course straight away. Transfer is possible, though, naturally, it does not often occur, since specialization has already begun; but we believe that candidates should do what they really want to do—subject, of course, to the other department concerned regarding their qualifications as satisfactory. If after a term of study we find a student not fitted for the Honours course we advise, though rarely insist on, transfer to the General course.

4. NUMBERS

As this is predominantly a residential college numbers are limited by the living accommodation available. In October 1965 and in each of the following two years a total of 25 students, men and women, will be eligible for admission to the Honours French course.

Information supplied by Professor H. J. Hunt

UNIVERSITY OF LONDON: UNIVERSITY COLLEGE

Department of French

I. COURSES OF STUDY

1. TYPES OF COURSES

(*a*) *B.A. French Honours:* a four-year course, with one Subsidiary subject, normally taken at the end of the second year. The third year is normally spent as an assistant in a French school. In special cases, students are excused the year in France and take their degree in three years.

No Joint Honours or General degrees.

(*b*) French as *Subsidiary* to another Honours subject (grammar, translation, literature): normally a two-year course, but sometimes compressed into one year.

2. CHARACTERISTICS OF COURSES

Honours course

In studying literature, we allow for some specialization according to individual preferences, but all students read at least some works from all the main periods from the 12th to the 20th centuries. Among Special Subjects, the Middle Ages, the Renaissance, and the contemporary period are always represented.

Modern French phonetics are dealt with in the Department of Phonetics; a certain amount of this work is a regular part of the French Honours course, but students who wish to can do more and take the College Certificate in French Phonetics.

The History of the French Language is a compulsory subject; it includes work on the development of the language in modern times. Comparative Philology is an optional non-examination subject.

Translation, essay-writing and oral work play a normal part in the course.

Subsidiary course

Translation, essay-writing, oral work. Literature with set books (students choose either a list of 17th–18th-century works or a list of 19th–20th-century works).

3. COMBINATION OF SUBJECTS

One Subsidiary subject, e.g. German, Italian, Spanish, English, Latin, History; Italian is the only one of these which can be started from scratch.

4. RESIDENCE ABROAD

See under I.1 (*a*) above.

5. METHODS OF STUDY

As is the case in most Arts departments, we work partly in classes with more or less formal lectures, partly in small tutorial groups. Each Honours student is attached to an individual member of staff for consultations.

II. ADMISSION TO COURSES

1. QUALIFICATIONS REQUIRED

The University of London entrance requirements for the Faculty of Arts (which include 'O' Level Latin).

2. SELECTION OF STUDENTS

(*i*) The application form is scrutinized and some applicants are rejected at this stage.

(*ii*) The applicants who appear most promising in (*i*) are tested by means of a two-hour written paper taken at school in January or February; there are special arrangements for invigilating those who have left school. The paper is designed to test mainly knowledge of French and handling of English; no special preparation is needed and there are no questions on literature. Applicants whose basic grammar is unsound or whose English is poor are eliminated.

(*iii*) Applicants who appear most promising under (*i*) and (*ii*) are asked to come for interview (normally in February and March), which is conducted partly in French but mostly in English. In recent years about one applicant in six has been interviewed, and about one in seventeen has been accepted.

(*iv*) Before offering a place to an applicant we attempt to sum up all the evidence gathered by (*i*), (*ii*) and (*iii*). It is impossible to put in order the various factors we consider, but they include: general intellectual keenness and initiative, linguistic ability, appreciation of literature and the fine arts, common sense, range of interests, ability to work with others and to join in the life of a community.

3. TRANSFER

(*a*) Students are admitted direct to Honours courses.

(*b*) Transfers are possible, but unusual.

4. NUMBERS

Thirty students are admitted annually.

Information supplied by Professor B. Woledge

UNIVERSITY OF LONDON:
WESTFIELD COLLEGE
Department of French Language and Literature

I. COURSES OF STUDY

Westfield College now admits men and women students and they are mainly resident. As many aspects of the London degree courses and examinations are at present under review it must be emphasized that the following rules apply to the situation as it exists in the academic year 1964-65.

1. TYPES OF COURSES

French may be studied in the following courses:

(a) *Honours.* A three-year course, with a Subsidiary subject normally completed by the end of the second year;

(b) *Subsidiary* to Honours in another subject. A five-term course normally completed by the end of the second year.

The College does not admit students to study for a General degree.

2. CHARACTERISTICS OF COURSES

The Honours course leads to the B.A. Examination of London University. This is on traditional lines and lays great stress on real ability in writing and speaking French, and in translation from and into French, requires the students to deal with literary topics and movements, individual authors and specially prescribed books, and demands some knowledge of the developments of the language and the literature from the earliest times to the present day. The two modern literature papers must be answered entirely in French. The oral examination carries as much weight as a written paper. In addition there is a Special Subject chosen from a list of ten or so. As far as possible these are provided for within the College, each member of the teaching staff dealing with his or her own speciality. We make a particular effort to make the element of 'option' a reality and thereby cater for all tastes, linguistic or literary, medieval or modern. We try to get a colleague from another College to supervise the work of a student who desires to take a subject which, for one reason or another, we are not teaching in any particular year.

Students may follow classes in languages other than those of their prescribed courses, e.g. in Spanish and Italian, and there is an opportunity for studying the less well known Romance languages. At present Rumanian is available for students who select Romance Philology as their Special Subject.

As a Subsidiary subject, translation from and into French, essay-writing in French and prescribed literary texts are studied over five terms (the summer term of the first year being normally spent abroad by students whose main language is German or Spanish).

3. COMBINATION OF SUBJECTS

The Subsidiary subjects studied with Honours French are German, Italian, Latin and Spanish; English and History will be added to this list in due course. There is no compulsory combination of subjects.

4. RESIDENCE ABROAD

There are no rules concerning residence abroad, but students are expected to use vacations for this purpose. In practice, all students spend some time in France. Financial help on a small scale is provided, when necessary, from a College fund.

Students may take a four-year course, spending the third year in France as assistants, under the official exchange scheme.

Students go where they please (or in the case of assistants where they are placed). No written exercises are required of them, but assistants must regularly attend some university courses during the whole of their year abroad.

5. METHODS OF STUDY

Teaching is by a combination of lectures, seminar classes and a tutorial system. A resident *lectrice* takes conversation classes with small groups of students throughout the whole of the three-year course. However, the principal method of study in this, as in all other University institutions, is the student's own reading, for which individual purchase, the College Library and the University Library provide the books. Guidance for this reading is provided in the tutorials and by advice for vacation reading, the results of which are tested by examinations at the beginning of the terms.

6. OTHER ACTIVITIES

Students run their own 'French Club', which is affiliated to the French Society of the University of London. The Department has a group membership in the French Institute.

II. ADMISSION TO COURSES

1. QUALIFICATIONS REQUIRED

A classical language at 'O' Level is a Faculty requirement.

For admission to the Honours course students are normally expected to have at least a grade B pass in French at 'A' Level and an 'A' Level pass in German or an 'O' Level pass in Italian, if they wish to take one of these subjects as subsidiary to French. Students taking Subsidiary French invariably have an 'A' Level pass. It is not possible to begin the study of French from scratch.

2. SELECTION OF STUDENTS

Applications for admission to the College are made through the Universities Central Council on Admissions. The process of departmental selection begins with a study of the applicant's qualifications as set out in the application form. The spread and quality of G.C.E. results are first considered. Evidence of general education and linguistic ability and referees' reports are carefully studied, and we try to make an assessment of character and the possibility of future development. Candidates we think to be promising are summoned for an interview conducted in English and in French, and we may ask applicants to demonstrate their ability to translate from and into French.

For intending scholars and exhibitioners there is an examination in which two French papers must be offered:

(1) prose composition and essay in French,
(2) translation from French and another question which may be of the commentary type, or require the ability to make an English précis of a passage of French, to draw conclusions from material supplied, or to define or illustrate the meanings of words or phrases.

Successful candidates are then interviewed.

3. TRANSFER

Students are admitted to the Honours course on entrance. At the end of the first year there is a departmental examination which must be passed if the student is to continue with the Honours course. As we do not take General students the question of transfer from one type of course to another does not arise. It is virtually impossible to change from one Honours subject to another after the three-year course has started.

4. NUMBERS

Up to 20 students will be admitted each year to the Honours School of French. Increases above this number must depend on the physical expansion of the College.

Information supplied by Professor R. C. Johnston

UNIVERSITY OF MANCHESTER

Department of French Studies

I. COURSES OF STUDY

1. TYPES OF COURSES

(*a*) *B.A. with Honours in French Studies.*

(*b*) *B.A. with Honours in Modern Languages.* French may be either the first or the second of the two languages studied, the other language being German, Italian, Russian or Spanish.

(*c*) *B.A. with Honours in French and Drama.*

(*d*) *General Degree of B.A.* for which French may be studied in combination with other subjects taught in the Faculty of Arts. Instruction is provided at three levels: Intermediate (1st year), General (2nd year), Special (3rd year).

(*a*) and (*d*) are three-year courses.

(*b*) and (*c*) are four-year courses.

2. CHARACTERISTICS OF COURSES

The following remarks are applicable to (*a*) and, with minor modifications, to (*b*) and (*c*) above.

The broad principles on which the course is based are those put forward by P. Mansell Jones in his article *Modern Humanities in the Technological Age* (M.U.P. 1957), namely that 'honours in our subject should be conceived as a type of humane study, a course in modern humanities'. At the centre of the curriculum is the study of French language, literature and thought, and no student is allowed to omit any one of these aspects of the course, but a system of options which comes into play at the beginning of the second year permits a first step towards specialization according to personal inclinations. A second step in this direction is taken at the beginning of the third year when students choose a Special Subject in which they pursue intensive study, leading to the writing of a short thesis on a topic arising from the Special Subject course.

The first-year syllabus is designed as an introduction to the study of French language, literature and thought, based on a small number of representative texts. The Preliminary Honours Examination taken at the end of the first year concludes this cycle. The second part of the course extends over two years and leads to the Final Honours Examination. Apart from courses intended to strengthen the students' command of written and spoken French, this second cycle includes altogether seven courses, at least three of which are literary (including one concerned with Old French texts), one linguistic and one concerned with the history of French thought. The sixth course can be taken either in literature or in philology or in the history of French art. The seventh is a Special Subject course taken in the final year. Instruction is offered in 16 Special Subjects catering for a wide range of interests: in literature, language, thought, history, history of art, political theory, etc. The study of French literature, apart from the Old French Texts course, is arranged according to *genres*: novel, drama, and lyric poetry, each of which forms the subject of a two-year course.

3. COMBINATION OF SUBJECTS

Students reading for the degree of B.A. with Honours in French Studies are required to take a course in a specified period of French history (usually the 17th and 18th centuries) in their second year. Their Subsidiary requirements include: (*a*) courses at Intermediate level in two subjects one of which must be Latin (good marks obtained at 'A' Level can exempt students from *one* of these courses), and (*b*) a course of General grade either in one of the subjects taken under (*a*) or in any other subject approved by the Board of the Faculty of Arts, e.g. English, History of Art, General Linguistics, Philosophy, etc. The Intermediate courses are normally taken in the first year, the General courses in the second year; but a student who comes to the University with an exemption mark in a Subsidiary subject is allowed to take it at General level in the first year.

4. RESIDENCE ABROAD

Existing arrangements, at present under review, enable all Honours students to spend the summer term of the second year at a French university. A wide choice is offered. Every encouragement is given to students to spend a year in France as assistants in French schools by allowing them to interrupt their course between the second and third year.

5. METHODS OF STUDY

Considerable emphasis is placed throughout the course on class work with small groups of students. This applies particularly to all forms of practical study, e.g. phonetics, conversation, prose composition, translation, *étude de textes* (a term recently adopted to replace the traditional *explication*), English essays and French *dissertations*. In *ex cathedra* lectures French is used sparingly in the first-year courses, but its use as a medium of instruction increases as the course progresses. Students are encouraged to make extensive use of the University Library which is particularly rich in the French field. The Reading Room of the French Department contains approximately 3000 volumes of its own kept on open shelves and is constantly adding to its collection of reference works and standard editions of French authors.

M.L.—C 2

6. OTHER ACTIVITIES

The students' French Society works in close collaboration with the teaching staff and helps to organize the extra-curricular activities of the Department such as public lectures by distinguished scholars from outside, informal talks by members of the staff on topics of general interest, staff-student debates, etc. The production of a French play, directed by a member of the staff with professional qualifications, is one of the features of the Society's annual programme.

II. ADMISSION TO COURSES

1. QUALIFICATIONS REQUIRED

Requirements for admission to the Honours School of French Studies or to the French part of the Honours School of Modern Languages are as follows:

In addition to the general entrance requirements agreed on by the constituent Universities of the Northern Universities Joint Matriculation Board, the Faculty of Arts requires a pass in Latin at either 'O' or 'A' Level in the G.C.E. examination. The French Department requires a mark at the G.C.E. 'A' Level of grade B in French, *and* two Bs *or* one A and one B or C in two other subjects. Although the department does not stipulate that candidates must take a paper at 'S' level, very careful consideration will be given to results obtained in such papers, whether in French or in any other subject, and candidates are encouraged to take them. These conditions may be varied in exceptional cases, but candidates offering two G.C.E. 'A' Level subjects only are likely to be handicapped in the present severe competition for places. It may well be that in the light of experience gained as a result of the change taking place in 1963 in methods of recruitment, the Department may be led to alter these requirements at short notice. It is difficult to foresee what precise changes, if any, might come about, but it appears at any rate most unlikely that the recommendation concerning the 'S' paper would be modified.

It is not permitted to take even the most elementary course in French (Intermediate I (1) and I (2)) without some previous knowledge of the language.

2. SELECTION OF STUDENTS

Candidates are normally selected on their performance at the G.C.E. 'A' Level, account being taken of head teachers' reports on school work. Applicants through the UCCA may also be offered places as a result of exceptional performance in the University Entrance Scholarship examination. This consists of three papers, of which one (General Studies) is compulsory, one is, naturally, French, and the third may be chosen from a wide range in either Arts or Science. The paper in French consists of translation from and into French, a short essay in French and questions on French grammar.

Interviews are given only in exceptional cases. Such interviews consist of an informal conversation, from which evidence of the candidate's range of interests, maturity, personality and ability to express himself can be acquired.

3. TRANSFER

Students are admitted to Honours courses on entrance, but transfer is possible.

4. NUMBERS

About 90 students are admitted annually to the Honours School.

Information supplied by Professors E. Vinaver and F. E. Sutcliffe

UNIVERSITY OF NEWCASTLE UPON TYNE

Department of French Studies

I. COURSES OF STUDY

1. TYPES OF COURSES

French can be studied in this University:

(*a*) as a *Single Honours* course;

(*b*) as one subject in a *Joint Honours* degree;

(*c*) as one of three subjects for a *General* degree. In the third year, a student has the option of studying only two subjects, taking an intensive course in one of them.

2. CHARACTERISTICS OF COURSES

The courses for both General and Honours degrees give training in the written and spoken practice of the French language and present a picture of the civilization of France through the medium of her literature. They aim at an education that is humanistic and which, owing to the central position of France in the development of the West, touches many aspects of European civilization as a whole.

In the General course, besides practice in the French language (essay-writing, translation and conversation), representative works from the 17th to the 20th centuries are studied.

In the Honours course, similar practical work is done but at a more advanced stage. The texts prescribed for detailed study and for general reading cover the whole range of French literature from the Middle Ages to the present day, and are studied in relation to the history and society of the age to which they belong. The first year is devoted to the study of the literature of the contemporary period. In addition, in the first two years of the course, undergraduates study the history of the French language, and, in their final year, choose one of several Special Subjects. Courses in the History of Art are available, and optional questions on art and music are included in the Final Honours papers.

Students reading French for a Joint Honours degree in French and German, or in French and Spanish, are normally excused all study of medieval French language and literature of and historical grammar.

3. COMBINATION OF SUBJECTS

For a Joint Honours degree French can be combined with German or Spanish.

For a General degree French can be combined with the usual range of B.A. subjects.

4. RESIDENCE ABROAD

Honours students are required, as an integral part of their studies, to intercalate a year as assistants in France or a French-speaking country, between the second and third years of their course.

General degree students who offer final examination papers in French are required to have spent at least a month during a vacation in a French-speaking country.

5. METHODS OF STUDY

For Honours students, lectures are supplemented by regular tutorials; and both General and Honours degree students are taken in small groups for conversation by a French lector. A language laboratory is shortly to be installed.

6. OTHER ACTIVITIES

There is a departmental society, *La Soirée Française*. A play is produced every year.

II. ADMISSION TO COURSES

1. QUALIFICATIONS REQUIRED

Both General and Honours degree students must have passed in French at 'A' Level. 'O' Level Latin is a Faculty requirement.

2. SELECTION OF STUDENTS

Selection is based on 'A' Level marks. Candidates are usually interviewed before a place is offered.

3. TRANSFER

Students are admitted to Honours courses mainly on entrance; but a few come in after first-year General studies.

4. NUMBERS

At present, about 20 students are admitted annually to the Honours School.

Information supplied by Professor P. J. Yarrow

UNIVERSITY OF NOTTINGHAM

Department of French

I. COURSES OF STUDY

1. TYPES OF COURSES

The Department of French offers three main courses:

(*a*) French as a *Single Honours* course;
(*b*) French in a *Joint Honours* course;
(*c*) French as a *Subsidiary* course.

There is no General degree in French. Students who, having started an Honours course, are found to be unequal to it, may be asked, after the first or second year, to change to a Pass degree course (see below).

French studies are divided into courses for Part I (first and second years) and for Part II (third year). Students reading French as a Single Honours subject take Part I and Part II in French, and Part I in some other subject. Students reading French in a Joint Honours course with Latin take in Part I papers A(*i*), A(*ii*) and B(*ii*) below, with three Latin papers and a French Oral; and in Part II they take (*i*), Option I (*iv*) and one paper chosen from Option II (*iv*), (*v*), (*vi*), Option III (*iv*), (*vi*) below, with three Latin papers and a French Oral. Students reading French in a Joint Honours course with German, Russian or Spanish take in Part I a special paper Translation from and into French, A(*iii*) and either B(*i*) or B(*ii*) below, with three papers in the second language and an Oral in both languages; and in Part II they take (*i*), (*iii*) below and any two of the nine papers set out in the three Options, with four papers in the second language and an Oral in both languages. *The level of achievement eventually reached in each of the two languages in the Joint Honours degree will be considerably higher than that needed for Subsidiary French in a Single Honours degree, but it will be less than that needed for Honours French in a Single Honours degree.* Students reading French as a Subsidiary subject take Part I, papers A(*i*), A(*ii*), A(*iii*) only in French, this in addition to their Part I and Part II in their chosen Honours subject. Students reading for a Pass degree have a course specially adapted to their personal needs and abilities.

Part I in French consists of five papers, divided into two sections:

A. (*i*) Translation into French;
    (*ii*) Translation from French and French essay;
    (*iii*) Outlines of French literature (1500 to 1900).

B. (*i*) Contemporary French literature, life and thought;
    (*ii*) History of the French language, with prescribed texts.

Single Honours students take both A and B courses; Subsidiary students take A only.

Part II in French, which is for Honours students only, consists of six papers:

(*i*) French essay;
(*ii*) Translation from and into French;
(*iii*) Commentary on unseen French texts.

With these three obligatory papers are taken three more chosen from one of the following options:

Option I:

(*iv*) Modern French linguistics;
(*v*) French dialects and patois; *or* Old Provençal; *or* The linguistics of the Iberian Peninsula;
(*vi*) A chosen *genre* of medieval French literature with prescribed texts.

Option II:

(*iv*) History of French thought and institutions;
(*v*) French philosophical writers;
(*vi*) The growth of French Liberalism.

Option III:

(*iv*) French literature of any two of the following centuries: 12th, 13th, 16th, 17th, 18th, 19th, 20th;
(*v*) History of French criticism;
(*vi*) One of the following subjects: *Les chansons de geste*, *Le Roman de la Rose*, Ronsard, Racine, Rousseau, Zola, Anouilh, Julien Green.

A French oral examination accompanies both Part I and Part II.

2. CHARACTERISTICS OF COURSES

The following features should be noted particularly.

(*a*) Particular importance is attached to proficiency in the language. In Part I, paper A(*i*), Translation into French, is a 'hurdle' paper; no student can go on to Part II Honours without having satisfied the examiners in this paper.

(*b*) The papers offered give the possibility of an unusually thorough training in French linguistics, culminating in very advanced work in Modern French linguistics and French dialectology.

(*c*) Similarly the papers offered permit a high degree of specialization in 20th-century French literature.

3. COMBINATION OF SUBJECTS

French Single Honours may be combined with Subsidiary English, Spanish, German, Russian (not beginners), Classics, Economics, Mathematics, History, Biblical Studies, American Studies, Music. French Joint Honours may be read with German, Latin, Spanish or Russian.

4. RESIDENCE ABROAD

All Honours students spend the third term of their first year under tuition at one of the following universities: Paris, Bordeaux, Caen, Grenoble, Lyon, Strasbourg, Toulouse. In the near future this term may be replaced by a compulsory year in a French university, intercalated between Part I and Part II. Until such time as this change is made, Honours students are being encouraged, but not compelled, to intercalate a year between Part I and Part II as paid assistants in French *lycées*.

5. METHODS OF STUDY

Both lecturing and tutorials are used, each lecture being supported by a tutorial in which the subject is considered in a practical way by a small group. Most of the lectures on literature are given in French, but not those on language or linguistics.

6. OTHER ACTIVITIES

The spoken language is perfected by tutorial groups given by French *lecteurs*, by classes in practical phonetics and by the use of tape recorders, wireless and gramophones. The University possesses a fully equipped language laboratory. There is an active *Cercle Français*, which brings French-speaking lecturers and films to the Department. Each year the Department produces a full-length modern French play, usually a first production in England.

II. ADMISSION TO COURSES

1. QUALIFICATIONS REQUIRED

Latin to 'A' Level if possible, although 'O' Level is accepted, together with two 'A' Level passes, of which French must be one, i.e. French with Latin, or, if Latin is at 'O' Level, then French with some other subject. 'S' paper qualifications are naturally preferred to mere 'A' Level passes.

2. SELECTION OF STUDENTS

Some 800 candidates apply for admission to the Department each year. This number is reduced to a short list of 150 by a careful scrutiny of the application forms, the careful filling in of which by candidates and head teachers is therefore of prime importance. The 150 candidates short-listed are each called for interview, given a short test (translation into French) and then seen by a team of members of the staff. Part of the interview is conducted in French. The matters discussed will usually be the candidate's reasons for wishing to read for an Honours degree in French; experience of travel, residence or study in France; personal preferences in French literature, music and art; ideas for an eventual career, etc.

3. TRANSFER

A candidate accepted for the Honours School of French can in no circumstance change to another Honours School. At the end of one or two terms, it may be suggested to him that he should change his Subsidiary subject, if he has failed badly in terminal examinations. If, at the end of either one or two years, he fails his examinations, wholly or partly, he may be moved from the Honours School and asked to do a Pass degree, this as an alternative to leaving the University.

4. NUMBERS

The annual intake of Honours students in French is 35, making an Honours School of 105. This is to be increased during the present quinquennium to 45. The number of Subsidiary students is about the same, this depending upon the requests from other Honours Schools. There are in addition some 20 graduates of Nottingham and elsewhere reading for Masters' or Doctors' degrees.

Information supplied by Professor L. Thorpe

UNIVERSITY OF OXFORD

Faculty of Medieval and Modern Languages (French) [1]

I. COURSES OF STUDY

1. TYPES OF COURSES

French may be studied

(a) as the subject for an *Honours degree in only one language*;

(b) as a subject for an *Honours degree in two languages*, of which French may be either the first or the second language.

(c) French may also be offered in the *Final Pass School*. (Undergraduates are now only rarely admitted to read for the Pass School.)

2. CHARACTERISTICS OF COURSES

In the first two terms of study undergraduates must work for the First Public Examination (normally the Preliminary Examination for Modern Languages) which in French demands prose composition; translation from French; prescribed texts (two papers) (a) chosen from 20th-century French literature and (b) illustrating French tragedy from Corneille to Villiers de l'Isle-Adam.

Undergraduates cannot read for Final Honours unless they have previously passed the First Public Examination in their first year of residence. Candidates offering French in the Final Honour School must take some or all of the following papers according to whether they offer it as sole (10 papers), first (7 papers), or second language (4 papers):

(1) Translation into French;

(2) Translation from French into English;

(3) Essay in French;

(4) History of the French language to 1250 (with prescribed texts);

(5) History of the French language with special reference to its present state (with prescribed texts);

(6) Period of literature: one or two of the following may be offered: (a) to 1515, (b) 1515–1715, (c) 1715–1914;

(7) Early texts prescribed for study as examples of literature;

(8) Prescribed authors: two of (a) Montaigne, Pascal, Molière, Racine and/or two of (b) Voltaire, Rousseau, Hugo, Flaubert.

[1] For further information on modern languages at Oxford see p. 348 below. Consult also the *Oxford University Examination Statutes*, where further details concerning the academic content of courses governing the Honours School of Modern and Medieval Languages and Literature are given.

Candidates offering French as sole language must take 1-5, 6 (two periods), 7, 8 (*a*) and (*b*); those offering it as first language must take 1-3, 5, 6 (one period), 7, 8 (*a*) or (*b*); and those offering it as second language 1, 2, 6 and 7.

A candidate aiming at a place in the First Class must also offer an optional subject, which may be taken in any language (there is a choice of 54 subjects in all, of which 14 are French or partly French subjects).

3. COMBINATION OF SUBJECTS

All combinations of subjects are set out in full in the Oxford University Examination Statutes.

4. RESIDENCE ABROAD

Residence abroad is encouraged whenever possible in vacations. In some colleges residence abroad is obligatory.

Some colleges encourage undergraduates to intercalate a year in France as assistants.

6. OTHER ACTIVITIES

Oxford has a *Maison Française*, which has a library of French books where students of French and others interested in France are welcomed.

It also has a French Club.

II. ADMISSION TO COURSES

1. QUALIFICATIONS REQUIRED

A sound knowledge of Latin is essential for undergraduates reading French as a sole or first language.

Except in the most exceptional cases, it would not be possible to start French from scratch, particularly since the normal rule in Colleges is that undergraduates who have not passed the First Public Examination by the end of their first year are sent down.

2. SELECTION OF STUDENTS

The selection of students is entirely in the hands of the Colleges. For particulars of College admission examinations see page 350 below.

The standard for admission to a College must be assumed to be higher than the minimum requirement laid down by the University for matriculation.

4. NUMBERS

Over 200 students are admitted annually to the Honour School.

Information supplied by Professor J. J. Seznec and Mr. A. D. Crow

UNIVERSITY OF READING

Department of French Studies

I. COURSES OF STUDY

1. TYPES OF COURSE

(a) *French Studies as a single subject course* lasting four years;

(b) *Combined subject courses* in:

French–German   Latin–French
German–French   French–Economics
French–Italian   English–French
Italian–French

All these courses last four years except English–French, which is a three-year course.

All courses leading to B.A. (single or combined subjects) are on the same academic footing: Honours are awarded on merit in the final examination. The General degree course has been replaced by specific listed courses in combined subjects.

(c) Special Subject: French is available as a Special Subject to students reading a number of degree courses: the particular subject being suited to the course in question.

2. CHARACTERISTICS OF COURSES

(i) (a) In all courses a high standard of linguistic proficiency is required of all students. In the final year, students are able to specialize in either certain literary options, romance philology, or the history of ideas. French social history and the history of institutions form an integral and large part of the course throughout. Special Subjects offer the possibility for additional fields as required.

(b) Teaching is by individual tutorial; also small groups and seminar classes. Lectures are kept to a minimum on the mornings of three days a week. The second year is organized as a single coherent course, with the study of literary texts (*explication*, tutorial essays, lectures, etc.) closely connected with the history of the language, social history, history of ideas. The fourth year is more specialized and comprises the treatment of special authors and topics.

(c) The Department has always specialized in the teaching of phonetics. Students record their exercises week by week in the same way as they attend weekly prose classes. Their proficiency is tested regularly and a phonetics test forms a separate part of the oral in the final degree examinations. Further developments are planned (in relation to Linguistics).

(ii) In the *French and Latin* course equal weight is given to the two subjects in the final examination. The French element is a good deal more selective than course (*i*) above, and students can emphasize either philological, literary or philosophical interests by choosing the papers they take; otherwise the demands of the course are the same as for French Studies (see also I.4, 5, 6).

(*iii*) In *Modern Languages* courses, it is possible to give greater weight to one or other language; in the final examination for Italian (or German) and French, for instance, there are four or five written papers in French Studies; in French and Italian (or German), on the other hand, six or seven in French Studies. There are possibilities in these courses for various experimental combinations and study programmes.

Arrangements for university study abroad are slightly different from those in French Studies (see I.4 below). Otherwise, the nature of the course is as described in paragraph I.2 (*i*).

(*iv*) In the *French and Economics* (four-year) course, the emphasis in French is on the contemporary language, the history of ideas in France, and modern European and French history and institutions. The Economics part comprises French Government and Politics, the History of Economic Thought (from the *Physiocrats* to the present day), Economic Organization (with specific reference to Modern France and Britain), Economic Theory, and either Economic Statistics or a further paper in Economic Theory or Organization or International Relations.

This integrated course is of interest to students whose future careers in business, public life or teaching would benefit by university studies having the kind of emphasis described.

3. COMBINATION OF SUBJECTS

For the First University Examination, any two other subjects taught in the Faculty are available. Thereafter in the final degree course one or two Special Subjects are taken from a list of courses available in the Faculty (e.g. Greek Drama, Latin Literature, Goethe, History of the Fine Arts in France, Italian Renaissance, an English topic or author, Aesthetics, a period of European history, etc.). Considerable latitude is available and new courses are devised in response to requirements. The Special Subject(s) form(s) part of the final degree examination.

The Special Subjects listed will be seen to be very varied in character and scope. They involve normally a weekly tutorial or seminar with written work throughout the four-year course. In some cases (e.g. Latin, German) the work will be of direct value to intending teachers: in all cases the aim is to provide a stimulating field of study which is both self-contained and of relevance to the main course.

4. RESIDENCE ABROAD

A full academic year (third year) is compulsorily spent at a French university; all arrangements, financial, academic, residential, etc., are made by, or under supervision of, the Department. Universities regularly attended include Strasbourg, Nancy, Grenoble, Dijon, Paris, Caen, Lille, Lyon, Poitiers, Toulouse, Bordeaux, etc. The arrangements are made on an individual basis; students' choices are taken into account and usually respected. Students follow courses for *Certificats de Licence* and for the *Agrégation*.

They are not required to sit French university examinations, but by their own wish frequently do.

While in France, students send essays back regularly (in addition to written work on the spot), correspond with their tutor, and are regularly visited in their university by a member of the Department (normally the Professor). Close contact is maintained with their immediate supervisors in France.

During this third year, students write a short thesis in French on a subject agreed between themselves and the Head of the Department.

In the Modern Languages courses, time is equally divided between universities in France and another country, half the year in each. Otherwise arrangements are the same.

In the *French and Economics* course arrangements are the same as for French Studies, except that students enrol in a French *Faculté de Droit et de Sciences sociales*.

5. METHODS OF STUDY

See I.2 above.

6. OTHER ACTIVITIES

In a closely integrated university, the various modern language clubs (French, German, Italian) play a lively part in student life.

II. ADMISSION TO COURSES

1. QUALIFICATIONS REQUIRED

(*a*) 'A' Level Latin is required, except for the French and Economics course; an 'O' Level pass may be accepted where a second modern foreign language is offered at 'A' Level.

(*b*) To candidates *not yet qualified* for matriculation, offers of places are normally made conditional upon reaching a standard of B or equivalent in two 'A' Level subjects, one of which must be French.

2. SELECTION OF STUDENTS

Selection is based on:

(*i*) Heads' reports,
(*ii*) Interviews and a short (one-hour) written test,
(*iii*) 'A' Level results only so far as involved in II.1 above.

Interviews. About two-thirds of candidates are interviewed. Those considered to have definitely no chances (school record, head teachers' report, etc.) are not interviewed.

Candidates indicating Reading as the university of their first choice are so far as possible interviewed earlier than others; nevertheless, all candidates applying before the closing date have equal consideration.

The interview lasts at least 30 minutes. Candidates are given opportunities to discuss their general reading, their curricular and extracurricular interests. Spoken French is briefly tested.

The Department is looking for students with lively intellectual interests from the start, as well as linguistic capacity.

3. TRANSFER

(a) Students when applying for admission indicate the course they wish to follow. They spend their first two terms, however, following courses in three subjects (including that or those in which they wish to continue) and in April sit the First University Examination in these subjects (nominally of equal weight).

(b) Students *may* without repeating a year transfer to a course other than that for which they were admitted, provided they have passed satisfactorily the appropriate subject or subjects in the First University Examination (taken at the beginning of the summer term in three subjects). E.g. A student admitted to read French, and including French and German in the first-university course could, if he wished, transfer to French–German, or German–French, or French–Economics, or German, or Philosophy, etc., provided his results in the relevant subjects in the First University Examination were satisfactory. Within the Faculty as a whole, about 20 per cent of first-year students do in fact avail themselves of this possibility of modifying to a greater or lesser extent their original intention on coming up.

4. NUMBERS

In the session 1962–63, 31 students were admitted to read French Studies, and 25 to read French as a combined subject. It is not the present intention that these numbers should be increased further.

Information supplied by Professor A. G. Lehmann

UNIVERSITY OF SHEFFIELD

Department of French

I. COURSES OF STUDY

1. TYPES OF COURSES

French can be studied in the following courses:

(*a*) *Special Honours in French:* French, a Special Subject (see I.2 below) and a Subsidiary subject;

(*b*) *Special Honours in a Dual Honours School:*

(*i*) Latin and French;

(*ii*) Modern Languages and Literature (French with English or German or Spanish);

(*iii*) Music and a Language;

(*iv*) Philosophy and a Language.

(No Special or Subsidiary subjects in any Dual Schools.)

(*c*) *General B.A. degree* in three subjects. Honours (two classes) awarded on all-round meritorious performance; also two Pass divisions.

All degree courses referred to above normally take three years and are divided into Intermediate (first) Year and the Final (second and third) Years.

(*d*) as *Subsidiary subject* to certain other Honours Schools. The examination is taken at the end of the second year and in that year a student can opt between the 17th–18th- and the 19th–20th-centuries literature programmes of the General degree course.

(*e*) as *Special Subject* to certain other Honours Schools. The examination is taken as part of the final examination and the programme is based on that for the General degree but reduced in scope.

(*f*) as *first- and second-year subject* in the course for the B.A. (Econ.) degree. The second-year course is a specially devised one of Subsidiary standard.

(*g*) as a *first-year subject* for degrees in Architecture.

2. CHARACTERISTICS OF COURSES

Options are possible mainly in the Honours School. Some parts of the Special Honours second-year are examined before the student's departure for France and not re-examined. For Finals, students have to choose one of eight Special Subjects: Romance Philology, Provençal, Spanish, German Literature, English Literature, a period of French History or Literature, or Latin.

3. COMBINATION OF SUBJECTS

For Special Honours in French, Latin is normally required as a first-year subject and as either a Subsidiary (one further year) or as a Special Subject (two further years).

For Dual Honours Schools, including French, a candidate accepted for both Honours Schools, has, at the end of the first year, no further Special Subject, Subsidiary or other Latin obligations.

For choice of Special Subjects see I.2 above.

For the General degree French is included among a list of 16 subjects, of which three have to be chosen; but there are no Latin requirements.

4. RESIDENCE ABROAD

Special Honours: one term's residence in a French university is compulsory, normally the third term of the second year. Honours students are encouraged but not obliged to spend a further year in France, usually under the official scheme for English assistants in French schools.

General degree: there are no obligatory requirements, but students are encouraged to spend as much time abroad as possible.

For the compulsory term, Honours students are scattered as widely as possible and concentration on one place is avoided. During this term all students are required to send in two essays from a wide choice. Students spending a year abroad in the interval between their second and third years are required to send in a monthly report of reading and general progress, occasional essays and other specimens of written work. Their queries are invited and answered.

5. METHODS OF STUDY

Numbers make tutorial tuition difficult for Intermediate and General students. The tutorial method is used for those parts of the Honours syllabus which allow options and elsewhere whenever possible. Conversation groups are kept as small as possible, especially in the final years and often take the form of tutorial groups.

6. OTHER ACTIVITIES

There is a flourishing *Cercle Français*. French plays are performed almost every year. Students can attend meetings of the Sheffield French Society. Lecturers from the *Institut Français du Royaume Uni* and other outside speakers visit the Department.

II. ADMISSION TO COURSES

1. QUALIFICATIONS REQUIRED

Basic requirements for admission to all degree courses are those of the Northern Universities Joint Matriculation Board. For Special

Honours in French or Dual Honours, including French, a reasonably good pass at 'A' Level in Latin is desirable; candidates who have only an 'O' Level pass (usually two years before entrance to the university) are required to provide evidence of some contact with Latin after 'O' Level.

French cannot be started from scratch.

2. SELECTION OF STUDENTS

There is no entrance examination apart from University Scholarships.

Method of selection. Application forms together with confidential reports from head teachers are carefully considered. Interviews are normally limited to applicants whose first choice is Sheffield and a relatively small number of very promising candidates. The interview (sometimes by a panel of departmental staff, sometimes by the Professor) is as informal as possible; it attempts to assess personality, nature of interest in French, likelihood of progress, reading habits, methods of work, powers of expression. It includes a brief reading and conversation test. The nature of the course is carefully explained to candidates.

Recommendations for firm or conditional acceptance are sent to the Dean of the Faculty and the nature of the recommendation is, in suitable cases, explained to the candidate. Most conditional acceptances are based on performance at forthcoming G.C.E. examinations, the 'A' Level grade normally required in French being B.

Much importance is attached to the head teacher's confidential report.

3. TRANSFER

(*a*) Students proposing to read for any Special Honours course involving French must take the Advanced Intermediate course in their first year. This first year is probationary and preparatory and definite admission to the Honours School is given at the end of it. Students not admitted to the Honours School read for the General degree.

(*b*) Transfer from Special Honours to General is thus made at the end of the first year. Transfer in the other direction is difficult, as it usually involves an additional year for the Advanced Intermediate course to be made up.

4. NUMBERS

Admission to the first (i.e. probationary Honours) year varies greatly from year to year. Up to now it has ranged between 30 and 50. Admission to the Honours School proper varies similarly from about

15 to 25. Admission to the ordinary Intermediate class (i.e. for students *not* proposing to read for Special Honours) is at present about 150; this class is split up into smaller groups for classwork. With the opening of the new Arts Building in 1965 these numbers will almost certainly be increased.

Information supplied by Professor H. W. Lawton

UNIVERSITY OF SOUTHAMPTON

Department of French

I. COURSES OF STUDY

1. TYPES OF COURSES

French is available as

(*a*) a *Single Honours* subject;

(*b*) a subject in a *Combined Honours* degree;

(*c*) a *Subsidiary* subject;

(*d*) an *Ancillary* subject.

Honours courses

Single Honours. French can be read as a Single Honours degree subject. This is a four-year course in which the student is required to spend the third academic year in France as an assistant in a French school. Students taking this course must in addition take an Ancillary subject for one year, e.g. English, German, Latin, Music, Spanish.

Combined Honours. French can also be read in combination with one other Honours subject. If the subject chosen is English, Latin, Music or Philosophy, the course will last for three years, and students will spend six months' continuous residence in France in the second year from the beginning of April to the end of September. This period will include at least one term at a French university. If the combining subject is German, History or Spanish, one year's residence abroad is required and the course will be of four years' duration.

2. CHARACTERISTICS OF COURSES

The courses have been drawn up so as to maintain a balance between the study of the language and the study of the literature, and between 'Old' French and 'Modern' French. They aim at developing a critical as well as a historical appreciation of literature and various aspects of French life.

Single Honours. This course is divided into two Parts, Part I being taken after two years and Part II after four years. Part I is general and comprehensive; Part II has been so arranged that students can, through their choice of Special Subjects, commentaries and the dissertation, give equal emphasis to the linguistic and literary sides, or specialize in one of these. Very few formal lectures will be given in Part II, and the teaching will consist almost entirely of tutorials and individual work with students.

Combined Honours. These courses are planned so that equal stress can be given to each of the subjects though in some instances more stress may be given to one of them.

3. COMBINATION OF SUBJECTS

Subjects usually read as Ancillary subjects by Honours French students are English, German, Latin, Music and Spanish, but it is possible to read other Arts Faculty subjects as Ancillary, with the permission of the Head of the Department. There are no compulsory combinations of subjects.

4. RESIDENCE ABROAD

One year, or six months, according to the course (see I.1 above).

5. METHODS OF STUDY

Great importance is attached to the tutorial system. The first-hand study of texts, and commentaries, are considered more important than reading about 'schools' and movements. Formal lectures are kept to a minimum. In addition to the regular staff, there are two *lecteurs* who conduct conversation and discussion groups in French throughout the session. There is also a Phonetics laboratory in which linguistic instruction is given by qualified members of the staff.

6. OTHER ACTIVITIES

There is a students' French Club; we are also in close relationship with the Modern Language Society, the *Alliance Française* and the Franco-British Society.

II. ADMISSION TO COURSES

1. QUALIFICATIONS REQUIRED

Admission to a Single Honours course in French requires three 'A' Level passes, including French and preferably Latin. A student may be admitted without 'A' Level Latin, provided he has passed 'O' Level Latin and has some compensation in the other 'A' Level marks.

Qualifications for entry to the Combined Honours courses are given in the University Calendar.

2. SELECTION OF STUDENTS

'A' Level results (see II.1 above). There is no entrance examination, but at the interview candidates are asked to speak in French and to read a passage of French prose or poetry. Great importance is attached to the head teacher's report.

3. TRANSFER

Transfers can, in exceptional cases, be arranged between Single and Combined Honours.

4. NUMBERS

Approximately 18 students are admitted annually to the Single Honours School of French and 24 to Combined Honours Schools, of which French is one subject.

Information supplied by Dr. E. Beaumont

UNIVERSITY OF WARWICK

School of French Studies and School of Literature[1]

I. COURSES OF STUDY

1. TYPES OF COURSES

French can be studied for an *Honours degree* in *either* the School of French Studies *or* the School of Literature.

2. CHARACTERISTICS OF COURSES

The Honours degree in French in both Schools will require knowledge to the same high level of the modern French language, both as written and as spoken, and of French literature during three of a possible five periods: to 1470; 1470–1630; 1630–1750; 1750–1870; 1870–present. Despite this division by periods, however, emphasis will be upon a literary-critical approach to texts far more than upon the history of French literature. A special subject will also be studied in the final year, taken from a list of both literary and non-literary possibilities.

In addition, the student reading in the *School of Literature* will undertake, throughout the three years of his course, a detailed study of selected authors and subjects drawn from European, including English, literature as a whole and follow courses dealing with the European epic, the European novel, European theatre, and, optionally, a subject in comparative literature. It is intended that in this way knowledge of the Western literary heritage in general shall complement and lend wider perspective to the student's work in French.

The student in the *School of French Studies* will extend his studies in a different way—by broadening his acquaintance with the civilization of France to include detailed knowledge of chosen aspects of French history, philosophy, political philosophy and/or contemporary political history and institutions. It is intended in this way to offer a degree course (not unlike those available in Classics and in Russian, American and similar 'regional' studies) that will provide more fully than is perhaps customary for those whose intellectual interests are historical, philosophical and/or political as much as literary or who seek an historical and philosophical background for their French literary studies. Each student will pursue during the second and third years of the course three of the following options, for which teaching will be provided in collaboration with the Schools of History, Philosophy and Politics:

(*a*) Philosophers of the 17th and 18th centuries;

[1] *Note.*—The information given is unavoidably provisional and should be confirmed by reference to the University Prospectus.

    (*b*) Philosophers of the 19th and 20th centuries;

    (*c*) Modern political philosophers;

    (*d*) A period of the history of France: (*i*) *c.* 1100–*c.* 1300; *or* (*ii*) *c.* 1450–*c.* 1650; *or* (*iii*) *c.* 1640–1789; *or* (*iv*) 1789–1945;[1]

    (*e*) A second period of the history of France;

    (*f*) Political history and institutions of France since 1945;

    (*g*) A literary option: *either* (*i*) prescribed authors *or* (*ii*) French literature to 1470: additional texts.

Note.—Options (*a*), (*b*), and (*c*) will require study of selected non-French as well as French thinkers. Those wishing to choose options (*c*) and/or (*f*) must follow a first-year course giving an introduction to government and politics. At least a good pass in 'O' Level history will be required of those choosing an option under (*d*). Those studying medieval French literature will be required in the final examination paper to show such knowledge of the medieval French language as is needed for the study of the literature as literature.

Students in both Schools of study will follow in the first year the same courses in French language and literature. In addition they will pursue a course in the School of Philosophy, obligatory for all freshmen, on Language and Logic, and they will also study and in the Preliminary Examination at the end of the first year be examined upon a secondary subject. For students in the School of Literature this subject must be the European epic; for students in the School of French Studies this subject may be literary, historical, philosophical or political or may be a second language (with literature), and it is expected that it will be selected with due regard for the student's intended choice of options at the end of the first year.

4. RESIDENCE ABROAD

It is expected that the majority of students will spend a year in France as assistants in French schools, between their second and third years of study. Those who do not do so will be required to attend French university courses of an approved nature and for a period to be laid down.

5. METHODS OF STUDY

Teaching will be by means of lectures, seminars and tutorials. All students will attend tutorials, in groups of not more than three.

II. ADMISSION TO COURSES

1. QUALIFICATIONS REQUIRED

In addition to satisfying university matriculation requirements, students of French in both Schools must have a good pass in French

---

[1] For reasons of staffing not all the alternatives under (*d*) will necessarily be available in any particular year.

at Advanced Level. For admission to the School of Literature applicants will be required in addition to have passed in 'A' Level English. A pass at 'O' Level in Latin will be required of those choosing to study medieval French literature.

2. SELECTION OF STUDENTS

Examination results, headmasters' reports and interviews, where these are thought desirable, will all be given due weight. Particular attention will be paid to evidence of decided intellectual interests of a literary, historical, philosophical or political nature, and interviews will be especially directed to ascertaining these interests.

3. TRANSFER

Students will make their final choice between the two Schools at the end of their first year; during this year there will therefore be marked ease of transfer.

4. NUMBERS

It is anticipated that about 30 students specializing in French will be admitted in 1965, about 50 in 1966 and about 65 in 1967.

Information supplied by Professor D. G. Charlton

UNIVERSITY OF WALES:
UNIVERSITY COLLEGE OF WALES, ABERYSTWYTH

Department of French and Romance Studies

I. SCHEMES OF STUDY

1. SCHEMES FOR THE DEGREE OF B.A.

(*a*) *Special in French* for three years, i.e. Part I, Special I, Special II; *or* joint schemes in French with other languages to be approved;

(*b*) *General Scheme*, i.e. Part I, General I and General II courses, three years;

(*c*) *Accessory:* at present a student taking Honours in another Department can take Accessory French: this is a two-year course consisting of Part I French and General I French. It is proposed to discontinue the Accessory courses from October 1964, or October 1965, as an obligation, but these may still be available on an optional basis, following proposals to integrate courses from the first year onwards for greater homogeneity of studies.

YEAR 1	YEAR 2	YEAR 3
PART I	PART II *Special Scheme* Special I 1st year	Special II 2nd year
	General Scheme General I 1st year	General II 2nd year

Students failing to gain Honours classification in either the Special or General Scheme may be awarded a B.A. (Pass) on the recommendation of the examining board.

2. CHARACTERISTICS OF COURSES

We make a special point of phonetics in second year for General and Special. We have recently instituted options *within* the Special Scheme for Italian and Spanish courses, lasting for two years in college, plus some work in the year spent abroad. Those choosing one of these languages are helped to spend the year in a part of France offering facilities for the second language (e.g. Toulouse or Grenoble). No formal demand for previous qualifications in the second language is enforced, but students are discouraged from attempting it if we do not deem them good enough. In place of it they can study aspects of modern French institutions. It is also possible to offer Spanish and Italian as subjects for Part I of a degree course. The aim of the present courses in Spanish and Italian is to give students a good working knowledge of the language, both written and spoken, and an introduction to the literature. Having specialists for Italian and Spanish, we try to extend all our linguistic and literary studies upon a comparative rather than a national basis in order to encourage a European approach.

3. COMBINATION OF SUBJECTS

(*a*) All students must follow three subjects *in all* in their first year. Their choice is free within the subjects provided in the Arts Faculty.

(*b*) Special students in French may be required to follow one Accessory course in another subject in their second year—choice free as in (*a*) above (but see I.1 (*c*) above).

(*c*) General students must follow two courses in second year, and two courses in third year.

(*d*) *No* compulsory combinations; other languages are the most frequent choice.

(*e*) An average Special group of 20–25 shows wide variety of combinations.

4. RESIDENCE ABROAD

(*a*) Special students are normally expected to follow at least one vacation course during their first two years at College, and must also spend one session in France, unless exempted on grounds of previous residence and proficiency in French. This session is intercalated between student's second and third College years, i.e. Special I and Special II.

(*b*) Students needing financial support are found self-supporting posts as English assistants in French schools.

(*c*) They are required to prepare and write during the year abroad a dissertation on a special subject of linguistics, literature, or general culture, at their choice.

(*d*) Students taking the General II course are normally required to follow at least one full-length vacation course before completing their degree.

5. METHODS OF STUDY

We use all standard methods: lectures, seminars, tutorials and oral classes (the latter taken by foreign assistants). Free use is made of the language laboratory.

6. OTHER ACTIVITIES

Any student can follow an additional course without examination. The flourishing departmental Society provides a full programme of social, dramatic and musical activities, the French play being a highlight of the College year. Lecturers from the *Institut Français du Royaume Uni* and other outside speakers visit the Department.

II. ADMISSION TO SCHEMES

1. QUALIFICATIONS REQUIRED

All entrants *must* have a good 'A' Level pass in French, or something deemed equivalent. No formal requirement in Latin for any course.

All entrants take the Part I course in their first year and then proceed to the Special Scheme, Accessory (supporting Special I in another subject for one year) or to the General Scheme.

2. SELECTION OF STUDENTS

Selection of students is based on:

(*a*) 'A' Level and 'S' paper results,

(*b*) interviews in selected cases which are not otherwise clear,

(*c*) entrance scholarship examination (also used as entrance test),

(*d*) personal reports, primarily those of head teachers.

The greatest weight is given to good performance in grammar, translation and prose composition, and candidates cannot give too much attention to these basic exercises.

3. TRANSFERS

(*a*) No student is finally accepted for either Scheme until the end of his first year.

(*b*) Transfer will not normally be possible.

4. NUMBERS

At the present time 20 to 25 students are accepted for Special yearly, and 15 to 20 for General. The annual entry into Part I is about 75 students.

Information supplied by Professor E. R. Briggs

UNIVERSITY OF WALES:
UNIVERSITY COLLEGE OF
NORTH WALES, BANGOR
Department of French and Romance Studies

I. COURSES OF STUDY

1. TYPES OF COURSES

French courses are divided as follows:

Part I: There is a common Part I with two streams:

(A) for Pass students;

(B) for intending Honours students.

In (A) the literary emphasis is on the 19th and 20th centuries;

In (B) it is equally divided between classical and modern.

Intending Honours students must also take a course in French linguistics.

Part II: Pass degree. French can be taken either as a Main subject (two years) or as an Auxiliary (one year), the latter being the first year of the Main course. In addition to the usual language work, the first year deals with classical and 19th-century literature, the second with further classical and modern texts but particularly with the 18th century.

Part II: Honours degree. Courses are given on:

(*i*) medieval and Renaissance literature;

(*ii*) literature from 1600 to 1850;

(*iii*) literature from 1850 (Symbolist poetry, novel, drama).

In addition, one of the following special subjects:

(*i*) the Development of French Philosophical Thought from 1800, combined with 19th-century French History and Civilization;

(*ii*) Romance Philology, with special reference to French, Provençal and Italian;

(*iii*) Italian.

Accessory courses in French for other Honours schools: English, Welsh, German, Economics and Music.

2. CHARACTERISTICS OF COURSES

See I.1 above.

A distinctive feature of the Honours course is the opportunity provided for the study of French philosophical thought.

3. COMBINATION OF SUBJECTS

The following subjects can be combined with the study of French in the Pass course: English, German, Italian, Russian, Welsh, Latin, Greek, Hebrew, History, Philosophy, Linguistics, Biblical Studies; also Economics, Education, Music, Mathematics, Welsh History and Archaeology.

Honours students take a one-year Accessory course which is examined at the end of the second (i.e. first Honours) year. Accessory courses to Honours French are Latin, English, Welsh, German, Italian, Russian, Romance Philology, Linguistics, Phonetics, History and Philosophy.

There is also a *Joint Honours course in French and German*, lasting four years. The course in French comprises the language work (prose composition, etc.) and, with the exception of the medieval texts and authors, the periods of literature prescribed for Single Honours in French. Candidates for Joint Honours do not take an Accessory subject.

4. RESIDENCE ABROAD

Honours students are required to spend a session in France as assistants in French schools between the first and second years of the Honours course. They are required to attend, wherever possible, a recognized university course in France. No set work is prescribed, but they are given advice as to reading, etc., and they are recommended to follow correspondence courses in advanced prose composition provided by the British Institute in Paris.

Students taking Joint Honours in French and German must spend one summer term of the first two Honours years at a French university and the other at Tübingen University.

5. METHODS OF STUDY

Teaching methods are a combination of lecture, seminar and tutorial.

II. ADMISSION TO COURSES

1. QUALIFICATIONS REQUIRED

For entry into Part I 'A' Level French is required. All students accepted for Honours (at the end of their Part I year) must have 'O' Level Latin (or Greek) or show proof of having reached an equivalent standard.

2. SELECTION OF STUDENTS

Admission of all Arts students is in the hands of the Dean. Entry is determined by 'A' Level results. In particular cases where it seems desirable in the light of head teachers' reports candidates are interviewed by the Department.

There is no special departmental selection on admission. Students, fulfilling the conditions mentioned in II.1 above, are permitted to enter the appropriate French class.

Selection of Honours students takes place at the end of the first (Part I) year and is based on examination results, oral and interview and general progress throughout the year. The selection is intensive, the criteria being not only a high degree of competence and ability to work independently, but evidence of critical judgment, power of reasoning and mental alertness.

3. TRANSFER

Honours students are selected at the end of the first (Part I) year (see II.2 above).

A student who has completed the first year of the Part II Pass course may, if proper evidence is forthcoming, be admitted to Honours courses making a four-year B.A. course necessary.

4. NUMBERS

Between 15 and 20 students are selected annually at the end of the first year for the Honours course (Single or Joint).

Information supplied by Professor I. W. Alexander

UNIVERSITY OF WALES:
UNIVERSITY COLLEGE, CARDIFF

Department of French

I. COURSES OF STUDY

1. TYPES OF COURSES

French is available in the following courses:

(*a*) *Part One*, which all first-year students of French pursue, consists of a close study of three prose texts (late 19th and 20th century) and an anthology of 19th- and 20th-century poetry, with special emphasis on *explication de textes*, in addition, of course, to the usual translation exercises and a course on phonetics and general linguistics.

(*b*) *Main* (Pass B.A.), pursued in their second and third years by Pass degree candidates: it conforms to much the same pattern as the Part One course, except that the texts are representative of a wider field (i.e. 17th, 18th and 19th centuries). We intend to introduce more history of literature at this stage. There is also a course on semantics.

(*c*) *Honours*, pursued by Honours students in their second and fourth years (their third year being spent in France). This covers the whole field of French literature and includes a study of Old French language and literature. It also includes a study of Italian, plus a course in French philosophy.

2. CHARACTERISTICS OF COURSES

We attach importance to

(*a*) *explication;*

(*b*) the use of the French language in literature papers. All lectures on literature are given in French, and at least half of each literature paper, at each stage, has to be answered in French. With one exception (an option between medieval language and medieval literature) all students follow the same course.

3. COMBINATION OF SUBJECTS

Italian, English, History and Philosophy are the other subjects usually studied by students of French. There is no compulsory combination of subjects, except that Honours students have to study Italian, with special reference to Dante and Petrarch; they also have to pursue a course of study in French philosophy.

4. RESIDENCE ABROAD

All Honours students are required to spend a year in France between the first and second year of their Honours course (i.e. in their third year). Students usually take posts as assistants in various parts of France. They are given comprehensive reading lists. They also send us, regularly, written exercises in Old French language. They are also recommended to follow correspondence courses in Advanced Prose Composition organized by the British Institute in Paris, and almost all of them do this.

5. METHODS OF STUDY

All classes are split up into small groups of about six for discussion, in French, of texts and special difficulties, and into groups of not more than 20 for prose composition.

6. OTHER ACTIVITIES

We have an active French society, whose proceedings are conducted, by the students, in French. Gramophone recitals and dramatic performances are a main feature of its activities.

II. ADMISSION TO COURSES

1. QUALIFICATIONS REQUIRED

We require a pass at 'A' Level of the G.C.E. of all students of French. Some knowledge of Latin is desirable but not an essential requirement.

2. SELECTION OF STUDENTS

We rely entirely on 'A' Level results; we also like students to have had a good mark in their prose composition and essay paper, though we have no hard-and-fast rule about this.

3. TRANSFER

Students are admitted to the Honours course at the end of their first year, on the results of the Part One examination.

Transfer is not possible.

4. NUMBERS

We admit, on an average, about 15 students to the Honours course every year.

Information supplied by Professor J. H. Thomas

UNIVERSITY OF WALES: UNIVERSITY COLLEGE OF SWANSEA

Department of Romance Languages

I. COURSES OF STUDY

1. TYPES OF COURSES

French can be studied in the following courses:

(*a*) *Honours* in French only;

(*b*) *Joint Honours* in French and German (five courses in French and three in German, or vice versa);

(*c*) French as a subject for the *General degree*.

The first-year course known as Part I is in three subjects (see I.3 below) and is followed by either two years of Honours courses (separated by a year abroad) or two years of General degree courses.

2. CHARACTERISTICS OF COURSES

In the Honours School four principal courses of two hours a week each, run through the two years (with a gap in France) and comprise: Old and Middle French language and literature (the latter treated as literature as far as possible, not as linguistic material); 17th-century drama; 18th-century novel and thought; 19th–20th-centuries novel and poetry.[1] There is an optional subject (two hours a week) in the final year, with a (fairly) free choice from about five subjects. All students follow a History of the Language course, which emphasizes the human and social aspects of language, and a Rhetoric course, covering the literary use of French from medieval to modern times. An optional course in Romance linguistics covers the work of traditional philologists, of linguistic geographers and of the sociological and structuralist schools. Normal language work, modern institutions, etc.

3. COMBINATION OF SUBJECTS

First-year students take a Part I course in three subjects. In theory these may be freely chosen from the eleven Arts departments; in practice they are limited to subjects passed at 'A' Level, except that Italian, Russian, Philosophy, Politics and Economics may be taken from scratch. The subjects most commonly studied with French are History, English, German, Italian, Philosophy, Classics. Part II of

---

[1] Of the last three one will henceforth be dropped in the final year.

the General degree will henceforth consist of two subjects normally chosen from those completed in Part I.

The only concomitant of an Honours subject is an Accessory course 'of Honours character' in another subject, pursued two hours a week for one year—most commonly Linguistics; or The Nature of Tragedy (Greek, English, French, German); or Literature and Society, 12th–14th Centuries.

German is the only subject that can be combined with French for an Honours degree (see I.1(*b*) above); Italian and Spanish will doubtless be added later.

4. RESIDENCE ABROAD

All Honours students are required to spend one academic year in France. They apply for posts as assistants (rejection is quite exceptional), intercalating this year between the two of the Honours courses. They thus go where sent, into the four corners of France.

Students send home two *versions* (prepared) per term, from French papers or journals at the student's choice; and a long French dissertation on an approved subject—*either* a contemporary author not in the syllabus *or* an aspect of French life observed by the writer.

5. METHODS OF STUDY

There are no survey courses: the syllabus is therefore selective. Literary work is closely linked to the study of texts, and accompanied by *explication de textes* (in a spirit permitting equal attention to content and expression), which is done in tutorial groups. Prose composition is being partially replaced by alternative teaching methods at elementary levels. The guiding principles of the Department may be studied in a book prepared by R. C. Knight and F. W. A. George, *Advice to the Student of French* (Blackwell).

6. OTHER ACTIVITIES

The annual French plays presented by the French Society are a feature of the Department's life.

II. ADMISSION TO COURSES

1. QUALIFICATIONS REQUIRED

There are no official requirements above those for matriculation; but only some other proof of competence would be accepted in place of an 'A' Level pass in French for admission to Part I. (French cannot be started from scratch.) There is no Latin requirement. There are no special requirements at entrance for Honours (but note II.3(*a*) below).

2. SELECTION OF STUDENTS

Places are offered on the results of the Open Scholarship examination (two subjects, with no special syllabus above 'A' Level, plus essay and general paper; this examination may be sat in school). Otherwise, the Department is guided by school reports and examination marks. Some candidates are interviewed by a member of the French Department, sometimes assisted by colleagues teaching subjects the candidate will take in Part I. They try to gauge mental activity and curiosity, width of interests and cultural background. For other candidates the Department requires a certain grade in the 'A' Level examination for lack of a better criterion (recently B in two subjects or C in three).

3. TRANSFER

(*a*) Admission to Honours is granted on the results of the June examination of Part I. In French (and some other subjects) the syllabus of the Part I course is slightly extended for intending Honours students. In exceptional cases candidates who have not satisfied this requirement may submit qualifying essays after the summer. It is common for candidates rejected by one Honours School to seek admittance to another.

(*b*) Any kind of transfer is theoretically possible, but in mid-course will usually need an extra year.

4. NUMBERS

The annual intake has risen to 20, including one to three Joint French and German Honours.

Information supplied by Professor R. C. Knight

ST. DAVID'S COLLEGE,[1]
LAMPETER
Department of French

I. COURSES OF STUDY

1. TYPES OF COURSES

French may be studied in the following courses:

(*a*) *Part One*, which is pursued by all first-year students of French, consists of a detailed study of five texts ranging from the 17th century to the 20th century. Courses are also taken in translation from and into French, essay-writing, phonetics and general linguistics.

(*b*) *Part Two*, which occupies two sessions during which students can read French for either of the following degrees:

> (*i*) *B.A. General degree.* This scheme of work is spread over the second and third years and involves the study of two main subjects. The courses in French cover the same fields as those mentioned for Part One, but there is greater emphasis on *explication de textes*. In addition, students follow courses in stylistics and semantics.

> (*ii*) *B.A. Honours degree.* This scheme of work occupies the second and fourth years (the third year being spent in France). The courses cover the whole field of French language and literature from the medieval to the modern. In addition, students take special courses in French philosophy (from Descartes onwards) and in German (including a study of Goethe).

2. CHARACTERISTICS OF COURSES

In all the courses mentioned, we attach particular importance to *explication de textes* and to a sound knowledge of the written and spoken language.

Study in vacation is an integral part of every course taken.

3. COMBINATION OF COURSES

General degree students in their first year combine the study of French with two subjects selected from the following: Greek, Latin, English, Welsh, Philosophy, History, Pure Mathematics, Biblical Studies, and Graeco-Roman Literature and Civilisation. German will be added in 1965–66. For their final examination they study two

---

[1] Founded in 1822, St. David's College, Lampeter, Cardiganshire, is not a constituent college of the University of Wales. It is autonomous and grants its own degrees.

Main subjects from the three read in the first year. There is no compulsory combination, but students receive advice from a Courses Committee upon entry.

Prospective Honours students read two other subjects (as above) during their first year, and then drop them so as to concentrate on French. There are no Joint Honours courses, but all Honours students in French are required to pursue the special courses in Philosophy and German mentioned in I.1(*b*)(*ii*).

4. RESIDENCE ABROAD

Honours students must intercalate a session in France (usually as assistants at a French school) between the first and second year of their Honours courses.

General degree students are encouraged to follow a vacation course in France some time during their final year.

5. METHODS OF STUDY

Teaching is by a combination of lectures, tutorials and oral French hours. As this is a residential college, the tutorial system is much in favour.

II. ADMISSION TO COURSES

1. QUALIFICATIONS REQUIRED

Entrants must have an 'A' Level pass in French. Students accepted for Honours must have some knowledge of Latin, but there is no formal requirement.

French cannot be started from scratch; but, in the case of French Honours candidates, it will be possible to do so in German.

2. SELECTION OF STUDENTS

This is based on:
(*a*) 'A' Level and 'S' paper results;
(*b*) Personal reports, especially from head teachers;
(*c*) Personal interview.

Selection of Honours students takes place at the end of the first (Part One) year and is based on examination results and general progress throughout the year.

3. TRANSFER

No distinction is made between Honours and General students during the first year (see II.2 above).

Transfer from General to Honours, or vice versa, is not normally possible thereafter.

4. NUMBERS

At present there is no restriction on the number of students admitted to the Honours School of French.

Information supplied by Dr. R. S. Jones

UNIVERSITY OF ABERDEEN

Department of French

I. COURSES OF STUDY

1. TYPES OF COURSES

French can be studied in this University:

(*a*) as part of an *Ordinary* (i.e. a 'Pass' or 'General') *degree* course.

(*b*) as one subject in a two-subject *Joint Honours degree* course in *Modern Languages*, and

(*c*) as a *Single Honours degree* course.

Ordinary degree. A three-year course, in which a student must complete seven 'degree courses'. To study the subject for one year (first-year or Ordinary course) counts as one such course; to study it for two years (i.e. Ordinary, and second-year or Advanced course) counts as two such courses. The language cannot be studied further than this in the Ordinary degree course. Thus French can be studied by Ordinary degree students for one or two years (consecutive or otherwise) in their three-year degree course. Examinations are held at the end of the Ordinary and Advanced courses.

In the *Joint Honours degree* course in *Modern Languages* and in the *Single Honours degree* course in *French Language and Literature*, French is studied for four years, termed Ordinary, Advanced, Junior Honours and Senior Honours years. The courses normally take five years, since students are encouraged to spend an academic session abroad, but it is possible to complete the degree in French Language and Literature in four by fulfilling the stipulated minimum requirements of nine months' residence in a French-speaking country during the long vacations. In the first two years the courses are those taken by students for the Ordinary degree and entrance to the Honours courses proper is only after students have successfully completed the Ordinary degree courses in French.

2. CHARACTERISTICS OF COURSES

(*a*) *Ordinary degree*

  (1) *Ordinary* (first-year course)

    (*a*) Translation and prose composition (one hour per week);

    (*b*) Literature and civilization (1800–1950) (four hours per week);

    (*c*) Tutorial (one hour per week).

  (2) *Advanced* (second-year course)

    (*a*) Translation, prose composition and free composition (one hour per week);

(*b*) Literature and civilization (1600–1800) (four hours per week);

(*c*) Phonetics and oral practice (one hour per week).

(*b*) *Honours degree*

(1) *Joint Honours in Modern Languages*

The course lasts two further years. Unlike the Ordinary degree course which aims at giving the students a general picture of French civilization and culture between 1600 and the present day, the Honours course treats certain aspects in much greater depth.

(*i*) *Literary courses*

(*a*) Aspects of medieval literature,	(*c*) Drama,
	(*d*) Novel,
(*b*) Lyric poetry,	(*e*) Ideas.

(*ii*) *History of the language*—historical syntax and semantics.

(*iii*) *Special subject*—literary or linguistic option according to candidate's preference.

(*iv*) *Language*—prose composition, translation, essays, oral work.

(*v*) Two outside subjects studied at the Ordinary level, one of which must not be a language.

(2) *French Language and Literature*

This course is more comprehensive than that of the Joint Honours outlined above, and more time is devoted to the study of the history of the language and of literature. Emphasis is also laid on oral work.

Two outside subjects are required—a language (which may be English) studied for two years up to the Advanced level, and a non-linguistic subject for one year.

Intending Honours students are strongly advised to follow the Ordinary level course in Latin if they have not a pass in Latin on the Higher standard of the Scottish Leaving Certificate or an equivalent qualification.

3. COMBINATION OF SUBJECTS

Ordinary degree. See I.1 above.

Joint Honours. French is most commonly combined with German, but it may also be studied with English, Italian, Latin or Spanish.

4. RESIDENCE ABROAD

A period of residence and study abroad is a compulsory requirement for all Honours students of French. Our regulations demand a minimum of six months spent in a French-speaking country for students taking the *Joint Honours degree,* and at least nine months for those taking *Honours in French Language and Literature.*

5. METHODS OF STUDY

All standard methods are used: lectures, seminars, tutorials and oral practice.

6. OTHER ACTIVITIES

A French play is produced annually by the students' French Society.

II. ADMISSION TO COURSES

1. QUALIFICATIONS REQUIRED

The Certificate of Fitness of the Scottish Universities Entrance Board including Higher French (or G.C.E. 'A' Level) is necessary. French cannot be started from scratch.

For an Honours degree in French Language and Literature, or a Joint Honours degree in French and Italian, or French and Spanish, a pass in Latin on the Higher grade of the Scottish Certificate of Education is desirable; for French–English and English–German a pass at the Ordinary grade is considered sufficient.

2. SELECTION OF STUDENTS

Selection for entrance is carried out on a Faculty basis, not by Departments. So far the French Department has been able to accept all first-year entrants who have the necessary qualifications (see II.1 above). Admission to an Honours course depends on a student's performance during the first two years of study.

3. TRANSFER

All students follow the same course during their first year. In their second year those who intend to read for Honours do some extra work, but a decision to take Honours can be left in certain special cases as late as the end of the second year.

4. NUMBERS

There are about 220 students in the Ordinary class and 70 in the Advanced class. Numbers in each year of the Honours classes have varied between 8 and 20, but they are expected to rise to over 30 by 1965.

Information supplied by Professor A. H. Diverres

UNIVERSITY OF EDINBURGH

Department of French

French Language and Literature
and Romance Linguistics

I. COURSES OF STUDY

At the University of Edinburgh, French studies are pursued in two separate but closely integrated sections of the Department. As each has its own Professor and specialized staff, it is possible to offer the student a wide choice of courses.

1. TYPES OF COURSES

Honours and General

(*a*) *M.A. Honours in Modern Languages.* The main language is studied for four years (the third year being spent abroad) and the Subsidiary language for two years.

(*b*) *M.A. Ordinary* in which various combinations of subjects allow the student the possibility of studying French for either one or two years.

2. CHARACTERISTICS OF COURSES

(*i*) *Honours courses*

Owing to our system of selection, the Senior Honours classes are relatively small, and the Special Subject, which forms a considerable part of the work in the final year, is conducted on a seminar basis.

(*a*) *French Language and Romance Linguistics.* Students in all courses are required to do French prose composition, essays and translations, and are examined in these at each level. All Honours students in Modern Languages take a two-year course in the History of the French Language and Medieval French Literature followed by an advanced course in the fourth year for those whose main language is French. There is a Special Subject in Romance Linguistics, involving the study of linguistic methodology, in particular, of linguistic geography, and the formation of the written forms of the principal Western Romance languages, with the study of early texts.

(*b*) *Literature.* In the first year, students follow a course designed to give them an understanding of the aims, resources and methods of literary study. This course is at present (1964) based on a 17th-century syllabus. In subsequent years the syllabus is related to other periods, from the Renaissance to the present day, and dealt with in lectures and in seminars. Emphasis is placed on the study of individual authors and texts rather than on literary history. The syllabus of the final examination is made available to students early in the penultimate year of their course (normally spent in France). In addition to essays set on the reading list, students are required to prepare during their year abroad a dissertation on a literary topic of their choice. In the final year, in addition to the General course, there is a choice of several Special Subjects in literature.

(*ii*) *Ordinary Courses*

(*a*) *Language.* Students are required to show proficiency in French prose composition, essay-writing and translation from French. Much emphasis is also laid on spoken French, which features largely in the curriculum and examinations.

(*b*) *Literature.* In both the first and the second years the syllabus is composed of texts from the 17th century to the present day, with the emphasis on the 20th century. In the second year, lectures are supplemented by seminars.

3. COMBINATIONS OF SUBJECTS

French can be combined in an Honours group with Celtic, English, German, Italian, Latin, Russian or Spanish. The Honours curriculum also includes the study of two 'outside subjects' for one year each. The subjects most commonly chosen are European History, Philosophy and English, but there is a wide range of other possibilities.

It is also possible, in certain cases, to take a degree in French Language and Literature, dispensing with the secondary language. Students who read for this degree take the Honours courses in French, together with an additional course, in each year, of medieval French language and literature, including Provençal.

Possible combinations of subjects for M.A. Ordinary are too numerous and complex to be set out here.

4. RESIDENCE ABROAD

Honours students are required to spend their entire third year in France. The majority of them secure posts as assistants in French schools, but some go as independent students. Besides the literary dissertation already mentioned (2(*i*)(*b*)) they are required to submit a *mémoire* on a subject of their own choice connected with the history, civilization or activities of the locality in which they reside.

II. ADMISSION TO COURSES

1. QUALIFICATIONS REQUIRED

For all students, a pass in French on the Higher grade in the Scottish Certificate of Education or the Scottish Universities Preliminary Examination.

For students reading for Honours in French, with or without another language, the same plus a pass in Latin on at least the

Ordinary grade in the Scottish Certificate of Education or the Preliminary Examination.

(For the purposes of these requirements, a pass at the 'A' Level of G.C.E. in French is accepted; a pass at the 'A' Level in Latin may be dispensed with in appropriate cases.)

No instruction is available for students who do not possess the minimum qualifications in French as set out above.

2. SELECTION OF STUDENTS

Selection of students is made on a Faculty and not a departmental basis. Generally speaking, the selection is made with reference to the performance of candidates in the Scottish Certificate of Education or, in the case of English candidates, in the G.C.E. 'A' Level.

3. TRANSFER

Students opt for Honours or Ordinary courses on entrance, but many prospective Honours students fall by the wayside at the end of either their first or second year and transfer to the Ordinary course. Transfer from Ordinary to Honours courses is occasionally possible in suitable cases.

4. NUMBERS

Approximately 100 students initially enrol as intending to pursue French either as the main or secondary language for an Honours degree, and some 200 others study French for other purposes.

Information supplied by Professor D. McMillan and
Professor A. J. Steele

UNIVERSITY OF GLASGOW

Department of French Studies

I. COURSES OF STUDY

1. TYPES OF COURSES

The peculiarity of Scottish Arts degrees is the large Pass degree contingent, the restricted Honours one. Since even prospective Honours students have two preliminary years before the two-year Honours course, it is of advantage to students of good ability who have not been very efficiently taught.

The syllabus is directly geared to this structure. The first-year course places less emphasis on *thème*, for those who go no further, than on French composition (essay) and *version*. Considerable time is spent on history (Revolution to 1940). The literature is conceived as a 'great books' programme. A further feature is a choice between additional History or an Introduction to Literary Criticism.

The *Ordinary class* (though meeting for lectures some 180-200 strong at 11 o'clock or at noon) is divided into groups of 36-40 students, each group being dealt with by a tutor who sees them once a week for *travaux pratiques* and once a week in groups of 12 for discussion of set books—as far as possible conducted in French. Intending Honours students and intending Higher (i.e. second-year) students have a greater proportion of translation into French and an introductory course of phonetics and linguistics. They are grouped as far as possible in separate sections of the class.

Higher class. This is at present divided for *travaux pratiques* into four sections, two of these largely composed of future Honours students who have some additional texts to study.

The syllabus comprises a course of French History, 17th to 18th century. The texts, it will be seen, are grouped under Classical Theatre, Novel, Poetry and French Thought. The Descartes texts are obligatory for intending Honours students, as this is found a useful introduction to a number of philosophical questions.

Honours class. This runs over two years and is always combined with another modern language or Latin or Modern History. The principle governing the syllabus is primarily the choice of individual texts, generally those which are more difficult. This is combined with a scheme of Special Options, of which two to be selected can be chosen from three distinct fields: (*a*) linguistic, (*b*) literary, (*c*) *civilisation*. Students can therefore give a definite slant to their syllabus.

CHARACTERISTICS OF COURSES

We avoid as far as possible literary periods or history of literature, ı favour of direct contact with texts, reintroducing an element of the short cut to periods and climates of opinion through Honours Options only.

3. COMBINATION OF SUBJECTS

French is usually combined with German. Other combinations are Italian, Spanish, Russian, Latin, Arabic and Modern History. There is no compulsory combination of Honours subjects.

4. RESIDENCE ABROAD

Normally all students spend nine months in France as assistants. This is not required by the University regulations. They go all over France and a few to Germany, Austria, Switzerland and Spain. They at present write three essays and some translation from Old French while abroad.

5. METHODS OF STUDY

The tutorial system in the first two years involves tutorial groups but is largely individual in the Honours years.

6. OTHER ACTIVITIES

There is an active French Society. We usually perform a French play some time during the session.

II. ADMISSION TO COURSES

1. QUALIFICATIONS REQUIRED

The only special qualification for the Ordinary class, with which all students must commence, is a pass in Higher French in the Scottish Certificate of Education or its equivalent (i.e. 'A' Level G.C.E.). Ordinary grade Latin in the Scottish Certificate of Education or 'O' Level Latin is a requirement for second-year French. These rules apply both to intending Honours and General students.

French cannot be started from scratch.

2. SELECTION OF STUDENTS

As in all Scottish universities there is no selection of students for a department as opposed to selection for the University. As regards the latter, candidates for admission who have two good 'A' Level passes or their Scottish equivalents are preferred to those with a large number of less good ones. Practice has been only to interview doubtful cases.

3. TRANSFER

(*a*) Honours students are selected later, but in any case potential Honours candidates receive special attention and are classified from the start (see I.1 above).

(*b*) Transfer is possible up to the end of the second year. It is only
at this point that the students are finally separated.

4. NUMBERS

The Faculty regulation demanding one foreign language for an
Ordinary Arts degree makes first-year numbers exceptionally large—
approaching 400. Second-year numbers are 150. There are about 25
Honours students in each of the two Honours years.

Information supplied by Dr. S. Jones

UNIVERSITY OF ST. ANDREWS

Department of French Language and Literature

I. COURSES OF STUDY

1. TYPES OF COURSES

Three types of courses must be distinguished:

(a) *Ordinary M.A.*;

(b) *Honours M.A.* in French only;

(c) *Honours M.A.* in French with another modern language.

The Ordinary M.A. is a three-year course and the two Honours M.A. courses last four years. All courses in French are available only in St. Salvator's College, St. Andrews, and not at Queen's College, Dundee.

All degree courses begin on a broad basis with four to five subjects taken by all students in the so-called *General classes*: the combination of General subjects is determined in some measure by the course which the student intends to take at Special or Honours level. General Philosophy is a compulsory subject in the preliminary stages of all the three courses. The more advanced Special course is taken in their second year by students intending to read Honours; those who wish to take an Ordinary M.A. degree will normally be enrolled in the Special class in their third year, but it is possible for them to do so in their second year, if they are better than average. The third and fourth years of Honours students are spent in the Junior Honours and Senior Honours classes. It is possible, but less usual, for a student to proceed to the Honours course after having spent three years on the Ordinary M.A. course.

2. CHARACTERISTICS OF COURSES

A very great number of students in the Faculty of Arts take the General or first-year French course, whether they intend to specialize in French or not. The course has recently been revised, so that it may cater for the non-specialist as well as for the intending specialist; it also tries to provide instruction likely to interest the student from England or Wales who may have spent three years in the sixth form and will have some knowledge of classical authors, and it must not be too advanced for the Scottish student, who tends to come up at an earlier age than the English student. In consequence, the course stresses more especially Modern France and comprises:

(a) Classes in composition, translation and essay-writing;

(b) Modern France (history and institutions) 1870 to the present day:

(*c*) The detailed study of three modern authors, of whom one will be a dramatist and two novelists; certain books by these authors will be prescribed for closer study;

(*d*) The close study of three acknowledged masterpieces written in French which has not 'dated'. These texts are selected from a variety of *genres*, so that students may also have the opportunity of learning something of the methods of approach to different forms of literature.

If a student intends to specialize in French for the Ordinary or Honours M.A. degree, his course may be expected to assume the following pattern:

(*a*) *Ordinary M.A.*—a three-year course, in which French is taken in the first and the third years: 1st year—General French and two other General subjects; 2nd year—General Philosophy and a fifth General subject; 3rd year—Special French and another Special subject.

The Special class, which is taken normally by intending Honours students in their second year, and by Ordinary degree students in their third year, comprises (*i*) Translation from and into French, and Essay work; (*ii*) 17th-century Literature; (*iii*) Literature 1800–1870; (*iv*) Introduction to Philology. In (*ii*) and (*iii*) provision is also made for study of the history and thought of the period. In the Special examination there is an oral test.

(*b*) *M.A. Honours in French Language and Literature.* 1st year— General French and two General subjects (one of which will usually be offered with French at Special level in the second year); 2nd year— General Philosophy, Special French and one other Special subject; 3rd and 4th years—Honours classes in French only.

The Honours course comprises the following papers: I. Translation from and into Modern French; II. Essay in French; III. Medieval Literature until 1300; IV. 16th-century Literature; V. 18th-century Literature; VI. French Literature 1870–1940; VII. History of the French Language; VIII. *Either* (*i*) Medieval Literature 1300–1500; *or* (*ii*) 17th-century Literature; *or* (*iii*) Literature 1789–1870; IX. Additional Subject I; X. Additional Subject II. No attempt is made to cover each period in an 'omnibus way'; certain texts are prescribed, and scope is given to the student who is also interested in the thought and history of the period in question. The Additional Subjects, which cover the literary, philosophical and linguistic fields, are not prescribed in advance, as they are determined after discussion between the staff and the students. Thus in recent years we have had, among others, the following subjects: Old Provençal, Occitan, Chrétien de Troyes, Poetry in the late 16th century, Molière and his Successors, the French Revolution, Currents of Thought 1870–1940, Music and Literature in the 19th century. These papers allow students to develop their special interests, and the subjects are dealt with in tutorials and not by lectures.

(c) *M.A. Honours in French with another modern language or English.* 1st year—General French and two other General subjects; 2nd year—General Philosophy and two Special subjects (namely the languages in which the students intend to take Honours); 3rd and 4th years—Honours classes in both languages.

The Joint Honours M.A. degree comprises five papers: (a) I. Translation from and into French; (b) II-IV. Three papers selected from the Pure Honours course papers III, IV, V, VI, VII; (c) V. *Either* Paper VIII *or* one of the Additional subjects of the pure Honours course.

In the final Honours examinations students are required to give an *exposé* in French on a topic chosen beforehand.

3. COMBINATION OF SUBJECTS

Ordinary M.A. A total number of five subjects is studied at the General level. The compulsory subject is Philosophy. Latin, or Greek, or Mathematics, or Hebrew, or two modern foreign languages must also be offered. One of the five subjects must be a language other than English. Students spend two years on these five subjects, usually three in the first year and two in the second. Two Special subjects are taken, French may be combined with another language, or Philosophy, or History. The usual combination is French with German or Spanish. It is possible for students to offer the combination of French-Arabic.[1]

Joint Honours M.A. Four General subjects, two Specials, plus Honours in French with another modern language, or with English.

Honours M.A. in French Language and Literature consists of four General courses (French, Philosophy and two other subjects), two Specials: French and one other freely chosen subject.

4. RESIDENCE ABROAD

One term abroad, spent in a university in a country speaking the language or one of the languages offered for Honours, is compulsory. This is a minimum and many students, probably most, go abroad in other years. The work demanded is attendance at definite university courses, either a special course for foreigners (usually taken if a suitable university, e.g. Lausanne, is selected), or appropriate *licence* or *agrégation* lectures. It is possible for a student to spend the whole of March to early October abroad. Compulsory university work is demanded only for the equivalent of the St. Andrews term.

5. METHODS OF STUDY

Group work with all classes, even in the first year. In the Special class, groups of five meet every week for the discussion of literary topics. At least three times a term students are taken in groups of three or four by members of staff for the discussion (in French) of the

[1] It is hoped that from October 1965 an Intermediate course will be introduced so that the French course will extend over three years.

essays they have written in French. Composition classes are also arranged regularly. The Special class receives about four lectures a week. In the Honours classes, formal lecturing is reduced to a minimum, and students are taken in small tutorial groups, as far as the staff-student ratio will allow. From his second year onwards, every student is put under the care of a member of staff who will deal with any problems that may arise in connection with his studies. The departmental library is being constantly enlarged and is at the disposal of all students taking French; we are also building up a stock of records (French plays, poetry readings and music) and of slides; and from time to time lectures are given on various cultural topics, not only by members of staff, but also by visiting lecturers from the French Institutes in London and Edinburgh, and sometimes by colleagues in other universities. The library also contains a good supply of current periodicals and newspapers. The tradition of putting on a French play once a year has now been restored.

II. ADMISSION TO COURSES

1. QUALIFICATION REQUIRED

The prerequisite for entrance to the University is the Certificate of Fitness of the Scottish Universities Entrance Board. For entrance to the Faculty of Arts the Certificate of Fitness must include or be supplemented by a Higher (or 'A' Level) pass in either Latin or Greek *or* two of French, German, Spanish or Arabic *or* Mathematics plus one of the four languages just mentioned. For entrance to the Department of French the student must have a Higher S.C.E. pass in French or an equivalent qualification.

French cannot be started from scratch.

2. SELECTION OF STUDENTS

Admission to the Faculty of Arts is given by the Dean, who takes into consideration examination passes and reports from schools; there are no interviews. As there are more applicants than places, the minimum requirements for admission are usually not sufficient to gain a place. Generally speaking, even students who do not intend to take French beyond General level, will find the first-year course strenuous if they have not reached grade C in their 'A' Level examinations; and, of course, any student wishing to go further in his study of French will need to be considerably better than that. This is not a statement based on entrance regulations, but one which reflects the performance of students admitted in the recent past, and which assumes that a student's result at 'A' Level is a fair assessment of his normal work. It is above all essential that a student wishing to read French should come up with a proper grasp of basic French grammar, some idea of what is involved in the study of a literary text, and especially the capacity to work on his own. It will be appreciated if he has read fairly widely in English literature.

3. TRANSFERS

The first year (General class) is common to all students of French. At present the Special class is intended to serve the interests of both the Ordinary degree and the Honours students; there is, however, a short course which is given as an introduction to medieval literature for intending Honours students and which does not lead to an examination. Students are selected for the Honours classes on their performance in the Special class during their second year.

It is also possible to complete the Ordinary M.A.—this takes three years—and then spend a further two years in Honours classes. At the end of the second year, students who no longer want to take Honours or who are rejected, may complete the Ordinary M.A. course in their third year, by taking a fifth General subject, the graduating Special French class and their second Special subject (see also I.1 above).

4. NUMBERS

Numbers in each year of the Honours classes vary from year to year; they range from 20 to 30, but may well rise in the fairly near future. There are about 100 students in the Special class and 170 in the General class.

Information supplied by Professor I. D. McFarlane

THE QUEEN'S UNIVERSITY
OF BELFAST

Department of French

I. COURSES OF STUDY

1. TYPES OF COURSES

In the first year French may be studied as one of the three subjects required for the University's First Examination in Arts. This examination is compulsory for all students in the Faculty of Arts in their first year. Thereafter, French may be studied as part of the following courses:

(*a*) as one of three subjects leading to the *General* degree (two further years of study);

(*b*) as a *Subsidiary* subject where this is required by another Honours School (one further year of study);

(*c*) as a *Single* or *Joint Honours* subject (three further years of study).

2. CHARACTERISTICS OF COURSES

Our courses have been planned on the following assumptions:

(*a*) that direct contact with texts is preferable to literary-historical surveys;

(*b*) that most texts can nevertheless only be fully understood when set against their social and historical background;

(*c*) that the older the text, the greater its difficulty.

Accordingly, we lay stress on French social, political and cultural history in each course and, with our less gifted students, move from the modern age to the past. In the first-year course, we study aspects of French Literature, History and Thought from 1870 onwards; in the first year of the General degree course (which also suffices for the Subsidiary pass course in French), the field of study is French Literature, History and Thought from 1748–1870; in the second and final year of the General degree course, the field of study is French Literature, History and Thought from 1600–1748. A one-year course in French Phonetics is also provided in this year. Prospective entrants to the Honours class take the same first-year course as all other students but follow, in addition, a survey course with extra prescribed texts on the literature of the period 1600–1748. Provisional entry to the Honours course is granted at the end of the student's first year in the University and largely on his performance in the First Arts

Examination. Thereafter he follows the same course as the first-year General degree student. A departmental examination near the end of the first Honours year determines whether the student may be admitted to the final two years of Honours studies, in which intensive study is made of a wide selection of the outstanding authors and topics in French Literature from 1600 to the present day.

A distinctive feature of French studies in this University is that there is a separate and autonomous Department of Medieval French in which may be studied Old, Middle and Renaissance French literature, and French philology. All Joint Honours students must study in the Medieval French Department for *at least* one year; Single Honours students for four years.

3. COMBINATION OF SUBJECTS

French may be combined with Celtic, English, German, Medieval French (to form the Single Honours course in French), Philosophy or Spanish. In the Joint Honours final examination, four basic papers are taken in each subject, plus two additional papers from the same subject or one from each.

4. RESIDENCE ABROAD

All Honours students are strongly recommended to spend an academic session in France, preferably as assistants between their first and second years of Honours studies. When this is not possible, Single Honours students are required to reside in France, following an approved course of study, from the end of the second term of their second Honours year till the end of August.

5. METHODS OF STUDY

Formal lectures, prose and translation classes, and conversation classes supervised by *lecteurs* are all employed, but the distinctive teaching method employed is the tutorial group. At every level students with one essay per fortnight meet in groups of from three to six to discuss it with a tutor. Use is also made of recordings of French drama and of lantern lectures and films.

6. OTHER ACTIVITIES

There is a lively students' French Society which organizes lectures, dances and wine-tasting sessions. Plays are occasionally produced, and there is a French Society football team.

II. ADMISSION TO COURSES

1. QUALIFICATIONS REQUIRED

(*a*) An Advanced Level pass or its equivalent in French is needed for admission to any course in French.

(*b*) An Ordinary Level pass or its equivalent in Latin is required of Honours students.

2. SELECTION OF STUDENTS

Selection of students, based on 'A' Level results, is made by the Faculty's Adviser of Studies. In addition there are General Entrance Scholarships based on a Special University examination.

3. TRANSFER

Since Honours students follow exactly the same courses as General degree students up till the time when they are finally admitted to or ejected from the French Honours School, it is possible to transfer without difficulty to the General degree course or else, as sometimes happens, to use French as a Subsidiary subject for an Honours degree in another subject.

4. NUMBERS

There are normally some 140-150 students in the First Arts class, 50-60 in each of the two General degree classes, and 15-20 in each of the three Honours classes.

Information supplied by Professor R. D. D. Gibson

GERMAN STUDIES

UNIVERSITY OF BIRMINGHAM
Department of German

I. COURSES OF STUDY

1. TYPES OF COURSES

The following courses in German are provided:

(a) *Special Honours*: a four-year course, in which German is studied for four years and a Subsidiary subject for two years.

(b) *Combined Honours:* this is a course offering various possibilities of combining subjects, including German and Russian at equal status for four years.

There is no Pass degree.

2. CHARACTERISTICS OF COURSES

(1) Students choose in their second year between modern (contemporary) literature and study of the older language. In their fourth year, they all take courses on contemporary literature, and contemporary language and modern linguistics. A course on medieval literature extends over the second and fourth years.

(2) The course in modern literature extends to the present day and includes recent works.

(3) All first-year students take for one term an Inter-Faculty course which brings together students of different Faculties round a theme that cuts across departmental disciplines.

(4) While the main emphasis is firmly on language and literature, students must also take courses on German philosophy and social history.

(5) In their second and fourth years, students may choose a course given jointly with the Department of Sociology, which introduces them to principles and methods of social science and leads to the investigation of certain aspects of modern German society.

(6) A ruling is in operation that the class obtained in Honours is related to the standard achieved in language papers.

3. COMBINATION OF SUBJECTS

German is combined with Russian, French or Spanish and occasionally Italian. Russian is increasingly popular. Other combinations are taken, but more rarely, e.g. English and Psychology.

4. RESIDENCE ABROAD

The third year of the course is (from 1965) spent at a German university and is preceded by attendance at a German Summer School. During this period students are required to follow a prescribed course of study and to submit written work (essays) to us.

5. METHODS OF STUDY

A radical modification of conventional teaching of prose composition has been introduced (see W. Lockwood, 'An Alternative to Prose Composition', *Modern Languages*, Vol. 36, No. 3, Sept. 1955, pp. 105-108, and R. Hinton Thomas, 'Prose Composition and the Teaching of Modern Foreign Languages', *ibid.*, Vol. 44, No. 2, June 1963, pp. 70-72). There is much essay work and several lecture courses are accompanied by seminars. Discussion and collaboration among students are encouraged in various ways.

6. OTHER ACTIVITIES

There is an active German Society, which produces a play annually or bi-annually. A compulsory residential reading party for first-year students is held in the last week of the Easter vacation.

II. ADMISSION TO COURSES

1. QUALIFICATIONS REQUIRED

No Latin is required for German Honours students.

A pass in German at 'A' Level for Special Honours and Combined Honours is required. This must be a *good* pass for Special Honours.

There is no teaching of beginners, except for a course for scientists.

2. SELECTION OF STUDENTS

We rely on:

(a) 'A' Level results,

(b) headmasters' and headmistresses' reports,

(c) interviews in many, but not all, cases (the very best and weakest are sometimes excluded),

(d) reports of 'other interests' of candidates.

We are influenced considerably by the wider interests of candidates and take into consideration whether or not they have held responsible office in school societies or participated in cultural activities. We appreciate it if teachers write to us about their candidates, especially if there are things about home circumstances that we should know.

3. TRANSFER

Students are admitted to the Honours course on entrance.

Transfer from Special Honours to Combined Honours, or vice versa, if possible. Transfer from one Special Honours School to another is very rarely possible.

4. NUMBERS

About 20 students are admitted to the Special Honours School per year.

Information supplied by Professor R. Pascal

UNIVERSITY OF BRISTOL
Department of German

I. COURSES OF STUDY

1. TYPES OF COURSES

The following courses are provided:

(*a*) *Special degree* in German (three years) with a Subsidiary subject to be studied for two years;

(*b*) *Double Special degree* in German and Drama.

(*c*) *A four-year course* in the *Joint School in Modern Foreign Languages:*[1] German and French.

(*d*) *B.A. General* and *B.A. (Econ.)*, in which German can be chosen among a list of many subjects to be studied as one of four subjects in the first year and as one of three for the final two years;

(*e*) *Subsidiary* German to be studied for two years in a number of Special Schools.

2. CHARACTERISTICS OF COURSES

The scope of study of German as a modern foreign language can be briefly summarized as follows:

(*a*) a technical mastery of speaking and writing it correctly and fluently;

(*b*) a sound training in the history, appreciation and criticism of literature (lyric, drama, novel, etc.);

(*c*) social history or *Kulturgeschichte* in its bearing on literature;

(*d*) seminars with analysis and interpretation, particularly for third-year Specialists and fourth-year Joint School Specialists, and for postgraduates.

General degree

Apart from undergoing a rigorous training in the German language, spoken and written, students are expected to attend courses on German literature, as well as on German history, art, thought and life.

The first-year course includes translation from and into German, set texts, outlines of literature and an introduction to German lyrical poetry. The second- and third-year courses include prescribed texts,

---

[1] It is Professor A. Closs's firm view that *all* Joint Schools in modern foreign languages should demand a *four-year* course. Three years are utterly unsatisfactory, as within a three-year course, the one main language cannot possibly be an equal partner with the other. About *half* of the work done by students in a normal Specialist course would have to be sacrificed!

an introduction to the history of the German language, translations, essays, conversation and outlines of literature.

Special degrees

In their first year students will attend lectures on medieval and modern literature, the elements of historical grammar, set books, essays, composition, etc. Specialist students are also expected to read among other chapters those dealing with German history and German art. Moreover, all Specialists are required to be acquainted with the essential elements of Germanic mythology and folklore.

The examination for Finalists (three-year course) comprises nine papers and ranges widely over the whole field of German studies. It should be emphasized that all Specialists study the *two* disciplines, i.e. medieval and modern; they must not just start with Luther and leave out German minnesongs, epics, romances and Old High German literature.

The Department lays great stress on the development of post-graduate courses, practical introduction to methods of literary research and instruction in palaeography.

Four-year Joint School in Modern Foreign Languages

For the four-year Joint School course, eight papers are prescribed and the course is arranged in the following manner:

	GERMAN	FRENCH
1st year	Subsidiary course—first year	Special I course (including course at Sorbonne)
2nd year	Special I course (and study abroad at a German university from the end of first week in June, including vacation course)	Special II course and French Part I Finals (3 papers)
3rd year	Special II course and sessional examination only. Summer: completion of required period of study in Germany	Special III course and French Part II Finals (5 papers plus oral)
4th year	Special III course and German Finals (8 papers and Oral)	Nil

Equal emphasis lies on *both* languages and literatures.
The above suggested stays abroad are compulsory.
All papers will be considered in awarding degree.

3. COMBINATION OF COURSES

German Special, and, as Subsidiary, either another language (old or modern) or Philosophy or Geography or Economics or History or Ancient History and Archaeology.

4. RESIDENCE ABROAD

General students reading German for three years must attend at a German, or German-speaking, university an authorized course of studies of at least *one month* to the satisfaction of the Professor of German.

Students taking a two-year Subsidiary course in German are requested, before taking the Final Examination, to produce evidence of having spent a minimum period of four weeks of supervised study in Germany, to the satisfaction of the Professor of German.

Special students (three-year course) are required to study at a German, or German-speaking, university for the *full summer term* of their first year. Students normally go to Lower Saxony, or to Mainz, Marburg or Frankfurt a. M. Essays and study of certain prescribed texts have to be prepared during the period of study abroad.

As to the four-year course in the Joint Special School, see the arrangement described in I.2 above.

5. METHODS OF STUDY

Lecturing and tutorials are evenly balanced throughout the three or four years (see also I.2 above).

II. ADMISSION TO COURSES

1. QUALIFICATIONS REQUIRED

Candidates who enter the German Special School must normally have 'A' Level German and 'O' Level Latin or Greek. Candidates for B.A. General or B.A. (Modern Studies) German courses must have passes at or above 'O' Level in German and in either Mathematics or a classical language.

2. SELECTION OF STUDENTS

We do not mainly rely on 'A' Level results, but candidates for Special German must have a minimum of two relevant Advanced Level passes at or above grade B, one of which must be German. There is no entrance examination but candidates are in some cases called for interview and on that occasion given an oral or written test. School records are taken up and, if the candidate has left school, other records are asked for.

3. TRANSFER

Students are admitted to the Special School on entrance, but transfers are possible.

4. NUMBERS

The usual number of Specialists annually admitted is about 45, though numbers are increasing steadily.

Information supplied by Professor A. Closs

UNIVERSITY OF CAMBRIDGE

Department of German[1]

I. COURSES OF STUDY

1. TYPES OF COURSES

The Modern and Medieval Languages Tripos is divided into two parts, which together normally involve three years of study. All courses are for Honours degrees, there is no Ordinary degree course in Cambridge in German, but a student may obtain an Ordinary degree as a kind of failed Honours in certain circumstances.

(a) *Part I.* A candidate for Honours in Part I of the Tripos must offer in the same academic year either two modern languages, or one modern and one classical language. To obtain Honours, he must reach the standard for Honours in each language, and take an oral examination in any *modern* language offered before sitting the written examination. He may try this twice, and his better performance is what is considered. Complete failure in the oral will cause him to be placed a class lower than he would otherwise have attained. He may take Part I *either* after one year's study *or* after two years, but if the latter, he must offer an additional, more advanced paper in the literature of *one* of his languages.

The written examination in each language consists in Part I of three linguistic papers (translation from and into German and an essay in German) and one literary paper. For this paper there is a choice of period, i.e. in German, a choice between the Classical-Romantic period and the Nineteenth Century. Each paper is divided into two sections, one relating to texts prescribed for detailed study, the other to authors or topics to be studied more generally, and to the historical and cultural background.

For the more advanced literary paper taken by the two-year students, there is a similar choice, but the subjects are more remote from ordinary school studies. In German the four possibilities are: a paper on Middle High German literature (with a Prescribed Texts and a General section), one on the Reformation and *Barock* period, one on the period 1880–1914, and one on aspects of the history of the German language. It will be seen that, in Part I, the older language and literature and philology only find a place in this more advanced group of papers, which the one-year student does not offer. No student is therefore examined in his first year on such subjects.

(b) *Part II.* After passing Part I, a number of students switch to entirely different schools of study. With its many two-part Triposes,

---

[1] Readers should also consult p. 340 of this *Guide*, where the general conditions of modern language studies at Cambridge are set out.

Cambridge offers a particularly flexible curriculum. Those who continue to study Modern Languages will be joined by a few from other schools (English or History, for instance) in Part II of the Tripos. Here they have very great freedom of choice among the 77 advanced literary and philological papers included among the subjects for Part II. If they devote two years to study for Part II, as will happen if they have required only one year for Part I, they must offer five subjects from the list, as well as an essay in one of the languages studied, and a paper in translation and composition, also in any one of the languages read by the student in Part II. If they take two years over Part I and give only one year to Part II (they may stay a fourth year and take two years if they choose, but this is rarely possible), the number of subjects is reduced to four.

There is no oral test for Part II.

2. CHARACTERISTICS OF COURSES

Comparing the Cambridge Modern Languages courses with those in most of the other British universities, one is struck by the great flexibility of the examination requirements, enabling a student to combine some study of Modern Languages with almost any other Arts subject or with Law, for example, and to engage in more specialized study of certain selected periods or topics in one or more literatures, than is usual elsewhere. This makes the course very stimulating to abler students, but sometimes less suited to more mediocre ones. One still finds, among some 350 students reading German for one or the other Parts of the Tripos, a wide range of ability and performance, the Department having no means of excluding unpromising candidates at an early stage. Because of the large number of options that are open to the student it is impossible to demand of them all, as is usual in other British universities, a certain minimum knowledge of the whole range of a particular literature, or some acquaintance with the history of its language and with its older forms. On the other hand, anyone who is interested in philology or in medieval literature can pursue these interests almost to the exclusion of anything else in Part II, if he so chooses. Many, however, take both Parts without any study of a medieval language, but to be successful, they will need to know the original texts really well in the periods of literature they offer.

Postgraduate studies. The opportunities for advanced study and research in German literature and related subjects are good in Cambridge, and they are made use of not only by Cambridge graduates but by research students who have graduated in Modern Languages in other universities. The minimum period of study for the Ph.D. degree is three years, part of which may be spent in study abroad.

3. COMBINATION OF SUBJECTS

It is impossible, as will have been seen in I.1 and I.2 above, to specialize in German alone from the outset of Part I, but in Part II a candidate may make up the required number of subjects from the German options without any others. The commonest combination in Part I is still French and German, and the majority offer a mixture of languages in Part II also, sometimes including one that they have begun at the University.

4. RESIDENCE ABROAD

No residence abroad is *required* of the student, though the great majority make good use of vacations for this purpose.

5. METHODS OF STUDY

The tutorial method of teaching which is traditional in Cambridge is applied in the supervisions which students of German, like all others, receive in their colleges. The University provides lectures for both Parts of the Tripos in considerable variety and composition and translation classes for Part I, as well as the opportunity of practice in conversational German with a German lector.

6. OTHER ACTIVITIES

There is a very active German Society, which provides a varied programme of talks and readings, music and films, and every year presents a full-length German play. A number of lectures are given in the Department every year by visiting German professors.

II. ADMISSION TO COURSES

1 and 2. QUALIFICATIONS REQUIRED AND SELECTION OF STUDENTS

The admission of students is entirely a matter for the colleges. The University Department of German has no control and imposes no tests of its own, except for the allocation of freshers to appropriate composition and translation classes. It is very unusual for students to begin the study of German at the University and no special teaching is provided for beginners, except certain courses for scientists.

4. NUMBERS

There are usually some 350 students in residence who are reading German for one or the other Part of the Tripos.

Information supplied by Professor W. H. Bruford

UNIVERSITY OF DURHAM

Department of German

I. COURSES OF STUDY

1. TYPES OF COURSES

   (*a*) *Honours in German*;

   (*b*) *Honours in German and French or Spanish* (Double Honours);[1]

   (*c*) German as a subject of the *General degree* of B.A.

   (*d*) Under present regulations, students reading German as a *Subsidiary subject* to another Honours subject normally attend, in their first and second years, the second- and third-year courses for the General degree.

2. CHARACTERISTICS OF COURSES

   For details, the calendar should be consulted. The course offers in addition to the normal work in language and literature non-examinable courses in history and lectures in German.

3. COMBINATION OF SUBJECTS

   For Single Honours in German candidates have to study an optional subject for two years, chosen from the list of subjects in the General degree.

   For Joint Honours combinations, see I.1(*b*) above.

   German as a subject in the General degree can be combined with a variety of other subjects.

4. RESIDENCE ABROAD

   For Honours students the normal requirement is to spend a year in a German-speaking country as an assistant under the official scheme, between the end of the second year of residence in Durham and the beginning of the third. There is now no compulsory term abroad and for the small minority who are unable or unwilling to spend the extra year abroad, an alternative requirement is to spend three months in one of the long vacations in a German-speaking country, and in fact to spend as much time abroad in vacations as possible.

   General students are required to spend at least one month in a German-speaking country.

5. METHODS OF STUDY

   Each student is given essay tutorials (more in the Honours course than in the General course) throughout his course, as well as lectures

[1] This course is regarded as exceptional rather than the rule and is reserved in practice for the potentially more able student.

and prose and translation classes, colloquial German with a *Lektor*, etc.

6. OTHER ACTIVITIES

Outside lecturers, films, music, etc. A lively German society.

II. ADMISSION TO COURSES

1. QUALIFICATIONS REQUIRED

Matriculation as per regulations for all courses. This includes Latin at 'O' Level as a *sine qua non*. For Honours German a minimum of 'Good' at 'A' Level in German and in one other subject is usually required. German cannot be started from scratch in this University.

Admission to the General degree course is via the individual colleges only.

Admission to the Honours School is via the individual colleges and the German Department.

2. SELECTION OF STUDENTS

Primary selection of candidates is made in every case by the individual colleges on the basis of candidates' application form, 'A' Level results and school reports. Honours candidates are interviewed both by the college concerned and the German Department, Double Honours candidates by both departments.

The interview in the case of the Department tries to establish the potentialities of the candidate for his subject, his interests and intellectual ability, as well as his possibilities as a potential member of an Honours School of German in a residential university. The college attempts a similar assessment from its own point of view. All candidates have this double interview, except those for the General degree, who are interviewed by the college only.

3. TRANSFER

The Preliminary Honours examination at the end of the first year helps the Head of Department to decide whether the candidate is suitable for an Honours course and whether he should be advised to continue or to transfer to a course for a General degree. In Double Honours a candidate may be allowed to proceed to a single Honours course with an optional subject.

4. NUMBERS

Recently about 30 students have been admitted to the Honours course, a small number of whom read for Double Honours; second-year General and Subsidiary students altogether number about 25. In the first year of the General degree course, numbers vary very greatly, but are usually small in German.

Information supplied by Professor D. F. S. Scott

UNIVERSITY OF EXETER

Department of German

I. COURSES OF STUDY

1. TYPES OF COURSES

German can be studied in the following courses:

(a) *Honours*;

(b) *Combined Honours:* normally German and French, German and Philosophy, German and Latin, German and Spanish, German and English, and German and Russian;

(c) *General*;

(d) *Additional* subject (equivalent to Subsidiary): with Honours French.

2. CHARACTERISTICS OF COURSES

The Honours course is divided into two parts, both of which are taken into account in assessing the final class. Part I is general, covering the outline of literature by set texts and also the historical background. Part II contains more specialized papers on a special subject and two prescribed periods (options available) and either history of the language or a paper of criticism. The language papers are distributed between the two parts, translation in Part I, prose and essay in Part II. The oral examination is in Part II. Combined Honours students usually omit medieval literature.

3. COMBINATION OF SUBJECTS

See I.1 above.

4. RESIDENCE ABROAD

Honours students are required to study at a German university in the summer *Semester* (1st May to 31st July) of the first year. Combined Honours students are encouraged to do this. It is, in fact, normal practice for them to go. Alternatively, Combined Honours students may spend a 'substantial portion' of one long vacation studying in Germany. General and Additional students are required to attend one vacation course in Germany.

Honours and Combined Honours students may go to the university of their choice, subject to my approval. They are required to write a thesis while in Germany.

5. METHODS OF STUDY

Teaching includes lectures, tutorials in small groups and the discussion of essays. There is weekly oral practice with a native German speaker.

II. ADMISSION TO COURSES

1. QUALIFICATIONS REQUIRED

Honours. The Arts Faculty requires pass at 'O' Level Latin. Pass at 'A' Level in German is necessary unless other qualifications are quite exceptional.

2. SELECTION OF STUDENTS

Combination of 'A' Level results, confidential references and, in appropriate cases, interview.

3. TRANSFER

Students are admitted to Honours courses on entrance; transfer is discouraged, but is sometimes possible.

4. NUMBERS

Approximately 30 students were admitted to the Honours and Combined Honours School in 1964, and this number is likely to increase in later years.

Information supplied by Professor H. B. Garland

UNIVERSITY OF HULL

Department of German

I. COURSES OF STUDY

1 and 2. TYPES AND CHIEF CHARACTERISTICS OF COURSES

There are only two possible degrees:

(a) *Special*

(b) *Joint*

Both of these are to be considered as Honours degrees, although there is a provision (not too often used) for the award of either of these degrees without Honours.

Special. This is a one-subject degree. Together with German as the main subject (which is studied for three years), a Subsidiary subject is taken, normally for the first five terms of the course, the sixth being spent at a German or Austrian university. As an alternative it is open to students who are successful in their application for such posts to spend (after their second year) not more than one intercalated academic year as English assistants in German schools. In this case the sixth term is spent at Hull. Students take courses in language and literature, with stress upon the present-day use of the language and on literature and literary history from 1700 to the present day; but medieval German language and literature are taught in all three years and the language and literature of the 16th and 17th centuries appear in the third year. There is also a *Special Subject* option: all students must choose one such; there are a good many options, both literary and linguistic.

Joint. This is a two-subject degree, one of the subjects being German and normally there is no further subject to be studied for part of the time. With the exception that there is no 16th- and 17th-century language and literature and rather little (in some circumstances no) Middle High German, the requirements of the degree are more or less those of the Special.

Students are expected to attend (normally in their first year) the two-term non-examinable general course in linguistics.

Swedish (now a separate Department) can be taken either as a subject for the Joint degree or as a Subsidiary subject.

3. COMBINATION OF SUBJECTS

Combinations with German are French (by far the most popular), also Swedish, Russian, Drama and English, and more occasionally

Theology, Italian or Spanish. In theory, other combinations with all subjects in the Arts Faculty are possible and sometimes found if there is no time-table clash.

4. RESIDENCE ABROAD

Special students must spend one summer term in a German-speaking university, or, alternatively, may spend one academic year as assistants in a German school (see I.1 and 2 above). No two people are allowed to go to the same university in any one year. Popular universities are Kiel, Munich, Tübingen, Münster, Innsbruck or Hamburg, but most universities in Federal Germany, West Berlin and Austria have been visited.

Joint students must spend one vacation (preferably attending a vacation course) in a German-speaking country.

5. METHODS OF STUDY

In all years students attend German conversation classes in small groups. There are also (compulsory for all years) two general lectures in German given by the *Lektors*.

6. OTHER ACTIVITIES

There is a students' *Deutscher Verein*, which has a fairly full programme of lectures, discussions, play readings, gramophone recitals, etc.

II. ADMISSION TO COURSES

1. QUALIFICATIONS REQUIRED

'A' Level German is required for both Special and Joint German; normally a bare pass, which is sufficient for matriculation, would not be sufficient for entry into either. There is no Latin requirement.

German cannot be started from scratch—even as a Subsidiary.

Swedish, often taken as a Joint Degree subject in combination with German, can be—and normally is—started from scratch.

2. SELECTION OF STUDENTS

Applicants tell us a good deal about themselves and this is read in conjunction with the head teachers' reports. Where applicants seem to be *prima facie* the right sort of students, they are called for interview. The interview is not designed to find out the candidate's knowledge but rather his reasons for wanting to study German—and at Hull. In accordance with a general agreement to desist from entrance tests, no written entrance test is given at the interview. On the basis of the interview, places are offered; in some cases the offer is provisional and is dependent on the attainment of a specific 'A' Level mark.

3. TRANSFER

Students are admitted to Honours courses on entrance. Transfer is possible, but as we have no General degree courses it is only rarely resorted to, and can only be a change of subject or subject grouping.

4. NUMBERS

Approximately 17 Special and 10 Joint students are admitted annually to the German Department.

Information supplied by Dr. C. Baier, Head of the Department of German

UNIVERSITY OF KEELE

Department of Modern Languages (German)

I. COURSES OF STUDY

The Degree course lasts four years, of which the first, or *Foundation Year*, consists of a compulsory course of lectures designed to introduce the student to some of the methods and information necessary to an estimate of the inheritance, problems and achievements of modern Western European man. This course, identical for students of all subjects, is supplemented by tutorial work adjusted to individual needs. During the last three years, students study two subjects at *Principal* level and two one-year *Subsidiary* subjects; one must be a science subject; and one Subsidiary subject may be replaced by a course in the Theory and Practice of Education (concurrent with the Principal courses) for the Diploma in Education.

There is no Pass or General degree course at this University.

1. TYPES OF COURSES

After the Foundation Year, during which tutorial courses in German are available, the following courses are available:

(1) *Principal*, i.e. a three-year course for students in their second, third or fourth year in the University. This is always taken with another Honours course, for example, English, French, History, Philosophy, Economics, Geography. The content is about that of the Honours German course in those Scottish universities which offer joint courses. Six papers for Finals cover prose, unseens, essay, classical and modern literature, Middle High German and historical language (Renaissance and Baroque literature are only lightly represented; Old High German, Gothic and Old Saxon only as special options).

(2) *Subsidiary German:* a one-year course (second or third year in the University) leading to a *reading* knowledge of German. About six representative works of literature are read in translation, and a short course on history and culture is given.

2. CHARACTERISTICS OF COURSES

In detail the Principal course consists of the following elements:

(*i*) prose, unseen and essay work, with special emphasis on proses;

(*ii*) literature, including set books from mid-18th century to the present day;

(*iii*) Middle High German literature;

(*iv*) Middle High German and an historical study of grammar.

In the final year students may take more or less 'tailor-made' options, for example, 20th-century poetry, 19th-century drama, additional Middle High German literature. The following have not been taken recently but can be made available: Baroque literature, Germanic philology, Older Germanic dialects, linguistics. The other Honours subject may suggest a suitable choice, e.g. medieval literature (French and German).

3. COMBINATION OF SUBJECTS

French, English and Economics are fairly common combinations with German. Philosophy and Geography are rare, but have occurred.

4. RESIDENCE ABROAD

A minimum of three months' residence is required, which sometimes includes an approved vacation course. One year's residence is desirable, if the student goes under the official scheme for assistants. Many students do, and they go between their third and fourth year in the University. No formal work is required of these. Another desirable form of residence abroad is a full *Semester* (usually summer) in a German or Austrian university. Students are required to register for lectures and a seminar, if possible, in German and in the other Honours subject.

5. METHODS OF STUDY

With small numbers, practically all teaching is tutorial, though the first Honours year students (Principal 1) have a weekly literature lecture in German—usually the first continuous German they have heard.

6. OTHER ACTIVITIES

A Modern Languages Society organizes film programmes, recorded plays, visits to performances within a 60-mile radius.

II. ADMISSION TO COURSES

1. QUALIFICATIONS REQUIRED

Principal. Generally only students with grade B or better in 'A' Level German, i.e. those who seem fully fitted to take Honours German, are admitted to the Principal course. The difference between ours and a Single Honours course is in scope rather than standard.

Exception: A student with little (or even no) German can be given special tuition during the University Foundation Year. There would have to be high qualifications in other languages or residence or similar favourable indications. In practice each graduation to date has contained one such student; as numbers are small, staff can be spared to 'nurse' them.

For the *Subsidiary* course, no qualifications are required. Candidates with 'O' Level German sometimes join, but the course is for starters from scratch. At present there is no Subsidiary for students with 'A' Level German.

No requirements in Latin are laid down for any course.

2. SELECTION OF STUDENTS

University requirements prevent selection by the departments. The university selection boards are aware of departmental requirements and often the department will be presented on the selection panel.

Generally only Honours students are being sought. There are no other kinds of degree, but special consideration is given to exceptional cases, e.g. older students, late developers, etc. A combination of 'A' Level results, head teachers' reports, and interview, is used for selection. As a rule no student is admitted without interview. Thus in one year recently from about 1,800 applicants 600 were selected for interview, and from the 600, 190 were offered places, subject to 'A' Level results.

Students have the whole Foundation Year in which to make contact with the Department of German. Usually those with 'A' Level German and proposing to read Honours German attend literary tutorials for one term and optional prose classes throughout the year. One effect of Foundation Year studies is to change original Honours subject intentions in many cases. Only those students who successfully complete the Foundation Year studies can remain in the University.

3. TRANSFER

See II.2 above.

4. NUMBERS

The average Honours population in German over the last five years was 7 students per year.

Information supplied by Professor K. Brooke

UNIVERSITY OF LEEDS
Department of German

I. COURSES OF STUDY

1. TYPES OF COURSES

German can be studied in the following courses:

(a) *Special Studies* ⎫ both are three-year courses;
(b) *Dual Honours Studies* ⎭

(c) *General Studies* (Honours are awarded in the General degree);

(d) *Subsidiary*—as a Subsidiary subject in some other Special Studies Schools.

2. CHARACTERISTICS OF COURSES

There are two alternative schemes of study for Special Honours:

(a) largely linguistic and philological,

(b) largely literary.

3. COMBINATION OF SUBJECTS

For Dual Honours Studies, German may be combined with any other modern language or with English.

For Special Studies, a three-year Subsidiary subject is necessary; this is usually French. The first-year course consists of German; another foreign language, or English; philosophy or history; and any other subject. In the second and third year only German and the Subsidiary subject are studied.

4. RESIDENCE ABROAD

Special Studies students are required to reside abroad during the third term of the second year. Some students intercalate a year abroad. General Studies students are required to spend at least one month at an approved course of study in a German-speaking country during the long vacation of their first or second year.

II. ADMISSION TO COURSES

1. QUALIFICATIONS REQUIRED

No special requirement in Latin is laid down.

For admission to the Special Studies School a suitable grade in 'A' Level German is necessary. Overall examination performance is looked at, and evidence of all-round ability desired.

The language is started from scratch for non-degree purposes and for scientists.

2. SELECTION OF STUDENTS

There is no entrance examination. Attention is paid to head teachers' reports, school estimates and so on. Selected candidates are interviewed (see also II.1 above).

3. TRANSFER

Students are admitted to the Honours course on entrance. Transfer is possible.

4. NUMBERS

The numbers vary.

Information supplied by Professor A. Gillies

UNIVERSITY OF LEICESTER

Department of German

I. COURSES OF STUDY

1. TYPES OF COURSES

(a) *B.A. German:* a three-year course, plus one intercalated year abroad (after the second year);

(b) *B.A. Combined Studies:* German may be taken for one, two or three years, with Honours (see also II.1 *Note* below).

2. CHARACTERISTICS OF COURSES

The syllabuses and courses and teaching methods may be said to be 'modern'. There is less philology than in most other German departments, more attention being given to more recent developments in the German language. In the courses where German is the main subject and in the third-year Combined Studies course, German institutions and recent German history are studied, together with some aspects of the sociology of the Germans. We do not teach 'history of literature' but Men and Movements in Literature and this in relation to the visual arts in the periods concerned.

Our student numbers are small; the staff-student ratio is very favourable to our tutorial system, so that students get a fair amount of individual attention.

3. COMBINATION OF SUBJECTS

German: French, Latin, English, History as a Supplementary subject. Other subjects may be taken in place of the above.

Combined Studies: a wide range of subjects including one compulsory subject for one year, *generally in another Faculty.*

4. RESIDENCE ABROAD

Students proceeding to the B.A. degree in German intercalate one year in Germany or Austria under the official scheme for assistants in schools. Students have a reading list to work through while abroad.

Combined Studies: If German is taken for three years, the student must attend abroad for three or four weeks an approved course of study in German.

5. METHODS OF STUDY

See I.2 above.

II. ADMISSION TO COURSES

1. QUALIFICATIONS REQUIRED

For admission to the B.A. German course, three 'A' Level subjects, including at least a B in German, are normally required as well as 'O' Level Latin.

For admission to the Combined Studies course, three 'A' Level subjects with a mark of C in each are required.

Note.—In the Department of German here, as in various other departments, the Combined Studies degree course is not regarded as inferior to the Special degree course. It is an Honours course for a different sort of mind and for a competence which may be wider than that of the specialist.

2. SELECTION OF STUDENTS

German. Strongly recommended candidates are generally interviewed. An entrance scholarship examination may be taken. We try to gauge potential, as well as to estimate the present level of achievement. We try to ensure that candidates have a genuine interest in German studies.

Combined Studies. Applicants are interviewed by a panel. Criteria are 'A' Level performance plus head teacher's report, and impressions gained by interview.

3. TRANSFER

Transfer is possible.

4. NUMBERS

Between 10 and 15 students are admitted annually to the German Department for the Specialist course; between 5 and 10 for the Combined Studies course.

Information supplied by Professor H. Powell

UNIVERSITY OF LIVERPOOL

Department of German

I. COURSES OF STUDY

1. TYPES OF COURSES

(a) *B.A. in General Studies* (with or without Honours): this normally involves the study of at least three subjects within the Faculty of Arts. At least one must be studied for three years though normally two are so studied.

(b) *B.A. with Honours:* after the First Preliminary year, one or two subjects are studied for the remaining two or three years. In the case of German either a term is spent at a German university (four months) during the last year, or a whole year in Germany is intercalated between the second and third years. If German is studied with another language, a year is intercalated in one of the countries concerned.

(c) *B.Com.:* this involves only an elementary translation course in a modern language which may be German.

We run a non-examinable course designed for non-linguists which aims to introduce German culture and literature to economists and others.

2. CHARACTERISTICS OF COURSES

Certain options are allowed in the Final year. Candidates may exercise a preference for medieval rather than modern literature, or for linguistic rather than literary work. One of these options allows them to take Dutch during their last year.

3. COMBINATION OF SUBJECTS

For General Studies any combination within the Faculty of Arts is possible. For Honours, German may be combined with English Literature, or with any other modern language. There are no compulsory combinations of subjects.

4. RESIDENCE ABROAD

See under I.1 above. Students go to any university in Germany, Austria or Switzerland, which they choose. They are required to attend lectures there and to write essays and proses which they send by mail to us here. If a year is intercalated, this is usually spent as assistant at a German school.

5. METHODS OF STUDY

We use the tutorial system throughout. There is a very small number of lectures, attendance at which is not obligatory.

6. OTHER ACTIVITIES

The undergraduates produce a German play annually which is always well received.

II. ADMISSION TO COURSES

1. QUALIFICATIONS REQUIRED

All candidates must have 'O' Level Latin at least.

For Honours candidates must reach an adequate standard in their 'A' Level examination.

General students may be admitted with a somewhat lower standard.

In no case can the language be started from scratch.

2. SELECTION OF STUDENTS

Students are selected by a combination of:

(1) 'A' Level results (see above),

(2) Head teachers' testimonials,

(3) Interviews.

All candidates for Honours are interviewed. No entrance examinations are set. Candidates for General Studies are normally interviewed, but not by this Department. Interviews, which normally last up to 20 minutes, are designed to assess the mental alertness and sensibility of candidates rather than their breadth of reading, though the latter is also taken into account.

3. TRANSFER

Normally students are admitted to Honours courses on entrance.

Transfer is possible at the end of the first year, either from General Studies to Honours or vice versa.

4. NUMBERS

Approximately 12 Honours students are admitted annually to the School.

Information supplied by Professor W. D. Williams

UNIVERSITY OF LONDON:
BEDFORD COLLEGE

Department of German

I. COURSES OF STUDY

Bedford College at present admits only women students to undergraduate courses; both men and women are admitted as postgraduate students.

1. TYPES OF COURSES

The following courses in German are provided:

(*a*) *Honours in German Language and Literature:* a three-year course, with one Subsidiary subject (examined normally at the end of the second year);

(*b*) *General:* German is studied as one of three subjects in a three-year course for the B.A. General degree;

(*c*) *Subsidiary:* German as a Subsidiary subject can be taken by students reading for Honours in another subject; this is a two-year course.

2. CHARACTERISTICS OF COURSES

Honours. Courses follow London University regulations. They cover the present-day language (translation, essays and oral work); medieval studies, linguistic and literary, with selected texts, and some reference to general linguistics; selected authors and topics from modern literature (1500 to the present day), with the special study of selected texts, and of the 'Age of Goethe'.[1]

[1] *Note.*—For examinations in and after 1966, the following revised Regulations and Syllabus will be introduced for the B.A. Honours degree in German:

The examination will consist of seven written papers and an oral examination.

(*a*) The German Language. The development of the German language from early Old High German on, with particular reference to Classical Middle High German and later times. Candidates will be further required to choose one of the following fields: (*i*) the development of the Old High German dialects in their relation to West Germanic, Primitive Germanic and Indo-European, in outline; (*ii*) (for Internal Students only) the German language of all periods in the light of modern linguistics together with passages in German for linguistic, including stylistic, analysis; (*iii*) Old High German texts, together with passages in Old Saxon.

(*b*) The Middle High German Classical Period. Knowledge of the following will be required: the Minnesang, Hartmann von Aue, Walther von der Vogelweide, the *Nibelungenlied*, Wolfram von Eschenbach, Gottfried von Strassburg. Command of Middle High German will be tested by passages for translation from prepared and unprepared texts. (*Contd. at the foot of p. 145*)

We concentrate on the analysis of major works of literature and thought, take account of European cross-currents, and pay special attention to the 20th century. Students are encouraged to take in their first year an additional *non-examination* subject.

General and Subsidiary. Courses are given on the modern language (translation, essays, oral work), prescribed books and periods from German literature, and a simple Middle High German text.

3. COMBINATION OF SUBJECTS

Honours students have a wide choice of Subsidiary subjects, including History, Philosophy, English, French, Italian, and Dutch; they should consult the University Regulations for the approved list. There is no compulsory combination of subjects. Subjects for which there is no teaching in this College may be studied at another College by arrangement.

4. RESIDENCE ABROAD

Honours students are expected to spend substantial periods during the vacations in a German-speaking country. Students normally spend the summer term of their first year at a German, Austrian or Swiss-German university, and every attempt is made to arrange exchanges. All students going abroad are advised to attend organized courses of study. The University Regulations also allow students to intercalate a year for study abroad if they wish.

5. METHODS OF STUDY

(1) Lectures
(2) Individual tutorials (essays)
(3) Seminar discussions
(4) Small groups for practical language work.

II. ADMISSION TO COURSES

1. QUALIFICATIONS REQUIRED

Admission is based on:

(*i*) Minimum entrance requirements for the University of London, Faculty of Arts, including a classical language at either 'O' or 'A' Level;

(*c*) The Age of Goethe.
(*d*) German Literature from the later Middle Ages to the present day (excluding the Age of Goethe).
(*e*) Works selected for commentary and criticism, from 1500 to the present day.
(*f*) Translation from and into German.
(*g*) Essay in German.
(*h*) An oral examination which shall test scholarship as well as command of the spoken language.
Subsidiary Subject. (As at present prescribed.)

(*ii*) An interview and/or satisfactory performance at the College's own entrance examination;

(*iii*) Late applicants may be considered for admission, after interview, on satisfactory performance in two or, preferably, three subjects at 'A' Level in G.C.E.

2. SELECTION OF STUDENTS

The College entrance examination will consist of *either* written papers in two subjects, one principal and one subsidiary (one paper each), together with an interview, *or* of an extended interview test alone. Any written examination in German will consist of passages for prose composition and translation into English, and either a short essay in German on some general topic, or a literary commentary in English on a passage of prose or verse.

School records are taken into account.

The examination of the London Intercollegiate Scholarships Board is accepted, if a satisfactory standard is reached, in lieu of the written paper at the entrance examination. Candidates are interviewed in the normal manner.

3. TRANSFER

Students are admitted to the Honours course on entrance. Transfer to another School or course is possible, though infrequent.

4. NUMBERS

About 20 students are admitted annually to the Honours School.

Information supplied by Professor R. Peacock

UNIVERSITY OF LONDON:
BIRKBECK COLLEGE
Department of German

I. COURSES OF STUDY

Birkbeck College is an evening college and normally admits only students in full-time employment.

1. TYPES OF COURSES

German can be taken in the following courses:

(a) *Honours German:* a single-subject degree with one Subsidiary subject;

(b) *German for the B.A. General degree:* German is studied as one of three subjects;

(c) *German as a Subsidiary subject:* German is studied as the second subject to another Honours degree subject.

2. CHARACTERISTICS OF COURSES

In accordance with the syllabus of London University, German studies include courses in: (a) the development of the German language; (b) German literature, medieval and modern; (c) translations, essays and oral work and (d) a subject for special study which may be linguistic, literary, philosophical or historical.[1]

3. COMBINATION OF SUBJECTS

French and English are normal combinations. A limited number of other combinations is possible where a clash does not occur in time-table; but as only 15 hours per week are available for all courses, the choice is necessarily restricted. No combination of subjects is compulsory.

4. RESIDENCE ABROAD

There are no compulsory requirements for residence abroad, since our students are all in full day-time employment; but we encourage them to attend German vacation courses. They usually go to Freiburg, Marburg or Tübingen.

II. ADMISSION TO COURSES

1. QUALIFICATIONS REQUIRED

For admission to this Department, German at 'A' Level G.C.E., or an equivalent qualification, is required.

[1] For regulations and syllabus for the Examinations in and after 1966, see p. 144, footnote 1.

We have elementary reading classes in German for students in the Faculties of Arts and Science taking degree courses in other subjects; but these classes are not open to outside students wishing to proceed to a degree in German.

2. SELECTION OF STUDENTS

Selection is based on 'A' Level results, plus an oral test at the interview. This consists of sight translation from and into German; and pronunciation is also assessed. All students are interviewed. Personal references are not required.

3. TRANSFER

Honours students are admitted on entrance.

Transfer is possible if there is a sufficiently good reason.

4. NUMBERS

Approximately 15 students are admitted annually to the Honours course.

Information supplied by Professor R. J. McClean

UNIVERSITY OF LONDON: KING'S COLLEGE

Department of German

I. COURSES OF STUDY

1. TYPES OF COURSES

Courses are as for other Colleges in the University of London:

(*a*) Four-year *Honours* course (plus one Subsidiary subject, the examination for which is usually taken after two years);

(*b*) *General:* German as one of three subjects, a three-year course;

(*c*) *German as a Subsidiary subject* to an Honours course in another subject; this is a two-year course.

2. CHARACTERISTICS OF COURSES

The principal course in the Department is that of the University of London German Honours course. This is traditionally language and literature (including medieval language and literature) and the standard is high. Each department in the University approaches the course in its own manner though a large amount of uniformity is achieved as ultimately all candidates from all colleges have to sit the same examination. As a result of discussions proceeding at present there will undoubtedly be some modifications in the future, and some of these modifications may be far-reaching.[1]

There is little time for non-examinable courses though students who are keen and who can with advantage carry the extra burden are encouraged to study some other subject. The department lays great stress on English literature and it expects all students to have a sustained interest in some aspect of the literature of their own country.

3. COMBINATION OF SUBJECTS

Normally German is combined with French, frequently with Latin, English or Spanish, and occasionally with Russian. We are, however, most liberal in this respect, and as long as no insuperable time-table difficulties arise we are happy to allow students to follow their own bent, and to choose any subject they like which is available, whether the subject can be studied at the college or not.

[1] For regulations and syllabus for the Examinations in and after 1966, see p. 144, footnote 1.

4. RESIDENCE ABROAD

All students must go abroad for their third year. We like them to leave as soon as they have completed their Subsidiary subject which means that they can get abroad by 1st July. We like them to stay in a German-speaking country all the time and return in October of the following year so that in the best case they have 15 months continuous residence. This is partly a financial problem. Each student is placed under a member of the staff who remains in constant touch. The students are given set work, an extensive reading list, and they are visited at least once. Full-time study at a German-speaking university is normal, occasionally students work as paid assistants in school where they give up to 12 periods per week English lessons. We prefer them to study at a university if this can possibly be managed. All students return to the college for their final year.

5. METHODS OF STUDY

We have small groups for tutorials as far as we are able with our limited staff. We try to have not too many set lectures with the whole group attending, though we should always have such courses, as we believe it is good for students to be confronted with the discipline of a course and good for them to work together.

6. OTHER ACTIVITIES

There is a flourishing German student society, which is run completely by the students. It is particularly well known in the University for its play productions.

II. ADMISSION TO COURSES

1. QUALIFICATIONS REQUIRED

For admission to this Department the entrant requires three subjects at 'A' Level, or two at 'A' Level and the requisite number of 'O' Level passes. These include Latin at least to 'O' Level: we like Latin to 'A' Level and normally give preference to Honours candidates with 'A' Level Latin and two further 'A' Level subjects.

2. SELECTION OF STUDENTS

We find it impossible to select on 'A' Level results only; so selected candidates are called for interview.

Criteria for selection: whilst we lay emphasis on good German we also seek applicants interested in literature. They are little use to us unless they read English literature with enjoyment and intelligence.

3. TRANSFER

Students are admitted to the Honours course on entrance.
Transfer is difficult but permissible.

4. NUMBERS

The overall number of students in the four years is at present 115. Between 25 and 30 enter the Department every year.

Information supplied by Professor F. Norman

UNIVERSITY OF LONDON: QUEEN MARY COLLEGE

Department of German

I. COURSES OF STUDY

1. TYPES OF COURSES

German can be studied for:

(*a*) *B.A. Honours:* a three-year course, with a Subsidiary subject for one or two years;

(*b*) *Subsidiary* (to Honours in another subject). The Subsidiary course in German takes a minimum of two years.

2. CHARACTERISTICS OF COURSES

The keynote of instruction in this Department is a competent foundation of modern German, and also historical grammar, on which to rear a sound knowledge and understanding of literature from *c.* 800 to the present day. Medieval German literature is given its full value. What we hope to find in students, and then to develop, is disciplined imagination, and this is the quality we look for in interviews, hard though it is to detect at the tender age of admission.[1]

3. COMBINATION OF SUBJECTS

French, English, Geography or Latin are more usually combined with German. Other combinations are possible. Swedish, Dutch and Philosophy have been read by German Honours students in the past. There are no compulsory combinations of subjects.

4. RESIDENCE ABROAD

One *Sommersemester* at a German-speaking university, normally in the second year, is all but obligatory in this Department.

If students co-operate by sending a list of lectures at their German university the staff examines it and makes counter-suggestions.

5. METHODS OF STUDY

In the Honours course there are chiefly small seminar groups and tutorials. (Five full-time members of staff, including one native German language assistant, to 45 Honours students affords a not unfavourable ratio.)

[1] For the new syllabus for German Honours courses which will come into force in 1966, see p. 144 above, footnote 1.

II. ADMISSION TO COURSES

1. QUALIFICATIONS REQUIRED

Honours students should normally have obtained B in German at 'A' Level and B in another language at 'A' Level. They also require 'O' Level Latin. (German is not started from scratch in this Department.)

Subsidiary students normally require at least C in German at 'A' Level.

2. SELECTION OF STUDENTS

Selection of students for this Department is based on the following data:

(*a*) 'A' Level results,

(*b*) Head teachers' reports,

(*c*) an interview.

Only those applicants whose school examination results offer some hope of broader achievement are interviewed. In the interview the general demeanour of the candidate is considered, particularly the prospective mutual educability of students. The ability to interpret orally a moderately difficult English poem, unseen, is expected. If the candidate cannot do this in his mother tongue there is no prospect that he will be able to do it in a foreign language. One half of the Final B.A. Examination involves the interpretation of literature, thus at the stage of admission those with purely linguistic interests and abilities are felt to be at a great disadvantage.

3. TRANSFER

Students are selected for Honours courses on entrance. Transfer is only possible in exceptional and convincing cases.

4. NUMBERS

Fifteen students are admitted annually to our Honours courses.

Information supplied by Professor A. T. Hatto

UNIVERSITY OF LONDON: ROYAL HOLLOWAY COLLEGE

Department of German

I. COURSES OF STUDY

Royal Holloway College at present admits only women under-graduates; but in October 1965 150 men will be eligible for admission as undergraduates, approximately doubling the present number of first-year students. This is the first stage of an expansion programme planned to establish in three years a college of a thousand students, with a balance between the sexes.

1. TYPES OF COURSES

(*a*) A three-year course for the *B.A. Honours* degree in German, with one Subsidiary subject examined after two years' study.

(*b*) A three-year course for the *B.A. General* degree, in which German may be one of three subjects, all studied for the three years.

(*c*) A two-year course in German as a *Subsidiary* subject, for students following the Honours French course.

2. CHARACTERISTICS OF COURSES

The content of all courses is that prescribed by the University of London for all Colleges. For the *B.A. Honours course* all students study the history of the German language; medieval and modern literature: the historical development in outline, with periods, authors or texts in greater intensity; modern German prose composition, translation, essay and oral work. In addition each student selects a Special Subject, either linguistic or literary, from a prescribed list, which may be studied at this or some other college. All students in their second and third year attend the intercollegiate lectures arranged for all Colleges, as well as the appropriate Special Subject class.[1]

Non-examination courses in some other subject (including Music, Art and Voice-production in addition to subjects taught in the Arts Faculty) may be taken by first-year students.

For the *B.A. General and Subsidiary* courses study is devoted to modern German prose composition, translation, essay and oral work, and to the periods of literature 1150–1250 and 1740–1926, with some prescribed texts treated in great detail and including extracts from one medieval one.

---

[1] For the revised regulations and syllabus for German Honours Courses which will be in operation on and after 1966, see p. 144 above, footnote 1.

3. COMBINATION OF SUBJECTS

Any Arts subject taught at this College may be taken as a Subsidiary subject or as one of the other two subjects in a General degree course. French is the most usual; English, Latin and History are also taken, and this is now the only College in the University of London at which Music may be studied as a Subsidiary subject or as one of the three subjects for the B.A. General degree. Other languages, e.g. Spanish and Italian, which are not at present taught at this College, may be taken at one of the other London Colleges by suitably qualified students, provided the time-table can be arranged.

Under the College's expansion plans for 1965–68 Spanish and Italian will be offered as Subsidiary subjects taught at the College, and it is envisaged that additional Subsidiary subjects, e.g. Russian and Philosophy, may be taught at the College in further phases of expansion.

4. RESIDENCE ABROAD

All Honours students spend the third term of their first year at a German-speaking university, usually Münster, exchanging with a German student. They are free to select the lectures which they attend, and no definite work is set for them for the term by this College. If students wish, a year may also be spent abroad as an assistant in a German-speaking school between the second and third year, but this is not obligatory.

5. METHODS OF STUDY

A certain number of formal lecture courses are given, and in addition there are seminars, tutorial and discussion classes. As numbers are small, there is ample opportunity for discussion, even within lecture courses. Essays are normally returned individually. A resident German *Assistentin* is appointed each year, with whom all students have a weekly half-hour conversation class, either singly or in pairs.

II. ADMISSION TO COURSES

1. QUALIFICATIONS REQUIRED

Minimum entrance requirements for the University of London Faculty of Arts which include a classical language (normally Latin or Greek) at 'O' Level. Latin at 'A' Level, while desirable, is not demanded nor is preference necessarily given to candidates who have taken it, as it is felt that a knowledge of English literature, for instance, is equally important. Candidates should normally have taken German at 'A' Level although exceptions may occasionally be made.

2. SELECTION OF STUDENTS

(*a*) A special examination is taken in November by candidates applying for a scholarship or exhibition. It consists of two papers: (*i*) translation from and into German; (*ii*) German literature in the

18th and 19th centuries. There is a wide choice of questions and candidates should be able to tackle this paper on the basis of their 'A' Level work. Those not recommended for an award may be advised to apply in the usual way for a vacancy, i.e. through the Universities' Central Council on Admissions.

(*b*) Applicants for places are considered on the basis of their academic record and head teacher's report, and selected candidates are interviewed. Candidates who have not yet taken 'A' Level may be offered places provisionally.

3. TRANSFER

A transfer from the B.A. Honours to the B.A. General course or vice versa may be arranged in cases in which this is felt to be in the student's best interests.

4. NUMBERS

As this is predominantly a residential College, numbers are limited by the living accommodation available. At present about 6 women undergraduates are normally admitted to the Honours German course, but in October 1965, and in each of the following two years, an additional 6 men students will be eligible for admission to the Honours German course.

Information supplied by Professor R. Tymms

UNIVERSITY OF LONDON: UNIVERSITY COLLEGE

Department of German

I. COURSES OF STUDY

1. TYPES OF COURSES

German may be studied at this College:

(*a*) for an *Honours* degree (see I.2 below);

(*b*) as a *Subsidiary* subject. This is a two-year course involving composition, translation, essay and German literature 1150–1250 and 1740–1926.

No student is admitted by the College to read for a *General* degree.

2. CHARACTERISTICS OF COURSES

The Honours course in German at all Colleges of the University of London requires the student to study the German language and German literature in the Middle Ages and the Age of Goethe, and allows him to study them at other periods that may interest him. There is no provision in the syllabus for the study of German history, geography, philosophy, etc.[1]

At this College, the emphasis is on the study of literature and in particular on the operation of language in literature. The periods on which attention is chiefly concentrated are the Middle Ages and the modern period since 1750. Applicants who have a 'flair for language' in its practical operations, or whose interest in Germany is a very broad one, would probably do better at a university where equal or greater emphasis is laid on these aspects.

3. COMBINATION OF SUBJECTS

French, English, Italian, Russian, Latin, History of Philosophy or History of Art are usually taken as Subsidiary to German. Other combinations are possible, in accordance with University regulations, though time-table difficulties sometimes make certain combinations difficult or impossible in practice. Subjects such as Russian or Spanish (for both of which 'A' Level is required) for which there is no teaching in this College may be studied elsewhere by arrangement.

4. RESIDENCE ABROAD

The German Honours course is normally a four-year course, and as an integral part of it, each student is expected to spend one year,

[1] For the revised regulations and syllabus which will be in operation for examinations in and after 1966, see p. 144 above, footnote 1.

normally the second, in Germany or Austria. This year abroad may be spent in full-time study at a university or as a paid assistant in a secondary school. The Head of the Department will advise students on their choice.

5. METHODS OF STUDY

We operate a modified tutorial system. Most classes are in small groups, and each student has the opportunity for individual consultation with one or more members of staff.

6. OTHER ACTIVITIES

There is an active German Society.

II. ADMISSION TO COURSES

1. QUALIFICATIONS REQUIRED

The College requires three passes at 'O' Level and two at 'A' Level *or* one pass at 'O' Level and three at 'A' Level.

These must include two languages other than English, one of which must be Latin or Greek. Thus a pass in Latin at 'A' Level is *not* a requirement.

2. SELECTION OF STUDENTS

For *Honours*, we consider a combination of G.C.E. results, head teachers' reports and interviews. Under present pressure from the schools, we have for the time being suspended our departmental entrance test, in order to see how the centralized admission procedure works.

On receipt of application forms from the Universities Central Council on Admissions we shall send out an acknowledgment with a request for some supplementary information. Some applications will be rejected on the information available at this stage; the remaining candidates will be invited for interview. No applicant can be accepted without interview.

For *Subsidiary:* Subsidiary students are admitted to the College by the Department in which they take their Honours subject. We normally require a pass in German at 'A' Level as a qualification to read Subsidiary German.

3. TRANSFER

Students are admitted to the Honours course on entrance. Transfer from one Honours school to another is possible providing that the other Department is willing and able to accept the student.

4. NUMBERS

Approximately 20 Honours students are admitted annually.

Information supplied by Professor Elizabeth M. Wilkinson

UNIVERSITY OF LONDON:
WESTFIELD COLLEGE

Department of German

I. COURSES OF STUDY

Westfield College admits men and women students as under-graduates.

1. TYPES OF COURSES

German can be studied

(*a*) for a Single *Honours degree in German,* or

(*b*) as a *Subsidiary* subject to an Honours degree in French or Spanish.

The College does not as a rule admit students to study for B.A. General, but occasionally a student is allowed to take a General course if it is found that she is unable to do the Honours course.

German as a Subsidiary subject follows the syllabus for the B.A. degree.

2. CHARACTERISTICS OF COURSES

All Honours candidates are required to take the following sections of the syllabus prescribed for the B.A. Honours in the University of London:

(*a*) The development of the German language, and prescribed Old High German texts;

(*b*) Prescribed and unprescribed Middle High German texts, and medieval literature (in relation to the texts, students will be required to make comments of literary, linguistic, cultural or metrical interest);

(*c*) German literature from 1500 to the present day;

(*d*) Prescribed modern texts (these change from time to time);

(*e*) Translation from and into German;

(*f*) Essay in German;

(*g*) An oral examination which shall test scholarship as well as command of the spoken language.

In addition to the above, every candidate must choose a subject for special study. Our students tend to take one or other of the modern subjects—Goethe, the Romantic Movement in German Literature (1795–1830), German Drama in the 19th century or German Lyric

Poetry since 1880. There are also at present two medieval options, i.e. either the Court Epic or the Heroic Epic.[1]

Courses for non-examinable subjects are usually taken in the first year, and every student is encouraged to follow one such course, which may be in another language or in history or theological lectures or something of the kind. These are sometimes taken in the University rather than in the College.

3. COMBINATION OF SUBJECTS

One Subsidiary subject must be taken in addition to the main subject. Any language other than German taught at Subsidiary level *in the College* may be combined with the main subject. The usual ones are French, Spanish, Italian. No previous knowledge of Spanish or Italian is required. History may also be taken at Subsidiary level.

4. RESIDENCE ABROAD

All first-year Honours students are required to go to Germany for the last term of their first year. They each exchange with a German student and matriculate at the appropriate university in Germany, so as to be able to follow the complete German course in Arts. We normally have students at nearly every university in Western Germany.

5. METHODS OF STUDY

The system here is a combination of lectures and tutorial classes. We are able to have small groups for discussion, and when our German exchange students arrive for the summer term, we rearrange the practical classes so as to mix German and English students at the appropriate level. This produces a much more lively discussion on the problems of language than would be possible if the German and the English students were separated.

The oral work is done by a full-time *Lektorin* who resides in College. As well as conducting small conversation groups, she assists in all sorts of ways with the practical teaching of the subject and with the performance and reading of plays in German.

II. ADMISSION TO COURSES

1. QUALIFICATIONS REQUIRED

Students must satisfy the University requirements for the Faculty of Arts, which include a pass in Latin at Ordinary *or* Advanced Level.

Admission to the College is through the Central Council, but a Scholarship Examination is held to enable us to make College awards. This examination consists of the following papers:

(1) Prose composition and essay in German;

[1] For the revised regulations and syllabus which will be in operation for examinations in and after 1966, see p. 144 above, footnote 1.

(2) Translation, and not more than two questions to be answered in English, designed to test the candidates' ability to handle material placed before them. No programme of literature is prescribed and no special preparation for this examination is desired. Candidates will be tested on their knowledge of the German language and their critical ability.

(3) Unprepared translation. Candidates must attempt at least one classical language. Those who wish to take French as a Subsidiary subject in the degree course must attempt the French passages unless they are taking prose composition, essay and translation in French. They must not attempt the German passages.

2. SELECTION OF STUDENTS

As admission is through the Central Council, particular attention is paid to heads' reports. Candidates whose applications look promising are required to come to the College for interview.

3. TRANSFER

Students are admitted to the Honours courses on entrance.

Transfer as a rule is not possible, but exceptions have been made in consultation with any other department to which a candidate may wish to transfer.

4. NUMBERS

We aim at 15–17 students per year. We now have approximately 30 Honours students in the Department.

Information supplied by Dr. M. Beare, Reader in German

UNIVERSITY OF MANCHESTER

Department of German

I. COURSES OF STUDY

1. TYPES OF COURSES

German can be studied for Honours or General degrees:

(*a*) for *Honours* degrees in the following Honours Schools: German Language and Literature (three years); German and Philosophy (three years); German and Drama (four years); Honours Modern Languages: German plus another modern language, e.g. French, Russian, etc. (four years).

All German Honours syllabuses, except that of German and Philosophy, include both linguistic and literary studies (medieval and modern). In the Honours School of German and Philosophy only the literary part of the German Honours course is taken.

(*b*) for the *General* degree or as *Subsidiary* subjects: German Intermediate Iiii is a beginners' course. German Intermediate Ii presupposes a pass at 'O' Level G.C.E. German General presupposes a pass at Intermediate Ii or at least grade B at 'A' Level G.C.E. German Special presupposes a pass at General level.

2. CHARACTERISTICS OF COURSES

In the Honours School of German Language and Literature the first five terms are devoted to the study of some of the most important German authors and *genres* of modern German literature in seminars, essay groups and lectures. The history of the German language is dealt with in lecture courses and a detailed study is made of some important Middle High German texts. There are classes in German essay-writing and prose composition as well as conversation classes in small groups. German history from antiquity to the present day is studied as an ancillary subject. A Preliminary Honours examination is taken at the end of the first year.

In the third year the student may choose between courses mainly in modern literature or mainly in medieval literature and linguistic subjects. While the Honours course is thus the same for all students in the first five terms, there is a wide choice of specialized subjects in the final year.

3. COMBINATION OF SUBJECTS

Students in the Honours School of German Language and Literature are obliged to take two Intermediate subjects, of which one must be either Latin, Greek or Philosophy, while the other may be chosen freely from a wide range of subjects. One Subsidiary subject must be taken up to General level. In Honours Modern Languages the one Subsidiary subject required is Latin.

4. RESIDENCE ABROAD

Students are required to spend the summer term of their second year at a university in Germany, Austria or Switzerland and to register for courses equivalent to a term at this University. Most of our students go to Germany. Students are encouraged to spend a year as an English assistant in a German-speaking country (usually after their second year).

5. METHODS OF STUDY

Most teaching is done in small tutorial groups or seminars.

6. OTHER ACTIVITIES

There is a German Society, which produces a German play annually.

II. ADMISSION TO COURSES

1. QUALIFICATIONS REQUIRED

Latin at 'O' Level is a Faculty requirement. For admission to the Honours School a mark of at least grade B in German and marks around grade B in all subjects taken at 'A' Level are normally required.

There is a beginners' course in German (see I.1(b)) but it is not possible to study German for an Honours degree without previous knowledge of the language.

2. SELECTION OF STUDENTS

Applicants who state that Manchester is their first choice are normally interviewed. The purpose of the interview is to assess the potentialities of the candidate for his subject, his intellectual ability and his general interests. Head teachers' reports and performance at 'A' Level in the G.C.E. examination are naturally taken into account.

3. TRANSFER

Students are admitted to Honours courses on entrance.

A transfer to the General Arts degree course is possible. A transfer from the General Arts degree course to an Honours course is possible but means an additional year.

4. NUMBERS

About 30 students are admitted annually to the Honours courses in German.

Information supplied by Professor R. E. Keller

UNIVERSITY OF NEWCASTLE UPON TYNE

Department of German and Scandinavian Studies

I. COURSES OF STUDY

1. TYPES OF COURSES

German may be studied in this University as follows:

(a) *Honours in German* (a three-year course and *one* year spent abroad);

(b) *Joint Honours in German and French,* or *German and Spanish* (a three-year course and *one* year spent abroad);

(c) *German as a subject in a General degree* (a three-year course with or without an additional special course in the third year which takes the place of a full subject at Final General standard);

(d) *German as a Subsidiary subject in another Honours School* (a two-year course covering the second- and third-year syllabuses of German for the General degree).

2. CHARACTERISTICS OF COURSES

The aims of the *Honours* course are: (1) to make students thoroughly proficient in the use of modern spoken and written German; (2) to acquaint them with the language in its classical medieval form, Middle High German, with the structure and history of the language, with the geography and history of German-speaking Europe and with German literature in the 12th and 13th centuries and from the 18th century to the present day. In addition students must work on some of the more specialized branches of Germanic studies, like Germanic philology with Gothic and Old High German, German literature of the 14th, 15th, 16th and 17th centuries, the learning of Dutch or of a Scandinavian language, the writing of an undergraduate dissertation.

Students reading German for an Honours degree in German and French or German and Spanish are excused detailed study of the German literature of most recent times as well as work in the more specialized branches of Germanic studies.

Among the special features to be noted are the stress laid on the geography, history and institutions of German-speaking Europe, the opportunity to acquire a modern Scandinavian language or Dutch; and comparatively wide options.

The aim of the *General* course is to give students a good knowledge of modern spoken and written German and to introduce them to the history and literature of Germany since the 18th century. In the first year the 20th century is studied, in the second the 19th and in the third the 18th. In the special course students return to the 20th century and make a detailed study of the life and literature of contemporary Germany.

3. COMBINATION OF SUBJECTS

The main Subsidiaries for German are French, Swedish, Norwegian, Danish, English, Modern History, but a wider choice is possible; e.g. Spanish, Economics, Philosophy, Psychology, Art and Architecture, and Music have all occurred.

4. RESIDENCE ABROAD

All students reading for Honours in German are required as an integral part of their course to intercalate after their second year of study *either* a year studying at a German-speaking university *or* a year as paid language assistants in a German-speaking country under the official scheme. Joint Honours students spend the summer-term of their second year of study at a German-speaking university and intercalate a year in France.

General degree students and students taking German as a Subsidiary are required to spend at least a month during a vacation in a German-speaking country.

5. METHODS OF STUDY

There are few set lectures; teaching is very largely tutorial. Two German lectors tutor small groups, and teaching staff is available for hours every week for consultation.

6. OTHER ACTIVITIES

We maintain close collaboration with the Modern Language Association. We show films, etc., provided by the German Embassy and arrange for students to see German films shown by the Tyneside Film Society; we sponsor Drama groups from Germany and readings by German authors and lectures by German scholars. We expect students to run their own Drama Group and Anglo-German Society without guidance by their teachers.

II. ADMISSION TO COURSES

1. QUALIFICATIONS REQUIRED

'O' Level Latin is a University matriculation requirement for all courses. For Single Honours or Joint Honours in German 'A' Level German is required.

For German in a General degree, 'O' Level German is required.

German cannot be started from scratch, but all Scandinavian languages (Swedish, Norwegian and Danish) are started from scratch.

2. SELECTION OF STUDENTS

A colleague and I select Honours students on the basis of a fifteen-minute interview, 'A' Level results, and head teachers' opinions. We try to interview all candidates except those with poor 'A' Level results who are not attempting to improve them. In interviews we discuss the candidate's interests and aspirations, speak German to him for a few minutes, perhaps ask him to translate a sentence into German or English, talk about the German books he has read.

We prefer students who want to work and become scholarly persons. We discourage those who think that a university is a finishing school for young gentlemen and young ladies. We are prejudiced in favour of tidy people. We like candidates who take English at school and can discuss English literature. We are impressed by candidates doing 'A' Level Latin, who can read and translate at sight a simple passage in that language. We do not much care whether candidates have been prefects, head boys, successful football and hockey players or not. We favour candidates who want to live and study abroad for a time. We are naturally interested in candidates who have asked for a place so that they can start Swedish, Norwegian or Danish as a Subsidiary subject. The 'A' Level performance demanded is lower for the candidate who interviews well, higher for the one who interviews badly. We appreciate from heads background information such as 'adopted child', 'father unwilling for her to study', 'painfully shy', etc.

Only the most brilliant candidates are accepted for Joint Honours, i.e. Honours in German and French, etc. General students are selected by the Senior Tutor in Arts.

3. TRANSFER

Students are admitted to Honours courses on entrance. Transfer to Honours is possible after the first-year General course. Students admitted to Honours courses on entrance who show themselves unable to stay the course may be permitted to transfer after their first year to the *second* year of the General course.

4. NUMBERS

Thirty students are admitted directly to the Honours courses in German.

Information supplied by Professor D. M. Mennie

UNIVERSITY OF NOTTINGHAM

Department of German

I. COURSES OF STUDY

1. TYPES OF COURSES

The Department of German offers two main courses:

I. (*a*) German as an *Honours* course, with one Subsidiary subject;

(*b*) German as part of a *Joint Honours degree*, combined with Philosophy; as part of a Joint Honours degree, combined with another modern foreign language; and

II. German as a *Subsidiary* subject.

2. CHARACTERISTICS OF COURSES

The course is designed to achieve a balance between linguistic and medieval studies on the one hand, and modern literature on the other; opportunity is given in the third year for more specialization.

3. COMBINATION OF SUBJECTS

Students must choose a Subsidiary subject from a fixed list. Most students of German take French, English, History or Latin.

4. RESIDENCE ABROAD

One term abroad (i.e. the third in the first year) is required. Students write one long essay in German while abroad.

II. ADMISSION TO COURSES

1. QUALIFICATIONS REQUIRED

For admission to this Department the student must have (1) Latin to 'O' Level; (2) four 'O' Level passes, including English language, one Science and one language other than English; (3) two 'A' Level passes.

German cannot be started from scratch.

2. SELECTION OF STUDENTS

Selection is based on 'A' Level results, school record and, when necessary, an interview.

3. TRANSFER

Transfer is made in certain circumstances to a Pass degree course after one or two years.

4. NUMBERS

Some 10 to 12 students join the German Department annually.

Information supplied by Professor K. C. King

UNIVERSITY OF OXFORD

Faculty of Medieval and Modern Languages (German) [1]

I. COURSES OF STUDY

1. TYPES OF COURSES

German may be studied

(a) as the subject for an *Honours degree in only one language*;

(b) as a subject for an *Honours degree in two languages*, of which German may be either the first or the second subject.

2. CHARACTERISTICS OF COURSES

Preliminary Examination for Modern Languages. In the first two terms of study undergraduates must work for the First Public Examination (normally the Preliminary Examination for Modern Languages) which in German demands:

(1) Translation from and into German;

(2) One paper involving the close textual study of selected works. At present these are Kleist's *Erzählungen* and Rilke's *Duineser Elegien*.

(3) One paper of prescribed texts to be studied in relation to general trends in literature or thought or to historical background. At present the subject prescribed for this paper is 'German Tragedy in the 18th Century'.

Honour School of Modern Languages (Second Public Examination). Candidates offering German must offer some or all of the following papers according to whether they offer German as sole (10 papers), first (7 papers), or second language (4 papers):

(1) Translation into German;

(2) Translation from German;

(3) Essay in German;

(4) History of the German language to 1050 (with prescribed texts);

(5) History of the German language with special reference to its present state (with prescribed texts);

(6) Period of literature: One or two of the following periods may be offered (a) to 1400, (b) 1500–1700, (c) 1760–1930;

---

[1] For general information concerning courses, admissions, residence abroad, etc., for undergraduates reading modern languages at Oxford, see p. 348.

(7) Medieval texts prescribed for study as examples of literature. These include selected portions of *Nibelungenlied*, Gottfried von Strassburg's *Tristan und Isolt* and poems by Walther von der Vogelweide;

(8) Modern prescribed authors: either (*a*) Goethe or (*b*) *two* of the following: Lessing, Schiller, Hebbel, Nietzsche.

A candidate offering German as sole language must offer papers 1-5 inclusive; two periods from 6; paper 7 and both alternatives in 8. A candidate offering German as a first language must offer papers 1-3; paper 5; one of the periods from 6; paper 7 and one of the alternatives in 8. A candidate offering German as a second language must offer papers 1 and 2; one of the periods from 6 and one of the alternatives in 8.

There are also 54 Optional Subjects in the Final Honours School of Modern Languages. A candidate aiming at a place in the First Class must take one of these. A candidate's choice of Optional Subject is not restricted to those concerned with the language or languages he offers in the compulsory papers.

II. ADMISSION TO COURSES

4. NUMBERS

The number of candidates offering German in the Final Honours Examination has been about 100 in recent years.

Information supplied by Professor E. L. Stahl

UNIVERSITY OF READING
Department of German

I. COURSES OF STUDY

1. TYPES OF COURSES

German is available

(*a*) as a *Single Subject* course lasting four years;

(*b*) *in combination with:*

French: The two subjects are combined either as German–French (7 papers in German and 5 in French) or French–German (7 papers in French and 5 in German). Both courses last four years.

Italian: six papers in German, four in Italian; the course lasting four years.

Latin: five papers in German, five in Latin, the course lasting four years.

(*c*) *in combination with:*

English: three papers in German, five in English.

Music: five papers in German, four papers and a practical in Music.

Philosophy: five papers in German, five papers in Philosophy.

These three courses last three years.

(*d*) as a *Special Subject* for students reading a number of degree courses.

Honours may be awarded on merit in the Final Examination. There are no Honours *courses*, and no 'General' or 'Pass' *courses*. A student following any of the above courses satisfactorily (but not meriting an Honours classification) will be awarded a Pass degree.

2. CHARACTERISTICS OF COURSES

(*i*) (*a*) The *Single Subject* course in German extends over ten terms from the completion of the First University Examination. The second and fourth years are spent in Reading and the third at a German-speaking university. The scheme of studies is as follows: Prose composition in German and the writing of essays in English and in German continue throughout. During the second year there is a slight emphasis on the new disciplines (the historical study of the German language and the reading of medieval texts). For the remaining two years a student will then, to a limited extent, be allowed to specialize. He may continue Old High German and add Primitive Germanic or Modern Danish or Modern Dutch (Scheme A). Or he can omit these and prepare for a fuller examination in modern German literature (Scheme B).

Of the nine three-hour papers taken in the final examination seven are common to Scheme A and Scheme B.

(*b*) *Teaching:* mainly in small groups and in seminar conditions. Formal lecturing is kept to a minimum. The emphasis in seminar work is on an orderly, critical approach. The medium is English.

(*c*) *Practical work:* a German *Lektor* and other members of staff conduct conversation classes in German, There is a weekly lecture in German by the *Lektor* who, in the term preceding the period of residence abroad, conducts a two-hour seminar on modern authors in German. Essays in German are written during the period abroad and sent back to Reading for correction. There are facilities for work with tape-recorders and in a language laboratory.

There are usually 10 to 12 native German students (students of English) at the University in the period October to March each year. Private exchange arrangements can be made with them.

(*ii*) *The Combined Subjects courses:*

(*a*) *German and French, German and Italian.* German is studied as in the Single Subject course. The range of topics is, however, reduced on the medieval and philological side.

Residence abroad: Students spend one semester at a German, Swiss or Austrian university, and the remainder of the year at either a French or an Italian university.

(*b*) *French and German, Latin and German.* Students of Latin and German spend a whole year, and students of French and German one semester, in a German-speaking country.

(*c*) *English Literature and German, Music and German, Philosophy and German.* Attendance at a recognized vacation course in Germany is required.

(*d*) *Note.*—Modern *Danish* or Modern *Dutch* can be taken from scratch within the course in German as a Single Subject, ending in each case with a three-hour paper; these courses can be made available by arrangement.

3. COMBINATION OF SUBJECTS

In the First University Examination students take three subjects of which German must be one; the choice of the two other subjects will normally be made with reference to the envisaged final course.

4. RESIDENCE ABROAD

This is referred to under I.2 (*i*) (*a*) and (*ii*) (*a-c*), above,

5. METHODS OF STUDY

See I.2 (*i*) (*b*) and (*c*) above.

6. OTHER ACTIVITIES

Visiting lecturers from Germany and Austria or from other British universities. The students' German Society invites speakers. Some play-reading.

II. ADMISSION TO COURSES

1. QUALIFICATIONS REQUIRED

'O' Level Latin is a requirement for German, as a Single Subject and in combination with English, French, Music and Philosophy. In combination with Italian and Latin, 'A' Level Latin is normally required.

2. SELECTION OF STUDENTS

Generally speaking, candidates are not interviewed in respect of German. Selection is made after a scrutiny of applications and headmasters' reports.

3. TRANSFER

Students are accepted for their degree course after a First University Examination (see I.3). Transfer after the beginning of second-year studies is not likely to be practicable.

4. NUMBERS

The annual intake into German Honours (now discontinued, see I.1 last para.) was latterly between 15 and 18. Of the 1963 entry 26 students were admitted to take German as a Single Subject or in a Combined Subjects course.

Information supplied by Professor F. P. Pickering

UNIVERSITY OF SHEFFIELD
Department of German

I. COURSES OF STUDY

1. TYPES OF COURSES

German can be studied in the following courses:

(*a*) *Intermediate*, preparatory to *Special*, and *Intermediate* preparatory to *General degree*. The latter may be a single-year course or may be integrated into Subsidiary (two-year course) to another Honours School, or into a General (three-year course);

(*b*) *Special degree in the Honours School of German Language and Literature;*

(*c*) *Special degree in the Honours School of Modern Languages and Literatures* (possible combinations are: French and German, Spanish and German);

(*d*) *Special degree in the Honours School of Music and German;*

(*e*) *Special degree in the Honours School of Philosophy and German;*

(*f*) as a subject in the *General degree of B.A.* (Honours, Class I and II are awarded on the attainment of a specified global mark in the three subjects presented for the General degree).

2. CHARACTERISTICS OF COURSES

Prospective Honours students attend in their Intermediate year a course in Middle High German. Considerable attention is also paid to the study of phonetics. Every week a tutorial, comprising German exchange students and some Honours students, discusses English and German pronunciation and intonation under the guidance of a lecturer and with the aid of a tape recorder.

'Outline' courses are *not* in general favour. As the General B.A. candidate is expected to have some knowledge of historical development in language and in literature, a series of texts is used to illustrate semantic and stylistic change. Illustrative texts also form the basis of study of the two years' Special degree course in literary criticism.

In addition to the prescribed philological work—Gothic, Old High German, Middle High German, and Early New High German—some attention is paid to German dialects in their present form, for which purpose a series of recordings is being assembled.

Danish and Dutch may be presented as special subjects within the Honours School of German. The course of study in these two subjects extends over two years.

3. COMBINATION OF SUBJECTS

Students of German in their Intermediate year are required to offer four subjects, one of which must be a subject other than a language, but beyond this, there is no clearly definable limit to the number of combinations permitted. French, Latin and English (in that order) are popular options, but other subjects occur as well, e.g. Philosophy, Modern History, Biblical History and Geography.

The commonest subject taken subsidiary to Honours German is French.

4. RESIDENCE ABROAD

One term (our third term and part of vacation in the student's second year of study) at a German university is required of students in the Honours School of German. In the Honours School of Modern Languages agreement is reached with the Heads of Department (French and Spanish) so that a student may go to one country for a term's study in regular courses at a university and to the other country for an equivalent period, during which he is usually required to attend a summer course.

When private funds or grants are available it has been found good to arrange for shorter periods of residence in Germany. Several students have found the benefit of interpolating a year of work in Germany immediately before the final year. This can be done, as is known, under the official exchange scheme. Essays in German and English are demanded of all students while abroad.

5. METHODS OF STUDY

The tutorial system is favoured in preference to lectures. Conversation groups are held by exchange students and by the *Lektor* or *Lektorin*.

6. OTHER ACTIVITIES

Play-readings and the production of plays in German are organized; students and staff have made their own puppet-theatre for production of German puppet plays. Visits are regularly arranged to attend play productions in German by students in other universities.

II. ADMISSION TO COURSES

1. QUALIFICATIONS REQUIRED

For admission to the Special degree in the Honours school in German, Latin or Greek are preferred but not obligatory. 'A' Level G.C.E. in German and two other subjects are required.

For the Special degree in Modern Languages, Latin is obligatory, and 'A' Level G.C.E. in German and two other subjects are required.

For the General degree of B.A. Latin is not obligatory and 'O' Level G.C.E. German is sufficient.

No beginners' courses in German are provided.

2. SELECTION OF STUDENTS

Provisional acceptance, and occasionally outright acceptance, is given. The condition stipulated is the attainment of about grade B in German and marks on the three subjects taken at 'A' Level of about grade B or C.

Formerly, almost all applicants were interviewed, but with the increase in numbers selection of candidates to be interviewed is now made. In all cases the personal reports of heads of schools are carefully studied. At the interview applicants are asked about the reading they have done (prescribed and additional) and about their general reading. They are often asked to read a passage of German prose or verse and are expected to talk in German on simple, general topics, etc., such as visits abroad. They are asked about their general interests, in and out of school, e.g. musical, dramatic, athletic.

Criteria: Some evidence of personal appreciation of texts is looked for. Careful attention is paid to pronunciation and grammar, but applicants are of course not expected at this stage to speak impeccable German. Alertness and thoughtfulness in answering specific and general questions are taken seriously into account. A good, polite manner of address and clarity of speech in English stand greatly in a candidate's favour, but no special credit is given for urbanity, and a regional accent is not regarded as detrimental.

What is borne chiefly in mind is the opportunity a student will have to do his best work in this University and what positive contribution he can make to the life of the University and to the School of German Studies.

3. TRANSFER

Prospective candidates for Honours are put in the Advanced Intermediate for the first year. This is a specific preparation for Honours work, and students find that they are from an early stage in close contact with the Honours school.

Transfer from Ordinary Intermediate (preparatory to General degree) is made for students who show special aptitude and a desire to read for Honours. If, on the other hand, after the December Terminal Examination, it is felt by the tutors that a prospective Honours student would be better advised to try for a General degree, he is invited to discuss the matter with the Head of the Department. Occasionally a student makes a plea to be transferred to the General course.

4. NUMBERS

About 8 students are admitted annually to the Honours school in German.

Information supplied by Professor W. F. Mainland

UNIVERSITY OF SOUTHAMPTON
Department of German

I. COURSES OF STUDY

1. TYPES OF COURSES

German is available as

(*a*) a *Single Honours* subject;

(*b*) a subject in a *Combined Honours* degree;

(*c*) a *Subsidiary* subject;

2. CHARACTERISTICS OF COURSES

The academic course covers language and literature. A bias towards either language or literature is given in the final year at the student's choice. Options for special study (changed from year to year) are available in the final year.

3. COMBINATION OF SUBJECTS

For students reading Single Honours one Subsidiary subject is required. The examination is taken at the end of the fifth term. Most Arts subjects are permissible.

For a Combined Honours degree German can be combined with one of the following subjects: English, French, Greek, History, Latin, Music, Philosophy or Spanish. Some of these combinations may involve a four-year course, with one year (the third) spent abroad.

4. RESIDENCE ABROAD

Single Honours German: One summer *Semester* (our sixth term) must be spent at a German-speaking university. As near six months' residence as possible is expected but not required. Students are deliberately distributed among the German-speaking universities of Germany, Austria and Switzerland. A long essay in German on a special subject is set by the Department to be sent in by the middle of September.

The Combined Honours course in French and German is a four-year course; the third year is spent abroad. For other combinations, see Calendar.

5. METHODS OF STUDY

Teaching methods include lecture courses, regular tutorials in small groups (with emphasis on discussion and essay work) and conversation groups; in the final year study is mainly conducted by means of seminars.

6. OTHER ACTIVITIES

A German Society organized by the students. Occasional dramatic productions.

II. ADMISSION TO COURSES

1. QUALIFICATIONS REQUIRED

For admission to the single Honours German course, an Advanced Level pass in German is necessary; 'O' Level Latin is preferred but not required. Otherwise no requirement in addition to Matriculation.

For Combined Honours entry requirements, see University Calendar.

German cannot be started from scratch at this University.

2. SELECTION OF STUDENTS

Selection is based on 'A' Level results, interview and Head's report. Not all applicants are interviewed. A short test may be set at the interview consisting of reading and discussing a German passage; otherwise knowledge of German literature, etc., is drawn out by question and answer.

3. TRANSFER

Students are admitted to Single or Combined Honours courses on entrance. Transfer from one to the other is possible during the first year.

4. NUMBERS

Approximately 20 Single Honours students and 15 Combined Honours students are admitted annually.

Information supplied by Professor W. I. Lucas

UNIVERSITY OF WALES:
UNIVERSITY COLLEGE OF WALES, ABERYSTWYTH

Department of German

I. COURSES OF STUDY

1. TYPES OF COURSES

German can be studied in the following courses:

(*a*) *Honours*. This course lasts four years, including a year abroad. In the first year at College students take two other subjects and specialization in German does not begin, therefore, until the second year. The final examination consists of two language papers and five literary or philological papers and an oral test. Some history and philosophy are included in the literary papers, which cover various centuries and special subjects.

(*b*) *Pass* degree. This is a three-year course, of which the first year is the same as for Honours students (see (*a*) above). Pass degree students continue to take three subjects in their second year and take two in their final year. The final examination consists of $1\frac{1}{2}$ language papers and $3\frac{1}{2}$ literary and history papers, and includes an oral test.

(*c*) *Accessory* German. This is an optional subsidiary course for students taking Honours in another subject, lasting two years, of which the first year is again as in (*a*) above. The examination consists of one language paper and one literary paper, including some history, and an oral test.

Both Honours and the Pass degree schemes are being revised and the Pass degree will shortly be replaced by a new type of classified General degree.

2. CHARACTERISTICS OF COURSES

The following special features should be noted:

(*a*) *Honours*

(*i*) Students specialize to a limited extent on either the medieval or modern side, the degree of specialization depending on individual students.

(*ii*) Swedish is taught as an option, open to all Honours students, in whichever branch of the Honours course they specialize. Danish or Dutch may be introduced later.

(*iii*) The literary and philological options vary from time to time.

In session 1963–64, for example, students were able to choose special papers on Old High German and Germanic Philology, Old Icelandic, Goethe or Schiller.

(*iv*) All students are given instruction in general phonetics.

(*b*) *Pass* degree. Apart from taking the usual language papers (composition, translation, essay) and the oral test, students cover 18th- and 19th-century literature and history. It is hoped to introduce options at a later date.

3. COMBINATION OF SUBJECTS

Students are free to choose which subjects they combine with German. The most usual combinations are with French, English, Geography and History and other possible combinations are: Latin, Russian, Welsh, Philosophy, Education, Economics, International Politics, Law, Art.

4. RESIDENCE ABROAD

Honours students are required to spend the year between the first and second year of their Honours course in Germany, Austria or Switzerland as assistants in schools or as students in universities. The majority go as assistants to the town or city which they personally prefer. They are required to keep up their reading and to do a short dissertation in German. An Exchange Scholarship to enable students to spend a year at a German university has been arranged.

Pass degree students are encouraged to do the same and are required at least to attend a vacation course at a German university before sitting for their degree examinations. This also applies to those taking German as an Accessory subject.

5. METHODS OF STUDY

A combination of tutorials, seminars, lectures and small oral groups is used. Considerable weight is attached to oral proficiency and the Department always has a *Lektor* or *Lektorin* on the staff for this purpose. Extensive use is made of the College language laboratory for oral work.

II. ADMISSION TO COURSES

1. QUALIFICATIONS REQUIRED

(*a*) All entrants to the Department must have an 'A' Level pass in German or its equivalent. Two 'A' Level passes are required for admission to the College. There is no Latin requirement, either for admission to the College or to the Department of German.

(*b*) Admission to Honours or Pass degree courses depends upon performance in the Part I examination in three subjects at the end of the first year.

2. SELECTION OF STUDENTS

Selection of students is undertaken by the Dean of the Faculty of Arts in consultation with Departments. It is based on:

(*a*) 'A' Level and 'S' paper results,

(*b*) Interviews in selected cases,

(*c*) Entrance scholarship examination (also used as an entrance test),

(*d*) Personal reports.

The Head of the Department of German will always be glad to receive information relating specifically to the ability in German of applicants for admission.

3. TRANSFER

Students are selected for Honours or the Pass degree course at the end of their first year, in which three subjects are taken. Transfer from Pass degree to Honours courses and from Honours courses to Pass degree courses is possible, but exceptional.

4. NUMBERS

There is no fixed quota of entrants to the Department of German or to Honours courses.

Information supplied by Professor C. P. Magill

UNIVERSITY OF WALES:
UNIVERSITY COLLEGE OF
NORTH WALES, BANGOR

Department of German

I. COURSES OF STUDY

1. TYPES OF COURSES

German can be studied in the following three courses:

(a) *Honours* German;

(b) *Joint Honours* in French and German;

(c) German as a subject in the *Pass* degree.

2. CHARACTERISTICS OF COURSES

The *Honours* course contains the usual ingredients: proses, unseens, set books, essays, literature (in depth from 1750 to 1950), Middle High German, history of the language, historical grammar. Apart from this, every student has the choice of:

(1) Gothic and Old High German;

(2) Modern Norwegian;

(3) Early New High German, Reformation and Baroque Literature.

Particular interest is taken in the history of the language.

The special feature of the Department is the Norwegian option.

Two lecturers in Russian are attached to the Department and a new Department in Linguistics was begun in October, 1960, providing further scope for those interested in linguistics.

The *Pass* degree course—consisting of German and one other subject of the candidate's choice—consists of instruction in the language (including proses, unseens, essays and conversational practice), lectures and set book classes on German literature from 1750 to 1850 and a course on the main aspects of German culture and institutions from the year 800 to today.

3. COMBINATION OF SUBJECTS

Combinations are possible with French, English, Latin, Biblical Studies, History, Music, Welsh and Philosophy. The most frequent combinations are with French, English, Philosophy, Latin and Music (in that order). There is no compulsory combination of subjects.

4. RESIDENCE ABROAD

All Honours students must spend the summer term of their second college year at Tübingen University, where special tuition is provided for them. They are also encouraged, but not compelled, to spend one year as assistants in Germany.

5. METHODS OF STUDY

Much stress is laid on teaching in small groups, tutorial instruction and the spoken language. There are two lectors, one for German and one for Norwegian, and two members of the Department are native German speakers. By an arrangement with Tübingen University there are always some Tübingen students at Bangor.

6. OTHER ACTIVITIES

There are regular functions, with recordings of German plays on long-playing records. A tape-recorder is used in phonetic exercises.

II. ADMISSION TO COURSES

1. QUALIFICATIONS REQUIRED

Apart from the normal matriculation standard there are no special qualifications required for entry into this Department. This applies to both Honours and Pass degrees. There is no Latin requirement for German Honours at Bangor.

The language can be started from scratch, and in three years a Pass degree can be obtained. For Honours four years are required if the student starts from scratch.

2. SELECTION OF STUDENTS

Selection of students for entry is undertaken by the Dean, usually after an interview by the Department, and is mainly based on 'A' Level results and heads' reports. All candidates who have passed their first-year examinations are entitled to admission to the Pass degree course if they have not been chosen for Honours. (For admission to the Honours course see II.3 below.)

3. TRANSFER

Honours teaching in Bangor only begins in the second year of the course, and Honours students are selected at the end of their first year. Their admission is based on performance in the first year's studies.

Transfer from Pass to Honours is possible at the end of the second year in College. This means another two years in the Honours school.

4. NUMBERS

Average admission to Honours annually is between 8 and 10, but this figure will be allowed to rise when the number of suitable applicants increases.

Information supplied by Professor K. Spalding

UNIVERSITY OF WALES:
UNIVERSITY COLLEGE, CARDIFF

Department of German

I. COURSES OF STUDY

1. TYPES OF COURSES

German is available in the following courses:

(*a*) as one of three subjects in Part I for all students who wish to take German for a Pass or Honours degree; thereafter

(*b*) as a Part II two-year course for a *Single Honours* degree (Honours One and Two);

(*c*) as a Part II two-year *Pass degree course* divided into Main One and Two;

(*d*) as an *Auxiliary* (one-year) course: Main students in other subjects have to take in the first year of their *Mains course* an Auxiliary course in a subject which they have not taken in Part I;

(*e*) as a *Preliminary course* for students with no previous knowledge, but not intended as a degree course (see also I.3 below).[1]

2. CHARACTERISTICS OF COURSES

Revision of German grammar and syntax is undertaken in Part I. This is accompanied by weekly translation work and by fortnightly German essays. Honours students have a special Modern German course, entailing the reading of current newspapers and periodicals and essays on a range of topical subjects.

In literature, the 'History of Literature' approach is avoided, but, on the basis of selected texts studied and discussed in detail, wider ideas and trends are considered. Students are supplied with comprehensive reading lists, and essay work figures prominently.

3. COMBINATION OF SUBJECTS

In Part I virtually any other two subjects may be taken, subject to limitations of time-table. Main students pursue two of these for the following two years, plus an Auxiliary subject; Honours students have only their Honours subject, which, in the case of German, includes two years of Swedish, studied within the Department.

4. RESIDENCE ABROAD

For Honours students, the third year, i.e. the year between

---

[1] The Pass degree will shortly be renamed *General* degree, and the Auxiliary course will most likely be abolished by October 1965.

M.L.—G

Honours I and Honours II, must be spent abroad. In the great majority of cases our students are appointed as assistants for the year in German schools; in a few cases, students sometimes gain awards to attend courses at German universities. The Main students are encouraged to spend at least one long vacation abroad.

5. METHODS OF STUDY

Classes at the Honours stage are sufficiently small to enable the teaching to be predominantly tutorial in character. Part I students are divided for tutorial purposes into groups of six, and each group meets the tutor once a week during the first two terms. The *Lektor* takes all students once a week in small groups of four to six for oral work. Regular use is made of tape recorders.

6. OTHER ACTIVITIES

The College German Society meets once a fortnight, for talks, debates, symposia, musical evenings, films, play production, book reviews, etc. The Department works in close collaboration with the local branch of the Modern Language Association and joins in all its activities.

II. ADMISSION TO COURSES

1. QUALIFICATIONS REQUIRED

(1) Latin is not stipulated.

(2) For Part I students, a pass at 'A' Level is normally required.

(3) German can be started from scratch, but not as a degree subject.

2. SELECTION OF STUDENTS

All incoming students are admitted by the Dean into the Faculty of Arts. A pass at 'A' Level secures entry into Part I German. At the end of a successfully completed Part I course suitable students are admitted into Honours or Main courses.

3. TRANSFER

Transfer is not easy, but as students have been in the Department for a session before the question of admission to Honours or Main courses arises their potential is fairly well recognized, and the need for transfer very rarely arises. Should the need arise, the Faculty considers each case individually.

4. NUMBERS

About 12 students are admitted to the Honours course each year.

Information supplied by Professor T. P. Williams

UNIVERSITY OF WALES: UNIVERSITY COLLEGE, SWANSEA

Department of German

I. COURSES OF STUDY

1. TYPES OF COURSES

German can be studied in the following courses:

(a) *Honours*. This is a four-year course, comprising two sessions at Swansea, followed by one intercalary session spent in a German-speaking country, and a fourth, final session at Swansea. An Accessory subject is taken during the second session.

(b) *Joint Honours* in French and German. This is a four-year course, in which the emphasis can either be mainly on French or on German. The third, intercalary year is spent in a German-speaking country if German is the major subject, and otherwise in France. Where French is the major subject, students are required to visit a German-speaking country in a vacation or vacations.

(c) *Pass degree*. This is a three-year course. If German is a *Main* subject, it is taken with two other subjects during the second session, and with one of these subjects during the third session. As an *Auxiliary* subject, German can be studied with two other subjects during the second session.

(d) *Accessory*. During the second year students taking Honours in subjects other than German may pursue an Accessory course in German, where the emphasis is primarily on the modern spoken and written language.

(e) *Part One*. All students taking German in the Faculty of Arts follow this course during their first session, together with two other subjects which are studied at a similar level.

2. CHARACTERISTICS OF COURSES

All courses include prose composition and essay work, and also German conversation classes. In addition *Part One* students read literary texts and attend a course of lectures given in German on aspects of society in Germany during the 18th and 19th centuries.

Pass degree students in their second and third sessions continue the study of the modern language and of selected literature from about 1750 onwards.

For the *Honours* course in German students pursue, in addition to the study of the modern language, courses on literature of the 18th, 19th and 20th century. Of the seven papers which are compulsory in the Honours examination, one is concerned with the history of the language, and one with some aspects of medieval literature and that of the 16th and 17th centuries. The eighth, optional Honours paper, may be either of a linguistic or literary character.

Candidates for *Joint Honours* in French and German take parts of the Honours course in Germany by arrangement.

3. COMBINATION OF SUBJECTS

In *Part One* and *Pass degree* courses a wide combination of subjects is possible, subject to the limitations which may be imposed by the time-table. German at Joint Honours level can only be combined with French. Accessory subjects are available in inter-departmental subjects.

A Lecturer in Russian is attached to the Department. For particulars of courses, see p. 294.

4. RESIDENCE ABROAD

Honours students spend one session abroad, if possible at a German university; otherwise they normally go as assistants in German schools. Pass degree students should spend at least one long vacation abroad.

5. METHODS OF STUDY

Both lectures and tutorial classes are held. The *Lektor* takes small groups for conversation and discussions in German.

6. OTHER ACTIVITIES

There is a German Society which shows films and arranges musical programmes and other activities.

II. ADMISSION TO COURSES

1. QUALIFICATIONS REQUIRED

'A' Level in German is required for admission to Part One. There is no Latin requirement.

2. SELECTION OF STUDENTS

Selection is based on 'A' Level results, on reports from headmasters and headmistresses, and in most cases on interview.

3. TRANSFER

After completing Part One at the end of the first session, students may be accepted for Honours or for the Pass degree course.

4. NUMBERS

There is not at present any fixed limit on the number of students. The approximate intake per year into the Honours and Joint Honours courses varies at present from 6 to 13.

Information supplied by Professor H. M. Waidson

UNIVERSITY OF ABERDEEN
Department of German

I. COURSES OF STUDY

1. TYPES OF COURSES

German can be studied in this University

(*a*) as part of an *Ordinary degree course*

(*b*) as part of a *Joint Honours degree course in Modern Languages*

(*c*) as a *Single Honours degree course.*

Ordinary (i.e. *General*) *degree:* a three-year course, in which a student must complete seven 'degree-courses'. To study a subject for one year (first-year or Ordinary course) counts as *one* such course; to study it for two years (i.e. Ordinary and second-year or Advanced course) counts as *two* such courses. The language cannot be studied further than this in the Ordinary degree course.

Thus German can be studied by Ordinary degree students for one or two years (consecutive or otherwise) in their three-year degree course. An examination is held at the end of each year.

In the *Joint Honours degree* course, German can be studied for four years, termed Ordinary, Advanced, Junior Honours and Senior Honours years. This course normally takes five years, which includes a year's residence abroad.[1]

The *Single Honours degree* course is normally a five-year course, one academic session being spent abroad.[2] As it is wholly devoted to the study of German language and literature it covers a somewhat wider field than the German part of the Joint Honours course and provides for a more intensive study of certain aspects of the subject.

2. CHARACTERISTICS OF COURSES

Joint Honours course

Ordinary course: composition and translation; detailed study of a number of set books (18th–20th centuries); general lectures on the history of German literature.

Advanced course: composition and translation; essays in German; phonetics; introduction to Early New or Middle High German and

---

[1] It is possible to complete the course in four years by fitting the compulsory minimum period of residence abroad into the long vacations. In the first two years the courses are those taken by students for the Ordinary degree (but see I.2 and II.3 below).

[2] It is possible to complete the course in four years by fitting the minimum requirement of nine months' residence in a German-speaking country into the long vacations.

(for prospective Honours students) Old High German, more difficult prescribed texts, oral practice.

Honours course: composition and translation work at a higher level; German philology (history of the language in its various aspects—phonology, morphology, semantics, historical syntax); Old High German and Middle High German literature. More detailed study of modern German literature (18th–20th centuries) in lecture and seminar courses. German political and social history.

Single Honours course

The programme of study resembles that of the Joint Honours course outlined above, but some topics (e.g. Middle High German Literature) are studied at greater depth. In addition, it includes two special subjects, which may be either medieval or modern, at the candidate's own choice.

3. COMBINATION OF SUBJECTS

Most of the students who opt for a Joint Honours course take French–German. Other possible combinations are German–English, German–Spanish, German–Swedish.

4. RESIDENCE ABROAD

A period of residence and study abroad is a compulsory requirement for all Honours students of German. Our regulations demand a minimum of six months spent in a German-speaking country for students taking Joint Honours courses, and at least nine months for students taking a Single Honours course in German.

5. METHODS OF STUDY

We lay great stress on essay work, with a great deal of individual tutorial instruction.

6. OTHER ACTIVITIES

There is an active German Club, run by the students with the co-operation of the staff. It meets once a fortnight and usually produces a short play at Christmas.

II. ADMISSION TO COURSES

1. QUALIFICATIONS REQUIRED

The Certificate of Fitness of the Scottish Universities Entrance Board including Higher German and for Honours students a pass in Latin, preferably at the Higher grade, are necessary.

2. SELECTION OF STUDENTS

Selection for entrance is carried out on a Faculty basis, not by departments. So far the German Department has been able to accept all first-year entrants equipped with the proper qualifications (see

II.1 above). Admission to an Honours course depends on a student's performance during the first two years of study.

3. TRANSFER

All students in this Department follow the same course during their first year. In their second year those who intend to read for Honours do some extra work; but transfer remains possible up to the end of their second year.

4. NUMBERS

Out of a first-year intake of some 90 students, about 35 to 40 go on to the Advanced course; of these, between half a dozen and a dozen normally proceed to an Honours course.

Information supplied by Professor W. Witte

UNIVERSITY OF EDINBURGH

Department of German

I. COURSES OF STUDY

1. TYPES OF COURSES

(a) *Ordinary M.A. course.* Two years' study of literature, history of language, translation, prose composition, essays.

(b) *Honours.* After the first-year class, which is taken by all students, those intending to take Honours enter in the second year the Intermediate Honours class; work is in common with the Second Ordinary class, plus study of medieval grammar and literature; also wider range of modern literature. The third Honours year is spent at university or school in Germany. The fourth Honours year, the final year, is spent again at Edinburgh.

2. CHARACTERISTICS OF COURSES

First and second years: two lectures per week on literature, including detailed study of prescribed texts; history of language (one hour); prose composition (one hour); tutorial work, conducted in German (one hour); also translation and essay work; lectures on German institutions and culture.

Intermediate Honours: as above, and in addition: work with medieval grammar and texts; further literature.

Senior Honours: the Final Honours course includes study of the development of the German language, German history, German literature, including medieval texts and a special subject from the fields of literature or language, modern or medieval.

3. COMBINATION OF SUBJECTS

For the Ordinary M.A. course, a wide range of combinations is possible. Those specializing in modern languages take a so-called Type 2 curriculum, i.e. a curriculum with the main emphasis on modern languages and literature.

For Honours, German may be taken with a secondary language (up to Intermediate Honours standard) chosen from Celtic, French, Italian, Latin, Russian, Spanish or Greek. Usually French; Russian, Spanish or Latin in rare cases. Two 'outside' subjects must also be studied for one year each, and one of these must be chosen from: British or European History, English Language or Literature, Fine Art, Geography, Logic and Metaphysics, Moral Philosophy, Phonetics, Political Economy, or Public Law. The other outside subject may be chosen from a list of qualifying courses.

4. RESIDENCE ABROAD

Honours students are required to spend nine months continuously at a German-speaking university or other approved institution. Most of them are at universities, some take teaching posts in German schools. They are required to write German essays and reports, marked by the staff in Edinburgh, and submit an essay of some 6,000 words on German life and/or institutions on their return, which is included in assessing the Honours work.

5. METHODS OF STUDY

Work in tutorials is based on prescribed texts, which are read and discussed in German.

II. ADMISSION TO COURSES

1. QUALIFICATIONS REQUIRED

For entrance to the First Ordinary class: a pass in German on the Higher grade in the Scottish Certificate of Education or the Scottish Universities Preliminary Examination or some equivalent evidence of proficiency (i.e. G.C.E. 'A' Level); no requirement made above this standard. For entrance to subsequent classes: satisfactory results in the previous class (including class-work and degree examinations).

There is no departmental requirement for Latin.

There is no class in elementary German leading to a degree course, but only to provide students from any faculty with a reading knowledge, mainly for research work.

2. SELECTION OF STUDENTS

There is no departmental selection.

3. TRANSFER

Honours students take the same class in the first year, and are then selected progressively in examinations at the end of the first, and at the end of the second year, when a higher standard of performance is required from them compared with the Ordinary degree students.

It is not usually possible for students to transfer from an Ordinary degree curriculum to an Honours curriculum after the first year unless they repeat the second year at a higher standard. Generally students begin by considering themselves future Honours students, and may revert to an Ordinary curriculum in the light of their results, at the end of either the first or the second year of study.

4. NUMBERS

The Intermediate Honours class (second year) usually has between 35 and 40 students. Junior (third year) and Senior Honours (fourth year) have between 15 and 20 each.

Information supplied by Professor E. C. Mason

M.L.—G 2

UNIVERSITY OF GLASGOW
Department of German

I. COURSES OF STUDY

1. TYPES OF COURSES

German can be taken as a subject in *Ordinary* and *Honours* degrees.

(*a*) The *Honours* degree involves the study of two modern languages equally for four years at this University, exclusive of periods of residence abroad, but German may also be studied with Music or Modern History.

(*b*) Students for the *Ordinary* degree may take one, two or three years of German. Of these the first two are identical with the first two years of the Honours degree course.

In the first year students have five lectures and two tutorials and are concerned with prose composition, history of language, history of literature and about ten set texts. In the second year Middle High German replaces history of the language. In the third-year course for Ordinary degree students more attention is paid to the geographical and historical context of German studies, though the main emphasis is on modern literature.

In the two final Honours years we have no lectures on history of literature but a considerably increased number of texts.

2. CHARACTERISTICS OF COURSES

The two years taken by most students including German in the Ordinary degree involves the study of:

(*i*) German literary history, 1700 to 1939;

(*ii*) History of language and an introduction to Middle High German;

(*iii*) Texts of the 17th to 20th centuries, representative mainly of the drama, the short story, and the lyric;

(*iv*) Prose composition.

Each student also has weekly conversation and tutorial classes. The size of these groups is about 8 to 12 students.

The Honours student has the above with two additional years, during which prose composition and Middle High German are continued throughout and selected texts are studied. The framework of the four-year course is conceived to give special attention to:

(*i*) Goethe   (*iii*) the drama
(*ii*) Romanticism   (*iv*) the *Novelle*

and to fill in the rest of the main figures, movements and *genres* as far as possible. At Honours level we treat the main topics in ten-week lecture courses, and lay great stress on a weekly tutorial held in groups of four, where the student reads two essays each ten-week term and has them corrected thoroughly afterwards in a private session with the tutor.

We have virtually no options at present. Old High German will probably be offered soon, as well as some choice of literary topics.

3. COMBINATION OF SUBJECTS

Usually French, occasionally Russian or Music, are offered as the other half of the Honours group of studies. Almost any of the modern languages could be the theoretical other half. It is also possible to combine German with Modern History.

As supporting subjects taken for one year, two are necessary: usually the popular subjects are History, Moral Philosophy, Latin and English.

4. RESIDENCE ABROAD

It is the almost universal practice, which we try to enforce, though there is no legal obligation, that Honours students spend the summer term of their second last year at a German university (1st May to 31st July). No special work is required, though the students are expected to attend lectures at the German university for about 12 hours per week.

A few students spend the year between their second and third years as assistant exchange teachers at a German school, but the majority of students spend this year in France.

5. METHODS OF STUDY

See I.2 above.

II. ADMISSION TO COURSES

1. QUALIFICATIONS REQUIRED

A pass in German at the Higher grade (Scottish examinations) or at the Advanced Level (English examinations) is required of all students entering the first-year class. Students taking German in the second year must also have Latin at the Ordinary grade. These requirements affect all students.

2. SELECTION OF STUDENTS

Departments do not admit students. The Faculty attends to admissions, taking into consideration entrance examination results and head teachers' reports; doubtful cases are interviewed.

Candidates for Honours are really not selected until the end of their second year. By that time their university record provides a means of natural selection.

3. TRANSFER

As explained in II.2, we have a good system whereby the students have two years at University to see how they are shaping for Honours and the staff at the same time are able to assess them. In general, the best students go on, though, of course, some choose not to.

4. NUMBERS

We find that of a first-year class of 150 about 20 will go on to complete the Honours course.

Information supplied by Professor W. W. Chambers

UNIVERSITY OF ST. ANDREWS

Department of German

I. COURSES OF STUDY

1. TYPES OF COURSES

German is available as a subject in the

(*a*) *Ordinary M.A.* degree in combination with another subject;

(*b*) *Honours M.A.* degree in combination with another language;

(*c*) *Honours M.A.* degree in German language and literature.

2. CHARACTERISTICS OF COURSES

For details, the University Calendar should be consulted.

3. COMBINATION OF SUBJECTS

For the Ordinary degree, German can be combined with a language or History; for the Honours degree with French, English or Spanish.

Honours students must take Subsidiary Philosophy and a Subsidiary language or History.

Ordinary degree students must take Subsidiary Philosophy and two other Subsidiary subjects.

4. RESIDENCE ABROAD

Honours students must spend the third term of the third year at a foreign university in one of the two countries whose languages are being studied. They go to various universities and are required to write an essay.

5. METHODS OF STUDY

Teaching methods include lectures, supplemented by tutorials.

II. ADMISSION TO COURSES

1. QUALIFICATIONS REQUIRED

For admission to the Faculty of Arts, students must all have 'A' Level passes or their equivalent in (*a*) a classical language, or (*b*) two modern foreign languages, or (*c*) mathematics and one modern foreign language. They must obtain an Attestation of Fitness from the Scottish Universities Entrance Board. Candidates for Honours in modern languages must have an 'A' Level pass in Latin or its equivalent.

'A' Level German G.C.E. or Higher German in the Scottish

Certificate of Education is required for admission to the first-year graduating class in German.

German may be started from scratch.

2. SELECTION OF STUDENTS

Admission to the Faculty of Arts is given by the Dean, who takes into consideration examination passes and reports from schools; there are no interviews. As there are more applicants than places, the minimum requirements for admission are usually not sufficient to gain a place.

3. TRANSFER

Admission to the Honours classes in German is not given until the end of the second year and depends on the student's record. Transfer is possible.

4. NUMBERS

Approximately 20 students are admitted each year to the Honours courses in German, making an Honours class of 40, as the course extends over two years.

Information supplied by Professor C. T. Carr

THE QUEEN'S UNIVERSITY OF BELFAST [1]

Department of German

I. COURSES OF STUDY

1. TYPES OF COURSES

In German there are courses leading to:

(*a*) *Honours in the School of German Language and Literature* (Single Honours);

(*b*) *Honours in the School of Medieval and Modern Languages* (Dual Honours): this is a Joint Honours School, German being read in conjunction with another language (see I.3 below);

(*c*) German as part of a *General* degree.

In certain cases it is possible for a 'Pass' degree to be awarded on an Honours examination. It is worth less than a Class III degree and is not awarded in any other circumstances: it is not the same as the 'General' degree.

In the first (or intermediate) year three subjects are normally studied leading to the First Examination in Arts.

Honours degree courses extend over four years in all and General degree courses over three years.

2. CHARACTERISTICS OF COURSES

As from October, 1960:

'*Dual*' Honours (i.e. Joint School)

Four basic courses:

(1) Unseen prose translation from and into German;
(2) Middle High German language and literature;
(3) German literature of the 18th century;
(4) German literature of the 19th century.

In addition students may choose *one* or *two* of the following (or *one* or *two* in their other language):

(1) Old High German and historical grammar;
(2) Gothic and Icelandic texts;
(3) The German 'Baroque' period with its literary and historical setting;

---

[1] This entry is an unrevised copy of the entry submitted by this Department to the 1961 edition. Applicants are strongly advised to check the information by reference to the current prospectus.

(4) Goethe's major works;

(5) Special aspects of drama and epic in the 19th century;

(6) History of the German lyric;

(7) German literature of the 20th century.

'*Single*' *Honours School*

The four basic courses as for 'Dual'. In addition:

(1) Old High German and historical grammar;

(2) Aspects of 17th-century literature and thought;

(3) From Age of Enlightenment to Storm and Stress;

(4) The Classical Age of Goethe and Schiller;

(5) The Romantic Movement, Realism and Naturalism;

(6) Aspects of German 20th-century literature;

(7) A seminar class dealing in alternate years with epic and drama, mainly of the 19th century.

In addition *two* of the following:

(8) Advanced Germanic philology, including the study of Gothic and Icelandic or Old Saxon texts;

(9) Special studies in Middle High German language and literature;

(10) The study of problems and trends in German 19th-century literature;

(11) The detailed study of selected works of contemporary literature;

(12) A two-year course in Swedish.

Wherever possible and practicable the courses of the two different Honours Schools are combined.

3. COMBINATION OF SUBJECTS

For the First Arts Examination (held at the end of the first academic year) almost any two Arts subjects can be combined with German. All Honours students in the Dual Language courses *must* follow a course in Medieval French in their first year. (There is a separate and independent Department of Medieval French.)

For Dual Honours, German is usually combined with French. Medieval French, Spanish and Celtic may also be chosen.

The qualification in Medieval French is not necessary for students reading 'Single' Honours German.

4. RESIDENCE ABROAD

Unless exempted by the Head of the Department all Single Honours candidates are required to spend a complete *Semester* at an approved German, Austrian or Swiss university. Exemptions are extremely rare. Certain students apply for faculty permission, which they have so far always received, to spend a whole session in Germany.

II. ADMISSION TO COURSES

1. QUALIFICATIONS REQUIRED

The minimum qualification to enter the first year course is an 'O' Level pass in German but an 'A' Level pass is desirable. Most students accepted for Honours do in fact have 'A' Level passes.

For General students a pass at 'O' Level is a sufficient qualification, backed up by passing the University first-year examination.

German cannot be started from scratch in this Department.

Latin is required of all Honours students in the Faculty of Arts except those reading Mathematics, Geography and Psychology.

2. SELECTION OF STUDENTS

'A' Level (in certain cases 'O' Level) results are decisive for admission of students to first-year courses.

3. TRANSFER

Students are admitted provisionally to the Honours School at the beginning of their second academic year. They are definitely accepted at the end of their second year on the basis of their results in a departmental Honours qualifying examination. Transfer is possible.

4. NUMBERS

The number varies. Session 1959–60 there were 7 finalists in the Single School, and 7 in the Dual (Joint) School. It is likely that the Single School will henceforth be somewhat reduced in size.

Information supplied by Professor H. E. Hinderks

SPANISH STUDIES

UNIVERSITY OF BIRMINGHAM
Department of Spanish [1]

I. COURSES OF STUDY

1. TYPES OF COURSES

Spanish is available in the following courses:

(*a*) *Honours:* a three-year course (including six months' compulsory residence abroad) covering Spanish history, Spanish literature (medieval to modern), Spanish language, Spanish philology (alternative to Portuguese language and literature), Latin-American institutions and literature.

(*b*) *Subsidiary:* a two-year course covering Spanish literature (16th century to modern), Spanish language, Latin-American studies.

(*c*) *Combined Subjects:* If Spanish is studied for three years, the student can either have begun the subject at school and will join the normal first-year course (Spanish history, Spanish literature (16th century to modern), Spanish language, Latin America), or can begin the subject in the Department taking the Preliminary course for one term and joining a slightly modified first-year course in January.

It is also possible for a student to take Spanish for one year only doing a one-year Preliminary course for the first year only.

The Combined Subjects degree is a full Honours degree in which students take three subjects for their first year carrying on with two of these three for the succeeding two years. Up to the present it has been a regulation in this degree that one of the three first-year subjects shall be a language. The intention was that this should give students a chance to begin the study of any modern language, but owing to administrative difficulties, this usually meant that they took Spanish as this Department was the only one offering a suitable course for them. As a result the regulation has ceased to operate in the University.

(The Combined Subjects course is the same as the old General degree course, with a change in name which describes its nature more accurately.)

2. CHARACTERISTICS OF COURSES

In the main, the first-year courses tend to stress factual and background information as students are normally weak in their knowledge of literary history. Their language work is also carefully studied,

---

[1] This entry is an unrevised copy of the entry submitted by this Department to the 1961 edition. Applicants are strongly advised to check the information by reference to the current prospectus.

both in prose classes and in conversation classes. Tutorial groups for these students tend to be small so that essays can be dealt with in detail. Honours students can begin Portuguese at this stage as an option instead of Philology.

The second-year course is usually more concentrated (it covers only two terms in view of the residence abroad) and students are encouraged to work more and more on their own initiative.

In the third year the number of lecture hours is lower, but more tutorial and essay work is done to develop critical appreciation.

Much of the teaching is done in Spanish and the second- and third-year essay work is normally in Spanish.

3. COMBINATION OF SUBJECTS

French is the most popular Subsidiary subject to Spanish in the Honours School, with other languages (German, Italian, Russian) a long way down the list. Other combinations are possible with History, English, Archaeology, Latin, Greek, Music, Psychology, Theology. There is no compulsory combination of subjects.

A student taking a Combined Subjects course can in theory take any two Arts subjects for three years. In practice, shortage of staff in certain departments may create difficulties, particularly in regard to tutorial work.

4. RESIDENCE ABROAD

Honours students are required to spend six months abroad in Spain and/or Portugal. They leave for Spain at the end of the spring term and spend the summer term at a Spanish university as normal students. They are free to travel where they like in the summer vacation but are recommended to attend a summer course for one month. They are given the book list for the following session before leaving and are expected to have read about half of the suggested texts during their stay in Spain. There is no examination held on their return and no 'holiday task' set. They are advised to do as much work as possible abroad, but it is emphasized that the purpose of going to Spain is to study the country and make contact with its people.

Combined Subjects students spend three months abroad only.

6. OTHER ACTIVITIES

The Department has an active Spanish Circle which meets every fortnight to hear talks, records, or occasionally a lecture by a Spanish visitor. The Circle produces a play in Spanish every year in December, and this year has instituted the holding of a dinner for staff and students. Such activities are encouraged by the Department as they provide a means of contacting students informally and also of widening their interests. In the past the experiment was made of holding a Spanish week-end at which students, departmental staff, and school children and their teachers could meet. Owing to the great pressure of work in the Department recently this activity ceased but it is planned to revive it in the near future.

II. ADMISSION TO COURSES

1. QUALIFICATIONS REQUIRED

Honours (Spanish main subject): Three passes at 'A' Level, one of which to be Spanish, are required by regulations. The Head of the Department may admit a student with two good 'A' passes and a reasonable performance in other subjects. In exceptional cases of this nature the marks gained on Scholarship papers would be seriously considered. A pass at 'O' Level in Latin is also required by the Department. There is no admission examination.

Honours with Spanish as Subsidiary subject: There is no specific requirement but normally students without at least C in 'A' Level Spanish would be advised against taking Spanish as a Subsidiary subject.

Combined Subjects: If Spanish is to be taken for three years, a mark of C would be the minimum 'A' Level requirement. It is, however, possible for students beginning Spanish in the Department to take an intensive Preliminary course for one term and join a modified first year.

2. SELECTION OF STUDENTS

Applications are 'weeded out' on the basis of examination results known up to the date of receipt (usually February preceding the new session). Only in very rare cases would applicants not be called for interview by the Department in the group wishing to take the Spanish Honours course. Subsidiary and Combined Subjects applicants are not interviewed by the Department. A preliminary classification is made before interview on the basis of results obtained to date and on the head's report. Particular attention is paid to potential academic ability and also to the character, outside interests and ambitions of the applicant. The Department prefers students whose attainments go beyond the ability to remember a mass of dictated notes on four set texts. At this stage of selection linguistic ability counts for more than a knowledge of the literature. There are no tests set. The interview is conducted by the Professor and one member of his staff. The applicant is encouraged to talk about his (or her) reasons for wishing to come to a university, to discuss any special interests in the study of Spanish, to give a brief account of extra-curricular activities including sport, and to give details of any foreign travel. The applicant is then asked if there are any questions or problems to be answered. The assessment is then made and if a provisional acceptance is given, the final decision to admit depends on the 'A' Level results. A mark of C would mean acceptance automatically.

3. TRANSFER

Admission to Honours courses is normally on entrance. This also applies to students taking Spanish as a Subsidiary subject in another Honours school.

Transfer is possible for students taking Combined Subjects courses; on occasion a good student has been admitted to the Honours course. It would also be possible for a student who has begun Spanish with the Department to be accepted as an Honours student (preferably as a student taking a four-year course, i.e. spending a year abroad instead of the normal compulsory six months).

4. NUMBERS

The normal intake into the Honours School per year is 15.

Information supplied by Dr. J. Gibbs, Lecturer in Spanish

UNIVERSITY OF BRISTOL
Department of Spanish and Portuguese

I. COURSES OF STUDY

1. TYPES OF COURSES

Spanish may be studied in this University in the following first-degree courses:

(a) *B.A. Special Honours in Spanish;*

(b) *B.A. Joint Honours in Latin and Spanish;*

(c) *B.A. Joint Honours in French and Spanish* (a four-year course);

(d) *B.A. Joint Honours in Drama and Spanish;*

(e) *B.A. General Honours* (in this case Spanish is one of three subjects studied for three years);

(f) *B.A. General Honours* (*Modern Studies*) (an Honours degree, with Spanish as one of three subjects studied for three years);

(g) a two-year *Subsidiary* subject to a Special School (e.g. French, German);

(h) a one-year *Additional* course for B.A. Special Honours English.

Portuguese and Catalan may be included in these courses. Portuguese is studied for three years, Catalan for two.

For *graduate courses*, see I.2 below.

2. CHARACTERISTICS OF COURSES

Emphasis is laid on Spanish studies as a discipline, i.e. their educative value in developing honesty, clarity of thought, persistency and the power of self-expression. The courses are designed to show the Spanish contribution, in literature, history and art, to Western civilization. Special attention is given to the history and culture of the Latin-American nations. During the first two years, students are introduced to the main fields of Spanish studies. In their third year they may specialize according to their chief interests: in Philology, Spanish Literature, Spanish America, Portuguese, Brazilian Literature and Civilization, or Catalan.

B.A. General Honours students normally choose Spanish courses of a more literary kind; B.A. General (Modern Studies) students usually specialize in Latin America; but all are encouraged to relate their Spanish studies to the other subjects of their university course.

Graduate courses. The Department provides graduate courses, seminars and supervision of dissertations leading to the degrees of M.A. and Ph.D. It welcomes especially graduates from other universities who wish to specialize in the history of Spanish drama. (These studies may be undertaken in conjunction with graduate courses in the Department of Drama.) It also welcomes graduates wishing to do specialized work in the Spanish-American, Portuguese and Brazilian fields.

3. COMBINATION OF SUBJECTS

For the Special degree, a Subsidiary subject has to be studied for two years. This is usually French, German, Russian, Latin, Italian or the History of Art.

For the B.A. General Honours degree and the B.A. General Honours (Modern Studies) degree almost any two subjects may be combined with Spanish, depending upon the time-table.

4. RESIDENCE ABROAD

Special Honours students must spend at least three months in Spain or a Spanish-speaking country; Joint School students spend up to three months in Spain or a Spanish-speaking country; B.A. General and B.A. General Honours (Modern Studies) students and students taking Spanish as a two-year Subsidiary course to a Special School, are required to spend a month in Spain or a Spanish-speaking country. Students generally attend Spanish university courses. Special Honours students may undertake study in Spanish libraries in preparation for their essay paper and for their dissertation.

5. METHODS OF STUDY

The requirements of each course are carefully adjusted to what may be reasonably expected of a student. He is encouraged to study in depth and to think for himself, not to be superficial or to copy other men's opinions. In the first two years, instruction is given in small tutorial groups, supplemented by lecture courses. In the third year, seminars are arranged on the subjects chosen for special study. Vacations are considered as a time for serious reading and reflection.

6. OTHER ACTIVITIES

Reading parties in Spain and Portugal. Spanish Circle. Spanish choir. The production of plays in Spanish and English.

II. ADMISSION TO COURSES

1. QUALIFICATIONS REQUIRED

(*a*) 'O' Level pass in Latin;

(*b*) The Faculty requirement of around grade B in two 'A' Level subjects, one of which must be Spanish. All students are Honours students, whether reading for the General or Special degree. There are no Pass courses.

Courses for beginners are provided for students from other departments and for students who wish to take Spanish (or Portuguese or

Catalan) as a non-examination subject. Special arrangements are made for students of History and Geography.

2. SELECTION OF STUDENTS

There is no entrance examination. Applicants for places are of two kinds: (*i*) A minority who already possess the required qualifications in two 'A' Level subjects. These applicants can be given a prompt reply. (*ii*) The majority, who are about to take the 'A' Level examination. Rarely, some of these applicants are given a firm offer of a place, but most, if accepted, are given a conditional offer (i.e. contingent upon their obtaining around grade B in Spanish and in one other subject at 'A' Level).

Applicants may be asked to come to Bristol. (The cost of travel, etc., is paid by the applicant. The University cannot assist with expenses.) As far as possible, all applicants who place Bristol as their first choice, and others who show promise, are interviewed. The interview takes about twenty minutes. It is not intended to test the applicant's knowledge (this will presumably be revealed in examination results), but to assess personality and general ability, to decide whether the applicant is developing and likely to benefit from three years at a university, or whether he is not likely to progress once divorced from his teacher. Head teachers' reports are given careful consideration. They are especially appreciated when they give a frank appraisal of the candidate.

Applicants for the B.A. General degree are seen by the Assistant Dean of the Faculty of Arts.

3. TRANSFER

Students are admitted to Honours courses on entrance.

It is possible, in certain cases, to transfer from one Honours course to another, provided the Board of the Faculty of Arts approves.

4. NUMBERS

At present 30 students are admitted annually for Special Spanish; and 5 for each of the Joint Schools. These numbers will rise proportionately within the next few years to an anticipated maximum of 50 for Special Spanish students.

Information supplied by Professor J. C. J. Metford

UNIVERSITY OF DURHAM

Department of Spanish

I. COURSES OF STUDY

1. TYPES OF COURSES

(*a*) *Single Honours in Spanish*. A first year of Preliminary Honours (language, introduction to medieval literature and linguistics, Golden Age and modern literature), followed by two years in which there are compulsory courses in history and all periods of literature, and optional courses in linguistics, Catalan and Portuguese.

(*b*) *Joint Honours*. The Preliminary examination is reduced and in Final Honours candidates will sit five papers in each language—two language papers and a choice of three from the Single Honours literary and history papers.

(*c*) *General*. Spanish may be taken in the General degree at first-, second- and third-year levels. First year is mainly elementary; in the second and third year courses in Golden Age and modern literature are prescribed.

2. CHARACTERISTICS OF COURSES

The Preliminary course offers an introduction to linguistics and to the literature of the various periods. The experience gained in this year should help the student to select the most suitable options for the Final courses, which end with a final examination of eight papers, six compulsory and two optional. The compulsory papers are: Translation, Essay, Medieval Literature, Golden Age Literature (two) and Modern Literature. The options offered are Linguistics, Portuguese, Catalan and further Modern Literature.

3. COMBINATION OF SUBJECTS

Most Honours students study Subsidiary French, though many other alternatives are provided for.

Many taking General courses are Honours students in French, German, English.

Almost any combination is possible in the General degree, from Religious Knowledge to Turkish.

4. RESIDENCE ABROAD

Honours. One term in a Spanish university is expected.

General. One month, preferably at an educational institution, in a Spanish-speaking country is expected.

5. METHODS OF TEACHING

No distinctive teaching methods are employed, the classes being normally small enough to permit the teacher freedom in this. Some lectures, both Honours and General, are given in Spanish, there being a Spaniard on the permanent staff. There is also a *lector*, who, as well as giving conversation classes, normally teaches Catalan.

II. ADMISSION TO COURSES

1. QUALIFICATIONS REQUIRED

For *Honours*, the Department does not lay down specifically any 'A' Level standard but adapts its requirements after an interview.

Entry into the *General* course for Spanish: the language may be started from scratch but evidence of some linguistic ability is looked for (not always found).

2. SELECTION OF STUDENTS

Selection of students is based on 'A' Level results (see II.1 above) and interviews. There are entrance scholarship examinations, details of which may be found in the appropriate pamphlets.

Interviews. Each applicant is interviewed, usually by at least two members of the staff. Questions are asked on Spanish reading interests and an attempt is made to judge the applicant's literary ability in his answers or his approach to the subject. More general questions are asked, too. The school report is always seen.

3. TRANSFER

The first year is preliminary to the Honours course and permission to proceed is decided after the examination at the end of this year. Personal estimation of the year's work is taken into consideration as well as examination results. After that, transfer is still possible but not common.

4. NUMBERS

It appears at the moment that the average annual intake into Honours will be 4 to 6. General numbers are difficult to forecast, especially as a complete redrafting of the system may occur in the next year or so.

Information supplied by Professor J. L. Brooks

UNIVERSITY OF ESSEX

School of Comparative Studies
(Departments of Government and Literature)
Schemes of Study with Spanish

I. COURSES OF STUDY

1. TYPES OF COURSES

Spanish can be studied in connection with the following schemes of study:

(*i*) *Government*

(*ii*) *Literature*

However, Spanish is not studied as a discipline in itself, but is considered rather as being complementary to the study and understanding of other disciplines.

Both schemes are of three years' duration and lead to the award of the B.A. degree with Honours. Students who do not already have a good knowledge of Spanish will be required to spend an additional year following an intensive course of language study at the University Language Centre. Previous knowledge of Spanish is not essential for entry to the Centre.

(*i*) *Government.* The scheme will be based on the comparative study of South American and British political institutions. It will include a general study of government in the world today with special emphasis on the action of social and economic forces in the structure of institutions, as well as in the conduct of politics. The scheme will also include a course on the history of political thought in Western Europe.

(*ii*) *Literature.* The scheme of study in Literature will include courses in modern history and in the development and structure of political and social institutions in Western Europe.

Emphasis will be placed on the literature of the last three centuries. Though literary study will be conducted with strict attention to chronology and in combination with political and social history, as much attention will be paid to critical elucidation and evaluation of specific works of literature as to literary history.

2. CHARACTERISTICS OF COURSES

In the first year, all students in the School will follow a common closely integrated group of courses. Students will not be required to decide upon their particular scheme of study until the end of the first year.

3. COMBINATION OF SUBJECTS

After the common first year, students will be required to follow either one or the other of the specialist schemes of study. There will be no ancillary or subsidiary subjects.

4. RESIDENCE ABROAD

Residence abroad will be encouraged.

II. ADMISSION TO COURSES

1. QUALIFICATIONS REQUIRED

Apart from the general entrance requirements of the University, applicants for admission to the School of Comparative Studies are required to have passed two subjects at Advanced Level. Applicants whose area of specialization is South America would normally be expected to have passed a language other than English at Advanced Level. This need not necessarily be Spanish, though in this case, a preliminary year of intensive language study at the University Language Centre would be necessary.

2. SELECTION OF STUDENTS

Selection is made on the basis of an applicant's performance both at Ordinary Level and Advanced Level, and careful attention is paid to reports obtained from the headmaster or headmistress. In most cases, applicants are invited to attend an informal interview with the professor of the Department.

3. TRANSFER

Special attention will, at all stages, be paid to the problems of students who wish to transfer from one scheme of study to another, although, in the case of transfer between two unlike subjects, a student's total period of study at the University may be extended beyond the normal three years.

Information supplied by the Registrar, University of Essex

UNIVERSITY OF EXETER

Department of Spanish

I. COURSES OF STUDY

1. TYPES OF COURSES

(a) *B.A. Honours.* This is a three-year course, which includes the following: the history of the language from Vulgar Latin to modern times; the history of Spanish literature in the medieval and modern periods; the history of Spanish thought and Spanish institutions; translation and oral work. In the final year of the course there is greater specialization, the Part II degree examination including papers on special periods or movements in Spanish literature and on special authors. A dissertation bearing on some aspect of the special period or movement studied is also required.

During the first two years of the Honours course, an Additional subject is also taken (see I.3 below).

(b) *B.A. Combined Honours including Spanish.* Spanish may be combined with another language (see I.3 below), the two subjects being studied *pari passu* for three years. The content of the course in Spanish is similar to that for B.A. Honours in Spanish, except that there is no Additional subject requirement and that students will normally not cover the history of the language or medieval literature.

(c) *Additional subject.* This is a two-year course, including Golden Age and modern literature and translation and oral work, for students in the Honours Schools of French or German.

2. CHARACTERISTICS OF COURSES

See under I.1 above and I.5 below.

3. COMBINATION OF SUBJECTS

(a) *B.A. Honours in Spanish.* An Additional subject is taken during the first two years, selected from the following list: English, European History, French, French History and Institutions, German, Italian, Latin, Philosophy, or another subject approved by the Faculty Board.

(b) *B.A. Combined Honours including Spanish.* Spanish may be combined with *either* French *or* German *or* Latin (see I.1(b) above).

4. RESIDENCE ABROAD

Honours students are, at present, required to attend a course of study in Spain or a Spanish-speaking country for at least a month during each of their two long vacations. Combined Honours students must attend one such course. Alternatively, students in either category may interpolate a year in Spain as an English assistant at a Spanish university or *Instituto de Segunda Enseñanza* under the official exchange scheme.

Students taking Spanish as an Additional subject are also required to attend one vacation course in Spain.

Apart from these formal requirements, students are given every encouragement to visit Spain and to get to know the country, people and way of life as widely as possible.

5. METHODS OF STUDY

Students are encouraged, and expected, to develop the habit of independent work (both during term and vacation), and to produce and discuss regular tutorial essays. Most of the teaching is done on a seminar and tutorial basis, and formal lecturing is kept to a minimum.

II. ADMISSION TO COURSES

1. QUALIFICATIONS REQUIRED

Departmental course requirements, as distinct from those of the University and Faculty generally, are:

(a) For Honours and Combined Honours courses: a good pass at 'A' Level Spanish (grade B), supported by a grade B in one other subject or two grade C marks. It may be added that a good 'A' Level Latin mark is welcomed as a desirable qualification.

(b) For Additional subject courses: a good pass in 'O' Level Spanish; or, alternatively, a pass in 'A' Level Latin or other evidence of linguistic ability may be accepted. Students for these courses may be accepted as beginners, and cases are examined on their individual merits. In the circumstances it should be realized that mediocre qualifications in Spanish will not normally carry more weight than a record which shows promise and ability in other languages.

2. SELECTION OF STUDENTS

The following considerations determine the selection of students:

(a) *G.C.E. 'A' Level results* when known (see II.1 above). Where 'A' Level has not been taken, or is being repeated, provisional acceptances may be given, on the strength of (b) and (c) below and subject to satisfactory results at 'A' Level.

(b) *Reports from the applicants' schools.* Careful consideration is given to these, and it is therefore particularly helpful when headmasters and others concerned avoid the use of superlatives in describing their more mediocre candidates, and preserve a sense of proportion between the qualities the candidate is claimed to possess.

(c) *Interviews.* These are held in the first half of the academic year, as applications reach the University, and are of some 15-20 minutes' duration. They are normally conducted by two members of the Department, and the qualities looked for are evidence of intellectual curiosity and general cultural interests as well as literary and linguistic ability. Enquiries may be made about the candidate's reading in English and other languages as well as in Spanish, and the interview may be conducted in part in Spanish.

The above remarks apply to applicants for Honours or Combined Honours. In the case of applicants for the Additional subject courses, interviews are normally in the hands of the Honours School, though a member of the staff of this Department frequently assists in interviewing such candidates.

3. TRANSFER

Honours and Combined Honours students are admitted on entrance. Transfer between these two categories, where desirable, is possible during or at the end of the first term.

4. NUMBERS

About 6 to 9 Honours (including Combined Honours) students are admitted annually.

Information supplied by Professor G. D. Trotter

M.L.—H

UNIVERSITY· OF HULL
Department of Spanish

I. COURSES OF STUDY

1. TYPES OF COURSES

Spanish is available in the following courses:

(*a*) *Ancillary:* taken in the first year with certain Special Honours subjects, for example, English and History;

(*b*) *Subsidiary:* taken over the first five terms with certain other Special Honours subjects (generally French);

(*c*) *Joint Honours:* taken over three years with one other Joint Honours subject.

A Special Honours degree in Hispanic Studies is to be introduced in the near future.

2. CHARACTERISTICS OF COURSES

Courses deal with the language and literature of Spain. The Joint Honours course concentrates on the literature of the 16th, 17th, 19th and 20th centuries; the projected Special Honours course in Hispanic Studies will include a wider range of Iberian languages and Hispanic literatures.

3. COMBINATION OF SUBJECTS

The most popular Joint Honours combination is with French. Combination with all subjects other than Italian is possible in the Faculty of Arts.

4. RESIDENCE ABROAD

Joint Honours and Subsidiary students complete a summer vacation course in Spain at the end of their first year.

5. METHODS OF STUDY

Teaching of literature is by monographic courses. Practical work stresses analysis, criticism, essay-writing and translation into Spanish. Joint Honours students have fortnightly tutorial classes.

II. ADMISSION TO COURSES

1. QUALIFICATIONS REQUIRED

All students must matriculate in the University.

Students wishing to take the *Ancillary* or *Subsidiary* courses must have a pass at 'A' Level in a modern or classical foreign language.

Candidates for the *Joint Honours* course must have a good pass in Spanish at 'O' Level, a pass in Latin at 'O' Level and a pass at 'A' Level in a modern or classical foreign language. (As almost every candidate for this course has taken or is taking Spanish at 'A' Level, a pass at 'A' Level will soon be a formal requirement.)

2. SELECTION OF STUDENTS

As there is no separate entrance examination, Joint Honours Spanish candidates are selected on 'O' and 'A' Level results, on the head teachers' reports and on interviews.

3. TRANSFER

As there is no General degree in Arts in this University, students are admitted directly to Honours Schools.

4. NUMBERS

In 1963 about 5 students were reading Joint Honours Spanish; this number may be expected to increase over the next few years.

Information supplied by Mr. C. B. Morris, Lecturer in charge of Spanish

UNIVERSITY OF LEEDS

Department of Spanish and Portuguese Languages and Literatures

I. COURSES OF STUDY

1. TYPES OF COURSES

Spanish can be studied in the following degree courses:

(*a*) *Special* (i.e. *Honours*). Literature from origins to the present day, largely omitting the 18th century. In the third year three special periods are studied: classical, modern and Hispanic American, as monograph courses with intensive seminar work. The history of the language is taken in the first and third years. Modern Spanish, translations from and into Spanish, are taken in all years. History: monograph courses of one term in each year; Geography: one term in the first year.

(*b*) *Dual Honours degree in modern languages.* Spanish can be combined with any other language, involving a programme of studies of about three-quarters of the single Special degree.

(*c*) *Spanish as part of a General degree course.* Literature of classical and modern periods and modern language studied over three years. Honours are awarded.

(*d*) *Subsidiary* to a Special course in some other subject for one or three years.

(*e*) *Combined Studies.* After one year of General Studies, a concentration on two subjects only, such as Spanish and English.

Portuguese may be an optional subject for Finals in the Special degree course.

2. CHARACTERISTICS OF COURSES

Centred on lists of required reading of literary texts (for detailed and general study) an attempt is made to set literature in periods of taste and national events. So all literature courses are paralleled by courses in history and preceded in the first year by a course in geography.

A good deal of written work is required, some of it for weekly seminars, which form an important part of all literary courses. Seminars are usually restricted to six or eight students and often taken by different members of staff, not only by the lecturer in the particular course.

In the final year of Special Studies several options are available to suit students who are more interested in literature, philology or civilization.

Selected students are invited to present a dissertation of 15-20,000 words, in lieu of two Final papers, on a literary subject. The selection is usually made among those students—about 90 per cent of each year—who spend a whole year abroad between the second and third years of the course.

The Department is a closely-knit unit in which there is a great deal of social activity involving staff and students.

Special emphasis is laid throughout on the spoken language in which the two native Spaniards and the one Portuguese on the staff play an important part. Some lectures in the language are given in each year of the course.

Courses are so arranged that students meet many members of staff in each year.

3. COMBINATION OF SUBJECTS

Spanish is studied in the following combinations: Special (i.e. Honours) Spanish with other modern languages, usually French, and in the future probably with Russian.

As a Subsidiary subject with French, German, English, Fine Art, Economics, Philosophy and quite regularly with Portuguese.

The study of Spanish does not demand any compulsory combination of subjects.

4. RESIDENCE ABROAD

Special students must spend one term in Spain attending university courses. They go to almost all Spanish universities.

General students are required to attend a summer school course in Spain for one month at some time during the three years.

In addition, students are encouraged, and grants are sought, to enable them to be in Spain on other occasions.

Special students write essays and sometimes do proses while abroad.

5. METHODS OF STUDY

See I.2 above.

6. OTHER ACTIVITIES

An active Spanish society arranges weekly meetings for outside lectures, poetry readings and the annual production of plays in the original.

From two to four distinguished Spaniards (professors and writers) are invited each year to the Department.

A very active and successful choir teaches a wide selection of folk songs which are also sung in public.

II. ADMISSION TO COURSES

1. QUALIFICATIONS REQUIRED

For admission to the Special (Honours) course students are required to have (*a*) Latin at 'O' Level or its equivalent, (*b*) grade B at 'A' Level in Spanish and marks at about C in usually two other 'A' Level subjects.

For Spanish as a subject in a General degree, no previous knowledge of Spanish is required; it can be taken from scratch. Possession of a high 'O' Level or of an 'A' Level in Spanish admits students to the second-year course in their first year and in successive years to following courses leading in their third year to a course equivalent in level to the second-year Special Studies course, though of less breadth. Success in this course qualifies for recommendation as teachers of Spanish in schools to 'O' Level.

Admission to courses in Portuguese is governed by similar conditions to those that apply to General Studies in Spanish, without any previous knowledge of the language.

2. SELECTION OF STUDENTS

'A' Level results, as indicated in II.1 above, together with interview are used for selection. The interview serves to get an impression of quality which can be compared with school testimonials, estimate of marks and results in trial examinations. All candidates are interviewed. Questions at interview attempt to reveal general interests of students (art, hobbies, fads and knowledge) as well as academic interests and ability to talk about them.

Note.—The most obvious defect in nearly all candidates is absence of historical knowledge. They seem to know almost nothing about biography or events of contemporary history which help in explaining the creation of literature.

3. TRANSFER

Students are admitted directly to the Honours School as indicated in II.1. They are also admitted from General Studies if a standard of first class is reached at the end of the first year. Three further years are then required.

Transfer is possible, then, into Honours as indicated above. Similarly transfer from Honours to General is effected if the results in the first-year Honours examination are not satisfactory, followed then by two further years.

4. NUMBERS

Between 15 and 20 students are admitted annually to the Honours School.

Information supplied by Professor R. F. Brown

UNIVERSITY OF LIVERPOOL
School of Hispanic Studies

I. COURSES OF STUDY

1. TYPES OF COURSES

(a) *Special Studies* (*Honours*) *in Hispanic Studies:* a three-year course (extended in certain circumstances to four) in which the main language is Spanish and seven of the ten final papers are concerned with the language, history and literature of Spain. Two further papers are on Portuguese language, history and literature. The tenth may be either (a) Spanish-American history and literature, or (b) Catalan language, history and literature, or (c) a special subject.

A student may, if he wishes, select Portuguese as his specialism. In this case, seven of the ten papers are Portuguese, two Spanish and the remaining paper optional as before.

(b) *General Studies* (*Honours and Pass*): both Spanish and Portuguese may be chosen by students following the course of General Studies, as either one-year, two-year or three-year subjects. A student is awarded Honours or a Pass degree on the combined results of his second- and third-year examinations.

(c) *Joint Special Studies* (*Honours*) *in Hispanic Studies and another subject:* a four-year course of this nature has been approved.

Catalan and Spanish-American Studies may be chosen as one-year subjects.

2. CHARACTERISTICS OF COURSES

Content of courses: the special and perhaps unique feature of the School is that it offers a degree in Hispanic Studies, with a full three-year course in Spanish and in Portuguese, for every student, and optional two-year courses in Catalan and Spanish-American. The courses cover the whole scope of Hispanic studies: linguistic, literary and historical, medieval and modern.

3. COMBINATION OF SUBJECTS

The Special Studies course is in Hispanic Studies. In addition to Spanish, Portuguese is obligatory, and Catalan and Spanish-American studies optional. Outside the School of Hispanic Studies, the student must follow a one-year course in one other subject of his own choice.

4. RESIDENCE ABROAD

All Special Studies students are required to follow a course of study at a university or other approved institution in Spain (or

Spanish America) and Portugal (or Brazil). They normally meet this requirement during the three months of the summer vacation preceding their final examination; of this period, six weeks are usually spent at the University of Coimbra, and the remaining period at a university in Spain. Students are also encouraged to go to both Spain and Portugal at other times.

5. METHODS OF STUDY

A full tutorial system is in operation, by means of which every student writes a weekly essay and, with one or at most two other students, discusses it with his tutor. Many of the courses are conducted by means of seminars, which are, of course, in addition to formal lectures.

6. OTHER ACTIVITIES

A vigorous student society organizes a full and varied programme of activities, including an annual production of a Spanish play and lectures by visiting scholars.

II. ADMISSION TO COURSES

1. QUALIFICATIONS REQUIRED

(1) *General Studies.* Students are admitted to courses in all four subjects in the school—Spanish, Portuguese, Catalan and Spanish-American studies—without previous knowledge of the subject. For admission to the Faculty, in addition to the matriculation requirements, they would be expected to reach a good aggregate mark in two, or preferably three, subjects at G.C.E. 'A' Level.

(2) *Special Studies.* Students may be admitted to the course on the result of the first-year examination in the University, either in General Studies or in Special Studies in another School.

Students admitted into Special Studies in their first year require Latin at 'O' Level and, at the 'A' Level, a good mark in Spanish and a good aggregate mark in two, or preferably three, subjects.

2. SELECTION OF STUDENTS

Students for Special Studies are selected on the strength of:

(*a*) Head's report (standardized questionnaire);

(*b*) Interview by, usually, three members of the Department, for some 15-20 minutes. Whenever possible, all candidates for admission are summoned to Liverpool, but the interview has been dispensed with in special cases (sickness, long distance, etc.).

(*c*) G.C.E. 'A' Level results.

There is no special entrance examination.

3. TRANSFER

Students are normally admitted to the Special Studies course on entrance, but they can be admitted (as indicated in II.1) on the results of the first-year examination, either of the General Studies examination or of the Special Studies examination in another School.

4. NUMBERS

The annual intake is between 10 and 12.

Information supplied by Professor Geoffrey Ribbans

M.L.—H 2

UNIVERSITY OF LONDON: KING'S COLLEGE

Department of Spanish Studies

I. COURSES OF STUDY

1 and 2. TYPES AND MAIN CHARACTERISTICS OF COURSES

Spanish can be studied in two courses:

(*a*) *B.A.Honours*

(1) The history of the language from Vulgar Latin;

(2) The history of Spanish literature from the 12th century to the present day;

(3) A special subject chosen from the following: (*i*) Romance philology, (*ii*) Catalan literature, (*iii*) a period of Spanish literature;

(4) Instruction in translation and writing the language.

(*b*) As *Subsidiary* subject to an Honours degree in another subject. A two-year course comprising the following:

(1) Translating and writing the language;

(2) Spanish literature of *either* the 16th and 17th centuries *or* the 19th and 20th centuries.

3. COMBINATION OF SUBJECTS

The Subsidiary subject most commonly combined with the course in Honours Spanish is French. Portuguese comes second and Latin third. There is no compulsory combination of subjects and all combinations are possible within the range of Arts subjects.

4. RESIDENCE ABROAD

First-year Honours students must spend the third term of their first year in residence at a Spanish university either following a special course arranged for them or attending such courses in language and literature as may be available. They are strongly recommended to spend the following long vacation in Spain also. Our students are free to go to any university they please but the majority choose Salamanca and Seville where my Department has made special arrangements for their tuition.

5. METHODS OF STUDY

We reduce formal lecturing to the minimum and give most of the tuition in seminars (discussion classes) or small tutorial groups.

6. OTHER ACTIVITIES

An important activity is the performance each year of a play or plays in Spanish.

II. ADMISSION TO COURSES

1. QUALIFICATIONS REQUIRED

For admission to this Department, students must fulfil the University of London minimum entrance requirements, with in addition:

(1) *Honours:* Spanish and at least one other subject to 'A' Level. Latin must have been passed at least 'O' Level.

(2) *Subsidiary:* Spanish at least to 'O' Level.

2. SELECTION OF STUDENTS

There is no entrance examination. On the basis of the G.C.E. results and the personal references and reports from the school, a short list of candidates is selected for interview. At the interview what is looked for is intellectual curiosity and as wide a range of cultural interests as possible. More importance is attached to mental alertness of this kind than to actual paper qualifications in academic subjects. On the basis of the interviews the candidates are graded in order of merit and places offered up to the number available. The rest are placed on a waiting list. We try, however, to take an immediate decision to accept or reject in order to facilitate the working of the UCCA scheme.

3. TRANSFER

(Does not apply.)

4. NUMBERS

The Faculty of Arts limits the number of Honours students of Spanish to 17 per annum.

Information supplied by Professor R. O. Jones

UNIVERSITY OF LONDON: QUEEN MARY COLLEGE

Department of Spanish Language and Literature

I. COURSES OF STUDY

1. TYPES OF COURSES

Spanish is available at two levels:

(*a*) *B.A. Honours in Spanish:* a three-year course. The third term of the first year is spent in Spain (see I.4). The Subsidiary subject selected is usually examined at the end of the second year.

(*b*) *Subsidiary:* a Subsidiary course to an Honours degree in another subject. This is normally completed in two years, and comprises the following: translating and writing the language, conversation, Spanish literature of *either* the 16th and 17th centuries *or* the 19th and 20th centuries.

The B.A. General course has been discontinued.

2. CHARACTERISTICS OF COURSES

The Finals examination in Honours Spanish tests linguistic proficiency, knowledge of the whole field of Spanish philology and of the history of Spanish literature. In addition, papers are set on a Special Subject chosen from *either* (*i*) Romance philology *or* (*ii*) a period of Spanish literature studied in great detail, mainly in set texts.

Our aim in the Honours course is to give students a sound command of the language both written and spoken, and, through the medium of the study of Spanish literature, to develop their capacities for literary appreciation. In the study of the cultural background to Spanish literature, special attention is paid to the interplay of the Arabic and Christian civilizations of medieval Spain. We also have a particular interest in Latin America, and an optional Special Subject in Latin-American literature is taught in the Department. At the moment we have the benefit of the services of two part-time Spanish conversational assistants, and conversation classes are obligatory at all levels.

3. COMBINATION OF SUBJECTS

The subject most commonly combined with the course in Spanish is French, with Portuguese a close second. There is no compulsory combination of subjects and all combinations are possible within the range of Arts subjects available.

4. RESIDENCE ABROAD

Honours students are required to spend the summer term of their first year at a Spanish university of their choice, and are recommended to spend the following long vacation in Spain also.

There are no requirements in force for Subsidiary students.

5. METHODS OF STUDY

The relatively small numbers of the Department allow formal lecturing to be reduced to the minimum, and most tuition is in discussion classes or tutorial groups.

6. OTHER ACTIVITIES

Amongst its other activities the Student Spanish Society is able, most years, to put on a play in Spanish. It has the advantage of having the splendid stage of the Great Hall (formerly the People's Palace) at its disposal, and has presented several extremely successful productions.

II. ADMISSION TO COURSES

1. QUALIFICATIONS REQUIRED

Applicants must fulfil the University of London entrance requirements, with in addition:

Honours: Spanish with a B at 'A' Level and another subject (preferably literary) at 'A' Level. Latin at least to 'O' Level.

Subsidiary: No fixed requirements. Spanish can be started within the Department.

2. SELECTION OF STUDENTS

Selection is by interview. Candidates are usually selected before 'A' Level results are known, so that admission is, in those cases, provisional. At the interview the qualities looked for are intellectual curiosity, strong cultural interests and evidence of wide reading. We normally interview all applicants who have satisfied or expect to satisfy our entrance requirements.

3. NUMBERS

Twelve to 15 students are admitted annually to the Honours course. Numbers are deliberately kept down to make for more satisfactory classes and closer staff-student relations.

Information supplied by Dr. L. P. Harvey, Reader in Spanish

UNIVERSITY OF LONDON:
WESTFIELD COLLEGE

Department of Spanish

I. COURSES OF STUDY

As from October 1965, Westfield College will admit men and women students to undergraduate courses; postgraduate courses are already open to men and women.

1 and 2. TYPES AND MAIN CHARACTERISTICS OF COURSES

Spanish can be studied in the following courses:

(a) *B.A. Honours:*

(i) The history of the language from its Vulgar Latin origins to the present day;

(ii) The history of Spanish literature from the 12th century to the present day;

(iii) A Special Subject chosen from the following: Romance philology, South-American literature, Catalan literature, a period of Spanish literature;

(iv) Instruction in translating and writing the language.

(b) *Subsidiary:* as Subsidiary subject to an Honours degree in another subject. A two-year course comprising the following:

(i) Translating and writing the language;

(ii) Spanish literature of *either* the 16th and 17th centuries *or* the 19th and 20th centuries.

3. COMBINATION OF SUBJECTS

As Subsidiary subjects to Honours Spanish, French or Italian or Portuguese are usually taken. There is no compulsory combination of subjects.

4. RESIDENCE ABROAD

The University of London does not require students to spend part of their course abroad. Students are, however, urged to spend the summer term of their first year in Spain.

5. METHODS OF STUDY

The tutorial system is combined with lectures and seminars (discussion classes).

II. ADMISSION TO COURSES

1. QUALIFICATIONS REQUIRED

Applicants must fulfil the University of London entrance requirements. Spanish cannot be started from scratch except as a Subsidiary subject.

2. SELECTION OF STUDENTS

Selection is by interview, including an oral test. Opportunity is given for candidates to show their ability to interpret orally a literary text, either in English or Spanish. The College offers annually a number of Scholarships and Exhibitions, open to all candidates for admission and awarded on the results of an examination held in the Michaelmas term.

3. TRANSFER

Students are admitted to the Honours course in Spanish on entrance. There is no alternative course available to which students can be transferred.

4. NUMBERS

The Department admits at present 8 or 9 students each year, but is expected to grow in the immediate future.

Information supplied by Professor J. E. Varey

UNIVERSITY OF MANCHESTER

Department of Spanish and Portuguese Studies

I. COURSES OF STUDY

1. TYPES OF COURSES

Spanish can be studied for Honours and for General Arts degrees:

(*a*) *Honours*

> *B.A. Honours in Spanish Studies* (three years);
>
> *B.A. Honours in Modern Languages* (in combination with French, German, Italian or Russian; four years);
>
> *B.A. Honours in Spanish and Classical Arabic* (four years).
>
> Spanish can also be taken as a *Subsidiary* subject for most Honours Schools.

(*b*) *General*

> as part of the *General degree of B.A.* at the three levels of *Intermediate*, *General* and *Special*;
>
> as part of the degree of *B.A. in Commerce, B.A. in Administration, B.A. in Theology*, and *B.A. in Music*.

Portuguese can be taken as a *Subsidiary* subject for most Honours Schools, as part of the General degree of B.A. at the three levels of *Intermediate, General* and *Special*, and as a Special Subject course (the works of Camões) for Spanish Honours Finals.

Latin-American Studies can be taken as a *Subsidiary* subject for most Honours Schools, as part of the General degree of B.A. at the levels of *General* and *Special*, and as a Special Subject course (the Latin-American novel in the 20th century) for Spanish Honours Finals.

2. CHARACTERISTICS OF COURSES

The Spanish Honours course is divided into *Part I* and *Part II*.

In *Part I* all students attend the same courses: on the Spanish language past and present, on Spanish history and on Spanish literature. In this last respect students examine closely a number of texts of widely varying types—from the Middle Ages to the present day—chosen both for their inherent quality and because they throw light on important aspects of Spanish thought and literature. It is hoped that through these courses students will acquire a better general idea of Spanish literature than through a manual-of-literature approach, that they will be made aware of some of the historical, literary and critical problems involved in the study of a civilization, and that they will be able to decide where their own particular enthusiasms lie and what they want to concentrate on in their *Part II* options and Special Subject.

In *Part II* there are compulsory courses and optional courses. The compulsory courses are: composition and unseen, essay in Spanish, syntax and semantics, Cervantes. The optional courses, of which each student must choose three, are: phonology and morphology, medieval literature, prose 1500–1700, poetry and drama 1500–1700, novel and essay since 1870, poetry and drama since 1870. Each student also takes a Special Subject, to be chosen from a group prescribed from year to year (e.g. Romance philology, the works of Lope de Vega, Spanish Romanticism, the Latin-American novel in the 20th century, etc.).

3. COMBINATION OF SUBJECTS

Honours Spanish may be combined in a four-year course with French, German, Italian, Russian or Arabic (see I.1(*a*) above). Students who take one of these combinations are allowed to omit one paper in the Spanish *Part II* Examination.

Students of Spanish Honours take two Subsidiary subjects, one of which must be Latin. Other popular choices are French, Portuguese and Latin-American Studies. Students with a Grade B at 'A' Level in an Arts subject other than Spanish can be recommended for exemption from the University's first-year examination in that subject. This is an important concession that all applicants should qualify for in their 'A' Level examination.

General Degree students can take Hispanic Studies—i.e. Spanish, Portuguese and Latin American—in seven of the nine courses required for their B.A. course. No previous knowledge of Spanish or Portuguese is required.

4. RESIDENCE ABROAD

Honours Spanish students may spend the summer term of their second year at a Spanish university. In practice, nearly all of them do so. The majority go to Madrid, some to Salamanca, Seville, Granada or Valladolid.

5. METHODS OF STUDY

As far as possible Honours classes are organized on a seminar basis. Conversation classes and discussion groups are arranged by the Spanish assistants.

6. OTHER ACTIVITIES

Lectures by visitors from Spanish universities. Active Spanish Society: play productions, talks, films, choir, soccer team, rugby team, etc.

II. ADMISSION TO COURSES

1 and 2. QUALIFICATIONS REQUIRED; SELECTION OF STUDENTS

Candidates for Honours Spanish have to satisfy the matriculation requirements of this University and are expected to have passed Latin at 'O' Level. In addition, the normal departmental 'A' Level requirement is *either* (*i*) not less than two grade B's and a grade C, *or* (*ii*) not less than a grade A and a grade B. In each case the candidate should have at least a grade B in Spanish. Headmasters' reports, 'S' papers, performance in the University of Manchester entrance scholarship examinations, period of Spanish study, interviews—all these can influence the final decision.

For the General degree, both Spanish and Portuguese can be started from scratch. Selection for entrance to the General degree course is in the hands of the Director of General Studies in the Faculty of Arts.

3. TRANSFER

Honours students in other modern languages who take Intermediate Spanish (from scratch) as a Subsidiary subject, may, if they obtain a First Class in Intermediate Spanish at the end of their first session, take Honours Spanish as second language for the Honours course in Modern Languages. General degree students also may be admitted to the Spanish Honours course if they show exceptional ability and have obtained a First Class in Intermediate Spanish.

Spanish Honours students who fail to satisfy the examiners in the Spanish *Part I* Examination are recommended for transfer to the General degree.

4. NUMBERS

The annual entry for Honours Spanish, or for Honours in Modern Languages with Spanish as first language, is generally about 15.

Information supplied by Professor H. Ramsden

UNIVERSITY OF
NEWCASTLE UPON TYNE

Department of Spanish
and Latin American Studies

I. COURSES OF STUDY

1. TYPES OF COURSES

(*a*) The following courses can be taken in the *Honours School of Spanish and Latin American Studies* at Newcastle:

(1) *B.A. with Honours in Spanish and Latin American Studies;*

(2) *B.A. with Honours in French and Spanish;* } Joint Honours

(3) *B.A. with Honours in Spanish and German;* } courses

(*b*) Spanish may be taken in all three years of the course for the *General degree of B.A.*

(*c*) It may also be taken for two years in the course for the *B.A. Economic Studies.*

(*d*) It is of course available as a *Subsidiary subject*, taken in one or two years, for certain other Honours Schools.

(*e*) Portuguese is taken for two years in the B.A. with Honours in Spanish and Latin American Studies (see above).

It may also be taken for one or two years in the B.A. Economic Studies course (but not, as yet, in the General degree of B.A.).

2. CHARACTERISTICS OF COURSES

B.A. with Honours in Spanish and Latin American Studies

The *First Year* of the course leads to the Preliminary Honours Examination. Apart from training in the use of the language students begin to study its history and to read medieval texts. They also have both an outline course on Spanish history and a similar course on the history of Latin America. Aspects of the literature of Spain are studied, and the students encouraged to form some idea of the development of Spanish literature as a whole (and its relation to history) in preparation for the fuller treatment to come in Second and Third Years.

In *Second and Third Years* the usual language work continues (Finals Papers 1 to 3) and the History of the Language is further studied (Paper 4). There is a separate course on Medieval Literature (Paper 5). Two courses on Spanish Literature cover the periods 1500 to 1700 and 1700 to the present day, respectively (Papers 6 and 7), and there is a paper on Spanish-American Literature (Paper 8). There is a course on the History and Institutions of Spain and Spanish America (Paper 9). Portuguese is studied in both years, and represented by a paper on the Portuguese Language and the Literature of Portugal and Brazil (10). A dissertation may be offered in place of one of the above papers.

It is possible for candidates to take a modified form of the above syllabus, containing a higher proportion of Latin-American Studies. If allowed to do this they would replace Papers 4 and 5 by the following: The Spanish and Portuguese Colonial Empires, and the History, Life and Literature of Mexico.

Candidates offering French with Spanish or German are excused a Subsidiary subject, and in their Final Examination take five papers in each subject: in Spanish, two language papers and three others chosen from 4 to 10 above.

The Joint Honours degree requires an appropriate level of ability and industry, and those who apply for admission to it should realize this.

General B.A. course

As mentioned above, the First Year course is for beginners and is mainly devoted to making rapid progress in the language, though three texts are studied, of which two at least are of a literary nature.

The Second Year course continues the study of the language, and studies aspects of Spanish literature: Cervantes, and modern literature from 1898 to the present day. Conversation classes are provided from this stage onwards.

The Third Year concentrates mainly on Spanish literature of the Golden Age. Candidates taking the Final General Examination must have spent at least a month in Spain.

Students who by concession enter the Second Year course in their first year (see II.3 below) and consequently take the Third Year course in their Second Year may, if they wish to continue the subject in their final year, be set a special literature paper based on part of the Honours syllabus.

As from October, 1964, an Intensive course in Spanish will be available. (Under new General B.A. regulations, an Intensive course may in certain subjects be taken in the final year; the Intensive subject plus one other would then be considered as an equivalent to the normal three subjects.) This too will be based on Honours work.

B.A. Economic Studies

The First Year course is as for the General B.A. degree. In Second Year, students have a smaller number of set books, which are less exclusively literary in character. They also have lectures on Latin-American history (including relevant periods of Peninsular history). Conversation classes are provided in Second Year.

3. COMBINATION OF SUBJECTS

Because Portuguese is studied for two years (second and third) of the Honours course, a Subsidiary subject is taken for one year only. This subject may be any of those available in the General degree; it is normally, but not always, taken at the Second Year level. French and English are popular Subsidiary subjects, especially with intending teachers; other students often choose History of Art and Architecture.

In the General degree of B.A. almost any combination of subjects is possible.

4. RESIDENCE ABROAD

Honours students are required to spend the third term of their second year at a Spanish university. They may, if they prefer, intercalate a whole year in Spain. (Attendance at a holiday course, e.g. between first and second years, or residence in a Spanish family, is also regarded as desirable.) Students choose a Spanish university after consultation with me. If they have chosen to offer a dissertation in their Final Honours Examination (see I.2 above) they are expected to work at this while in Spain.

General students are required to spend a month in Spain before they may sit the Final General Examination in Spanish. Students who do not reach this level are of course strongly recommended to visit the country.

5. METHODS OF STUDY

The lecture is necessarily the basis of instruction, owing to the limitations of teaching staff, but every effort is made to divide classes into tutorial groups as they become larger. In any case, all students do a regular essay in a small tutorial group.

A tape recorder is used for language work, and the University will have a language laboratory in the near future.

6. OTHER ACTIVITIES

There is a flourishing Spanish Circle, which organizes lectures from visiting speakers on literary and other subjects, and arranges for the showing of Spanish films. A Spanish play is usually produced every year, and an annual dinner held.

II. ADMISSION TO COURSES

1. QUALIFICATIONS REQUIRED

Latin or Classical Greek (to at least Ordinary Level) is required for admission to all Honours degrees in modern languages and to the General degree of B.A.; but not for the B.A. Economic Studies.

The general requirements for matriculation in all faculties of the university, including Arts, are that the candidate must have passed in

English Language and in either four or five other subjects. These subjects must include (*a*) a language other than English and (*b*) either mathematics or an approved science subject; and at least two of the total number of subjects must have been passed at Advanced Level. Where only four subjects have been taken in addition to English Language there are certain requirements about the nature of these subjects and the number of sittings (see *University Calendar*, Volume II, page 2).

The study of Spanish in the General course normally begins from scratch, and that of Portuguese in the B.A. Economic Studies always does so. A student who has done Spanish at school may, by concession, take the Second Year General Examination in his first year.

For Honours see II.2 and 3 below.

2. SELECTION OF STUDENTS

Students for the B.A. General degree are admitted by the Senior Tutor after interview and will usually be allowed to take Spanish if they so desire.

Applicants for the Honours School are almost always interviewed in the spring preceding the October in which they wish to enter the University. Interviews are with the Head of the Department, who may be assisted by a colleague. When applicants are not called to interview it is either because their qualifications are felt to be inadequate or because too long a journey is involved. Before an interview a reference has been obtained from the applicant's headmaster or headmistress. In the interview I look mainly for enthusiasm, probable capacity for hard work, and some indication of Honours quality in intelligence and judgment. After the interview candidates who have not yet taken Advanced Level examinations—a majority—may be given conditional acceptance; they are then expected to obtain at least category B, though a lower mark may be accepted in exceptional cases. Candidates who are already qualified for entry, by possessing two Advanced Level subjects, may be offered admission on the spot. The few candidates who are not interviewed will either be turned down or given conditional acceptance on the same terms as the others.

3. TRANSFER

(*a*) The majority of entrants come direct from the sixth form into the Honours School.

(*b*) Transfer is possible from the First Year of the General degree course to the First Year of Honours. Students who transfer in this way will normally have done one year's Spanish only; but First Year General students may (as stated in II.2 above) obtain a concession to take Second Year Spanish in the First Year Examination, if they have studied the subject to 'A' or at the very least 'O' Level, and students in this position are sometimes considered as being aspirants to the

Honours School. When transfer takes place, the total length of the course is four years.[1]

4. NUMBERS

(*a*) The number of Honours students given direct admission in October 1963 was 9 (and the total in the Honours School 25). Admissions are expected to increase by about 1 per year.

(*b*) The total number of students taking Spanish is at present in the neighbourhood of 80, but is expected to increase.

*Information supplied by Dr. K. S. Reid, Reader in Spanish
and Latin American Studies*

[1] Students (of whatever provenance) who after taking the Preliminary Honours Examination are not allowed to proceed in the Honours School, may apply for admission to the Second Year of the General degree course. They thus obtain a degree in the same number of years as if they had remained in Honours.

UNIVERSITY OF NOTTINGHAM

Department of Spanish

I. COURSES OF STUDY

1. TYPES OF COURSES

The Department of Spanish offers three main courses:

(*a*) Spanish as a *Single Honours* course;

(*b*) Spanish as a *Joint Honours* course as from October 1964;

(*c*) Spanish as a *Subsidiary* course.

There is no General degree in Spanish. Students who, having started an Honours course, are found to be unequal to it, may be asked to transfer to a Pass degree.

Spanish studies are divided into courses for Part I (first and second years) and for Part II (third year). Students reading Spanish as a single Honours course take Part I in Spanish with some other Subsidiary subject, and Part II in Spanish alone. Students reading Spanish in a Joint Honours course will study Spanish and another language jointly for three years. Students reading Spanish as a Subsidiary subject take Part I only, in addition to Part I and II in their chosen Honours subject from another field. Students reading for a Pass degree have a course specially adapted to their personal needs.

2. CHARACTERISTICS OF COURSES

All courses are concerned with the language, literature and history of Spain, and Single Honours candidates can specialize in the first two fields.

Part I

(*a*) *Subsidiary*. Students attend courses in practical, oral and written work, conversation with a native speaker and practise skills in the language laboratory. There are courses in Spanish history and literature ranging from the 19th to 20th centuries together with a selection of set books. All these courses last two years.

(*b*) *Single Honours*. Students attend the above and in addition courses in the history of the Spanish language, medieval and Golden Age literature.

(*c*) *Joint Honours*. These students will balance equally their courses of study over the two main languages chosen. Only students with a high level of ability in both languages may take this course.

Part II

(*a*) *Single Honours*. Only the Honours subject is studied in this year and beyond the usual practical and essay work, students will be allowed to choose from among a series of options ranging from linguistics to medieval and modern literature, including Portuguese and Catalan.

(*b*) *Joint Honours.* Students will be able to choose a more limited number of courses from the same range of options.

3. COMBINATION OF SUBJECTS

Spanish as a Single Honours subject can be combined with Subsidiary English, French, German, Russian (not beginners), Classics, History, Biblical Studies, American Studies, Music (time-table permitting); as a Joint Honours subject it can be combined with Latin, French, German, Russian.

4. RESIDENCE ABROAD

Single Honours students are required to attend one term at a Spanish university, normally the last term of the first academic session. The majority go to Salamanca, Seville or Barcelona. Students are advised to stay on as long as possible after the term has ended, in order to get the utmost advantage from their visit to the Peninsula. With Joint Honours students, it will be arranged for an equal amount of time to be spent in each country; attendance at a summer school may be admitted as an equivalent.

Subsidiary students are also encouraged to go abroad. Those who begin Spanish in the University are required to attend a vacation course in Spain, usually in the vacation following the first academic year.

5. METHODS OF STUDY

Normal teaching methods include lectures, tutorials, conversation classes and language laboratory. As far as possible and especially in the third year, Honours students are taught in small groups. It should be emphasized that students are expected to read, without lectures, certain texts on their own, and regular essay-writing is a feature of departmental instruction.

6. OTHER ACTIVITIES

There is an active Spanish Society which arranges lectures and meetings. Each year a short play is produced. In addition to this, lectures by visitors from Spanish and other universities are arranged by the Department.

II. ADMISSION TO COURSES

1. QUALIFICATIONS REQUIRED

Latin at 'O' Level G.C.E. and two 'A' Level passes are required for admission to the courses described in I.1 (*a*) and (*b*).

Spanish can be taken from scratch but not by Honours students. Beginners are required to attend one vacation course in Spain.

Note.—For residential requirements for Subsidiary students who are beginners, see also I.4 above.

2. SELECTION OF STUDENTS

Students are chosen on the basis of an interview and school reports. Up to the present all candidates have been interviewed. Interviews are carried out by the Head of the Department and his deputy, who interview the same candidates and discuss results. A short practical test usually forms part of the interview. Some of the interview is carried out in Spanish. Questions range over the whole field of the candidate's interests in order to judge potential. There is no laid-down limit as to the percentage to be reached in 'A' Level subjects.

3. TRANSFER

Students are admitted to Honours courses on entrance. Transfer is possible but not very practicable except in the first weeks of the opening session.

4. NUMBERS

Approximately 9 Single Honours students are admitted annually to this Department.

Information supplied by Professor R. B. Tate

UNIVERSITY OF OXFORD
Faculty of Medieval
and Modern Languages (Spanish) [1, 2]

I. COURSES OF STUDY

1. TYPES OF COURSES

Spanish may be studied

(a) as the subject for an *Honours degree in only one language*;

(b) as a subject for an *Honours degree in two languages*, of which Spanish may be either the first or the second subject.

2. CHARACTERISTICS OF COURSES

Preliminary Examination for Modern Languages (*First Public Examination*). In the first two terms of study undergraduates must work for the First Public Examination (normally the Preliminary Examination for Modern Languages). The subjects in Spanish are: translation from and into Spanish; one paper involving the close textual study of selected works of three 20th-century authors; one paper of prescribed texts to be studied in relation to general trends in literature or thought or to historical background—the subject at present prescribed in Spanish for this paper is 'The Spanish Ballad Tradition'.

Honour School for Modern Languages (*Second Public Examination*). Candidates offering Spanish must offer some or all of the following papers according to whether they offer Spanish as sole (10 papers), first (7 papers) or second language (4 papers).

(1) Translation into Spanish;

(2) Translation from Spanish;

(3) Essay in Spanish;

(4) History of the Spanish language to 1250 (with prescribed texts);

(5) History of the Spanish language with special reference to its present state (with prescribed texts);

(6) Period of literature: one or two of the following periods may be offered: (a) to 1499, (b) 1543–1681, (c) the literature of Spain and Spanish America, 1811–1947;

---

[1] For general information concerning courses, admissions, residence abroad, etc., for undergraduates reading modern languages at Oxford, see p. 348.

[2] Portuguese may be offered as sole, first or second language. The structure of the examination is the same as that in other languages. For details see *Examination Statutes*.

(7) Medieval texts prescribed for study as examples of literature: *Cantar de Mio Cid*; Juan Ruiz, *Libro de Buen Amor*; Fernando de Rojas, *La Celestina*;

(8) Prescribed authors: two of (*a*) Luis de León, Cervantes, Góngora, Calderón and/or two of (*b*) Pérez Galdós, Leopoldo Alas, Miguel de Unamuno, Pablo Neruda.

A candidate offering Spanish as sole language must offer papers 1-5 inclusive; two periods from 6; paper 7; and two authors from each group in 8. A candidate offering Spanish as a first language must offer papers 1-3; paper 5; one of the periods listed in 6; paper 7; and two authors (both selected from the same group) in 8. A candidate offering Spanish as a second language must offer papers 1 and 2; one of the periods listed in 6; and two authors (both selected from the same group) in 8.

There are also 54 Optional Subjects in the Final Honours School of Modern Languages. A candidate aiming at a place in the First Class must take one of these. A candidate's choice of Optional Subject is not restricted to one concerned with the language or languages offered in the compulsory papers. There are 11 Iberian or Latin-American Optional Subjects.

II. ADMISSION TO COURSES

1. QUALIFICATIONS REQUIRED

Generally speaking, Colleges are unwilling to offer places to candidates for admission wishing to read Spanish unless they already have a good grounding in the language. However, candidates of proved linguistic ability who do not know the language are sometimes admitted to read Spanish provided they take steps to obtain a knowledge of it between the time they are accepted for admission and the time they come into residence.

4. NUMBERS

The number of candidates offering Spanish in the Final Honours Examination has varied in recent years between 30 and 50.

Information supplied by Professor P. E. Russell

UNIVERSITY OF SHEFFIELD
Department of Spanish

I. COURSES OF STUDY

1. TYPES OF COURSES

Spanish can be studied in the following courses:

(*a*) *Special Honours in Spanish* (Single Honours);

(*b*) *Special Honours in Modern Languages and Literatures, Special Honours in Latin and Spanish, Special Honours in Music and Spanish, Special Honours in Philosophy and Spanish* (Dual Honours);

(*c*) *General degree of B.A.* (which can be awarded as an Honours or a Pass degree depending upon performance in the final examinations);

(*d*) as a *Subsidiary subject* (taken in the second year) or as a *Special Subject* (read for two years and examined in the final examinations) to other Honours Schools;

(*e*) as an Intermediate and General degree subject for the degree of B.A. (Econ.).

The courses listed under (*a*), (*b*) and (*c*) are of three years' duration, but (*a*) or (*b*) may last for four years if a candidate begins Spanish on coming up to the University.

2. CHARACTERISTICS OF COURSES

(*a*) and (*b*) Honours courses follow the usual pattern of work divided between language, literature and history. All students attend weekly classes in spoken Spanish given by native Spanish speakers. Single Honours candidates must also opt for Catalan or Portuguese or a Special period or author as a Special Subject. Most of them choose Portuguese. This part of the course runs for two years, as does that on Peninsular history. Certain periods of Latin-American literature and history are covered in the Special Honours courses. Single Honours students also read a Special Subject outside the Department, usually French. All Honours candidates must read Latin for one year, Single Honours candidates for two, unless they choose an alternative to part of the medieval course (this can be again a special author or period of history or period of language).

The General courses (*c*) (which are read together with those in two other subjects in the Faculty) again deal, although in briefer form, with language and literature, from 1500 to the present day, but not history or philology.

3. COMBINATION OF SUBJECTS

Honours students must all read one year of Latin.[1] Single Honours candidates are strongly advised also to read French as a Special Subject. Special Subjects within the Spanish Department have already been referred to (see I.2 above). Instead of a second year of Latin, Single Honours candidates, who prefer an internal option to the full medieval course, may choose History, Philosophy or Economics.

All subjects of the Faculty can be read with Spanish for the General degree, although an attempt is made to dissuade undergraduates from reading three languages for this course.

4. RESIDENCE ABROAD

The time required for foreign residence for Honours students is three months. All Honours students must spend the summer term of their second year at a Spanish university. With Joint candidates who also read French, the residence in Spain can be postponed until July and August when attendance at a summer course may be admitted as an equivalent. Single Honours candidates reading Portuguese as a Special Subject are also expected to visit Portugal during their residence abroad. Those who opt for Catalan normally spend the summer term at Barcelona.

While abroad students are asked to attend whatever lectures will help them and may also interest them, e.g. they are encouraged to attend lectures on art. During their stay abroad they are also expected to prepare for the First Part of their Final examinations at Sheffield which takes place during the September following their stay in Spain. General students are strongly encouraged (but not required by regulation) to go abroad. Most of them, in fact, do so, although often without any assistance from their Local Authorities.

5. METHODS OF STUDY

The tutorial discussion system is in operation with us and applies to Honours candidates throughout their course and to General students during their second and third years. Many of our lectures take the form of reading, translation and comment upon set books, although each course is introduced by a series of formal lectures. Honours students are expected to read, without lectures, certain texts on their own and then to meet one of their lecturers from time to time to discuss their reading and present an essay on it. All students are expected to write essays on their set books, General students during the last two years. Not all the course is covered in this way, but a good selection of authors and subjects is chosen. Essays are in English and in Spanish. We also give occasional, non-examinable lectures, with slides, on Spanish art, etc.

---

[1] As from 1965 the first-year undergraduate course in the Faculty of Arts will be made up of three (instead of four) subjects. Latin will, then, nor longer be a compulsory subject for Honours Spanish, but candidates will *normally* be expected to read this subject in their first year.

6. OTHER ACTIVITIES

Our students have an active society, which arranges for lectures, social gatherings, etc.

II. ADMISSION TO COURSES

1. QUALIFICATIONS REQUIRED

Normally a student must come up with a mark B at 'A' Level in Spanish as a minimum requirement. He must also have at least a good mark (C) in 'O' Level Latin. Most candidates also have an 'A' Level mark in French. Faculty regulations require all applicants to Honours Schools to have two 'A' Level subjects with B, one of them being in the Special Subject chosen for Honours.

General students may be taken from the first-year beginners' course, to which are admitted only students with a good mark in Latin or French (preferably at 'A' Level). Several General students come with 'A' Level Spanish.

2. SELECTION OF STUDENTS

As indicated in II.1 candidates must have certain 'A' Level and other marks. Only those candidates who already possess 'A' Level marks (sometimes even those with only 'O' Level marks) are interviewed, and also those with adequate Latin qualifications.

Interviews take the form of discussion of career, reading in English, and enquiries about general interests. A test is also given in reading and translating Spanish. Special preference is sometimes given to candidates who put this University as their first choice, but only if other things are equal.

Teachers might keep in mind that it is desirable for pupils wishing to read Honours Spanish to keep up their Latin if they do not take it beyond 'O' Level. Further, general literary and other reading, in English and other languages, often allows a candidate to give a better impression at an interview and shows that he can place within a wider field his specialized Spanish reading.

3. TRANSFER

Students are now admitted directly to Honours, although all first-year students must satisfy certain Intermediate requirements, i.e. they have to sit a University examination at the end of their first year. This will, of course, include their Special Subject, Latin, probably French and another non-linguistic subject. Exemption in one of these (but not the Honours subject) may be granted at an 'A' Level mark of B. After the Intermediate an Honours student may be transferred to the General course if the results of his examination do not show that he can undertake a full Honours course.

4. NUMBERS

Up to a total of seven or eight students are admitted to the Special Honours School each year. The first-year Intermediate courses generally number about 50 to 60 and are divided between beginners and those with G.C.E. qualifications in Spanish. General courses are attended by an average of 15 to 20 undergraduates each year. These latter classes also include those reading Spanish as a Special Subject, usually for French Honours.

Information supplied by Professor F. W. Pierce

UNIVERSITY OF SOUTHAMPTON

Department of Spanish

I. COURSES OF STUDY

1. TYPES OF COURSES

Students are accepted for Honours degree courses only, and Spanish may be taken:

(*a*) as a *Single Honours* subject;

(*b*) as a *Combined Honours* subject;

(*c*) as a *Subsidiary* or *Ancillary* subject for students reading a Single Honours subject other than Spanish.

Under (*b*) Spanish can be combined with English, French, German, History, Latin and Music. There is also a Spanish with History and Portuguese option, which gives particular attention to Latin-American literature and history.

Under (*c*) Spanish language and literature can be studied as a Subsidiary or Ancillary subject to any other Arts Single Honours course and, in addition, to Economics and Social Science courses. Such Subsidiary and Ancillary courses are of five and three terms' duration respectively.

2. CHARACTERISTICS OF COURSES

The Combined Honours course with French is a four-year course and is divided into Part I and Part II, with a qualifying examination at the end of the first year. The Single Honours and other Combined Honours courses are of three or four years' duration, involving a qualifying examination after one year and an examination at the end of the final year. Departments also hold sessional examinations to test the progress of students.

The study of Spanish as the whole or part of an Honours course is chiefly concerned with the language (written and spoken) and its history, and with the literature of Spain and Spanish America. Importance is attached to proficiency in the spoken language. Lectures and classes are all conducted in Spanish from the second year onwards and the Spanish *lector* takes conversation groups for one hour a week throughout the course. A language laboratory will be in use from October 1964. Selected periods of Spanish literature are studied in the first two years and representative texts are set for detailed literary and linguistic analysis. In the final year, Special Subjects in Spanish or Spanish-American literature are selected for close study, and in Combined Honours courses one or more of these subjects must be related to the other discipline being studied. Thus

M.L.—I

when Spanish is being studied with French, German or English, a Special Subject in comparative literature has to be taken. In the Spanish and History combinations, a literary subject with historical implications, such as political or social themes in the novel or theatre at a given period in Spain or Latin America, is studied. In the Spanish and Music course, the work of selected Spanish composers is examined in detail, and a subject in Spanish literature related to Spanish music (the 19th-century folklore movement or the use of music in the 17th-century theatre, for example) is selected for special study. Students are encouraged to attend relevant History and Geography lectures even when these are not required by their course. Attendance at Faculty Lectures and at University Open Lectures (specially arranged and not necessarily on Arts subjects) is equally encouraged.

3. COMBINATION OF SUBJECTS

See I.1 and 2 above.

4. RESIDENCE ABROAD

The Combined Honours courses are mostly of three years' duration and a compulsory period of at least three months is spent normally at a Spanish university course. Students studying French and Spanish, however, who must take four years over the course, spend one year in France. Single Honours students may take either three or four years over the course. Three-year students must spend at least four months at a Spanish university, and those who are taking four years must study for a whole session in Spain.

5. METHODS OF STUDY

All students, whether Single Honours, Combined Honours or Subsidiary and Ancillary, have a weekly tutorial hour relating to the lectures they attend, and an hour of conversation with a resident Spaniard.

6. OTHER ACTIVITIES

There is a Spanish Society which arranges lectures and social activities for those interested in all aspects of Spanish and Latin-American culture. Those interested are also encouraged to attend the meetings of the Southampton Modern Language Society.

II. ADMISSION TO COURSES

1. QUALIFICATIONS REQUIRED

Apart from the normal University matriculation requirements, all courses involving Spanish listed in I.1 and I.2 above normally require a good Advanced Level pass in Spanish and one other subject, and at least an Ordinary Level pass in Latin. For a Combined Honours course a good Advanced Level pass in both subjects to be studied is normally necessary. It is not possible to start Spanish from scratch at the University.

2. SELECTION OF STUDENTS

Students are chosen on the basis of an interview and the information given by the candidate and his or her school on the Universities Central Council application form. Periods spent fruitfully abroad are always taken into account. Part of the interview is conducted in Spanish, and the other language or relevant skill for a Combined Honours course is tested. No written test is, however, required. It is also possible to gain entrance as a Scholar or Exhibitioner, with a special examination which candidates can sit in February each year.

3. TRANSFER

It is sometimes possible to transfer to a Single Honours course after one year of the Combined Honours course. It is also sometimes possible to transfer to Combined Honours from a Single Honours and Subsidiary or Ancillary course after one year.

4. NUMBERS

The numbers admitted each year may vary slightly according to the quality of applicants and the combinations involved. Not more than 10 students each year can usually be accepted for the various combinations.

Information supplied by Professor O. N. V. Glendinning

UNIVERSITY OF WALES:
UNIVERSITY COLLEGE, CARDIFF

Department of Hispanic Studies

I. COURSES OF STUDY

The Department of Hispanic Studies, comprising a Spanish and a Portuguese section, is one of the few in the United Kingdom at present offering an Honours course in Portuguese, which among European languages is now surpassed only by English, Spanish and Russian in number of speakers. Courses are provided in the literature, civilization and languages of Spain and Spanish America and of Portugal, Portuguese Africa and Brazil.

1. TYPES OF COURSES

(a) *Part One* (first year, in which three subjects are read): (1) Spanish, (2) Portuguese;

(b) *Honours* (second and third years): *either* (1) Hispanic Studies (i.e. Spanish and Portuguese) *or* (2) Portuguese and Brazilian Area Studies;

(c) *Pass degree* (second and third year, in which two Main subjects are read, with an Auxiliary subject taken in the second year only): *Main:* (1) Spanish *and/or* (2) Portuguese; *Auxiliary:* Latin-American Studies.

2. CHARACTERISTICS OF COURSES

The Part One and Main courses in Spanish and Portuguese, and the Hispanic Studies Honours course, deal with the literature, civilization and languages of the Iberian Peninsula (including, in the Honours course, Catalonia) and Latin America; the Honours course in Portuguese and Brazilian Area Studies and the Auxiliary course in Latin-American Studies are designed for those whose interests incline towards history and the social sciences as well as literature.

3. COMBINATION OF SUBJECTS

Faculty regulations require three Part One subjects to be read in the first year, before admission to an Honours School is considered; for prospective Honours candidates in Hispanic Studies these would preferably be Spanish, Portuguese and English; intending specialists in Portuguese and Brazilian Area Studies will find the most appropriate Part One subjects to be Portuguese, Spanish, and either History or Economics or English.

4. RESIDENCE ABROAD

All Honours candidates attend the summer course at the University of Coimbra and a reading course at the National Library in Lisbon during their first long vacation; Area Studies specialists then return to Cardiff, while those reading Hispanic Studies go on to a two-month Michaelmas term course at the University of Madrid. During their second long vacation the latter also attend a course at the Institut d'Estudis Catalans in Barcelona; candidates for the Area Studies degree go instead to either a Brazilian or a Portuguese-African university, according to their field of specialization, for a further period of study extending from the Easter vacation of their second year in College to the following Christmas. The time spent abroad does not increase the overall length of the course.

5. METHODS OF STUDY

Teaching is almost entirely by seminar discussion courses conducted in the appropriate language, and by tutorial supervisions. The 'practical' work consists of the writing of critical essays in Spanish, Portuguese and English, and of stylistic analyses; no translation is done. Conversation classes directed by native speakers supplement the courses in both Spanish and Portuguese.

6. OTHER ACTIVITIES

As the undergraduate and teaching members of the Department (and those graduates still in residence) tend more than is customary to regard themselves and each other as constituting a single community engaged in a common pursuit, informal and unorganized social and intellectual contacts are frequent (and often indistinguishable); there is also an active Hispanic Society in which both the junior and senior members of the Department participate.

II. ADMISSION TO COURSES

1. QUALIFICATIONS REQUIRED

To be admitted to the various courses the following qualifications are required:

Part One Spanish: 'A' Level Spanish (normally);[1]

Part One Portuguese: some knowledge of a Romance language or of Latin;

Honours Hispanic Studies: high average in Part One Spanish *and* Portuguese or distinction in Part One Spanish and completion of summer course at Coimbra;

Honours Portuguese and Brazilian Area Studies: high average in Part One Portuguese *and* Spanish; or distinction in Part One Portuguese;

---

[1] Special arrangements are made for candidates without previous knowledge of Spanish who have attained minimum 'A' Level grades of A and B in two other languages (which may include English or Latin).

Main Spanish and *Main Portuguese:* by College regulations, a pass in the corresponding Part One course admits to these courses; alternatively, those who have not read one or other subject in Part One may qualify for the corresponding Main course by passing specified vacation courses in the Peninsula, provided they are also pursuing the *other* Main course.

Auxiliary Latin-American Studies: unrestricted.

The ideal 'A' Level programme of a prospective entrant would be: (1) Spanish, (2) English and (3) a second Romance language or Latin (for Hispanic Studies), or History or Economics (for Portuguese and Brazilian Area Studies).

2. SELECTION OF STUDENTS

Admission to the College is granted by the Faculty of Arts, not the Department; once admitted, students apply to the Department for admission to specific courses. Those with 'A' Level Spanish marks below B, not counterbalanced by at least a B in another language (preferably English), are encouraged to opt for Part One Portuguese, where they will be on an equal footing with the rest of the class, rather than (or as well as) Part One Spanish.

3. TRANSFER

Admission to Honours courses does not take place until the end of the first year.

Transfer from the combined Main courses to Honours Hispanic Studies, and vice versa, is possible; but there is no provision for transfer between the Area Studies Honours course and Main Portuguese.

4. NUMBERS

Twelve to 15 students on the average are admitted annually to each Part One course, and 4 or 5 to the Honours School of Hispanic Studies; the new Portuguese and Brazilian Area Studies Honours course is expected to take a further 3 or 4.

Information supplied by Professor Stephen Reckert

UNIVERSITY OF ABERDEEN

Department of Spanish

I. COURSES OF STUDY

1. TYPES OF COURSES

Spanish can be studied in the following courses:

(*a*) *Ordinary*

(*b*) *Advanced*

(*c*) *Dual Honours* in Spanish, with Latin, French, German or Italian. There is no Single Honours course.

The Dual Honours course in Spanish lasts two years after Ordinary and Advanced, and the Senior and Junior Honours classes are taken together, in such a way that a cycle of (roughly) Middle Ages is studied one year, and Modern the next.

(*d*) There is an Elementary non-examinable course in Spanish for beginners, who can then go on to Ordinary in the following year.

2. CHARACTERISTICS OF COURSES

We stress close attention to actual works. 'Background' remains background. We study authors rather than periods, and works rather than authors. As the Department is small, with a staff of two lecturers, all Honours courses are dual. We therefore concentrate on main Castilian authors. We try to give equal treatment to medieval and modern periods, philology and literature, but there is a Golden Age bias. Unfortunately, no Portuguese or Catalan are taught here.

3. COMBINATION OF SUBJECTS

Students for the Ordinary M.A. take seven courses: five at Ordinary level, two at Advanced level (i.e. second year). At least one subject must be taken from each of the following divisions: (1) Logic and Metaphysics, Moral Philosophy; (2) English Literature; (3) Arabic, Celtic, French, German, Greek, Hebrew, Italian, Latin, Spanish, Swedish, Syriac; (4) Botany, Chemistry, Geology, Mathematics, Natural Philosophy, Zoology; (5) Civil (Roman) Law, Geography, History (British), History (Economic), History (Modern European), History (Scottish), International Relations, Political Economy, Political Theory, Psychology. For Dual Honours combinations see I.1 above.

Honours students take, in addition to their Dual Honours course, two outside subjects, which are normally studied in the first two years before entering upon the Honours course. Only *one* of these two courses need come from a non-linguistic division. Thus the outside subjects for a French-Spanish Honours course might be Latin and any subject from divisions 1, 2, 4, etc., above. The choice of these subjects is almost entirely left to the student, except that those students who are deficient in Latin are strongly advised to take the Ordinary course in Latin, while others are advised to take the Advanced course in Latin.

4. RESIDENCE ABROAD

It is normally required that a student taking a Dual Honours course in Modern Languages should spend a total of a year abroad in the countries where the languages of his course are spoken, dividing this period equally between each.

5. METHODS OF STUDY

Tutorials are held from the beginning with all intending Honours students in the Ordinary class and with all students in the Advanced course. Honours classes are all small and the stress is on reading and discussion. We cannot give choices of special subjects but we are able to allow for students' individual interests.

II. ADMISSION TO COURSES

1. QUALIFICATIONS REQUIRED

Students require for admission the Certificate of Attestation of Fitness (Scottish Universities).

The Ordinary course is normally taken by students who have taken Spanish up to at least 'O' Level at school.

Students are sometimes permitted to start from scratch if they have taken the non-graduating Elementary course (see I.1 above) or if their linguistic attainments are exceptional, e.g. if they have 'A' Level Latin or French. Such students are selected by interview by the Head of the Department.

2. SELECTION OF STUDENTS

All students enter upon the Ordinary degree course first. They are interviewed by Advisers of Studies, who contact heads of departments where necessary. (For intending Honours students see II.3 below.)

3. TRANSFER

Students intending to study Honours are noted in their first year, and they are advised to take Latin. In order to be admitted to the Honours course a student must have passed the examination concluding the Ordinary and Advanced class. The Head of the Department has no right to exclude from the Honours course any student who has taken only the Ordinary course, but he can, and does, exercise powers of dissuasion where he thinks fit, and so far all Honours students in Spanish have passed the Advanced first; but a student who has passed Advanced will not necessarily be advised to take Honours.

A student who wishes to switch during his Honours course (e.g. from French and Spanish to English and Spanish) will normally lose a year in the process. During his first two years he has plenty of choice.

4. NUMBERS

Our numbers are small. There is no limit, but so far up to 4 students have been annually admitted to the Honours courses.

Information supplied by Mr. T. E. May, Lecturer in Spanish

UNIVERSITY OF EDINBURGH

Department of Hispanic Studies

I. COURSES OF STUDY

1. TYPES OF COURSES

The following courses in Hispanic Studies are provided:

(*a*) *Elementary* class;

(*b*) Classes for the *Ordinary degree*;

(*c*) the *Honours* courses.

2. CHARACTERISTICS OF COURSES

The Ordinary degree courses cover Spanish language and the history and literature of Spain from 1500 to 1700 and from 1870 to the present day.

The Honours course in Modern Languages comprises the historical study of the Spanish language in its development from Vulgar Latin; the linguistic study of early texts; the historical and critical study of Spanish literature from the 11th century to the present day; the history of Spain from 1474.

The Honours course in Hispanic Studies comprises the above with the exclusion of Spanish medieval literature but with the addition of the development of the Spanish language in America, Portuguese language, Spanish-America and Brazilian literatures, and the history of Latin America.

3. COMBINATION OF SUBJECTS

For the Honours degree in Modern Languages Spanish can be taken either as a primary or as a secondary language. As a primary language it is combined with one of the following: English, Arabic, Celtic, French, German, Italian, Latin. This secondary language is taken to Intermediate Honours (second year) standard. As a secondary language Spanish, up to Intermediate Honours, is taken with one of the above languages (other than English). For the Honours degree course in Hispanic Studies the secondary language is replaced by Portuguese for which, however, there is no separate Intermediate Honours examination.

4. RESIDENCE ABROAD

For Final Honours, one year abroad—normally the third year in a four-year course—is required.

II. ADMISSION TO COURSES

1. QUALIFICATIONS REQUIRED

Entrance requirements: a pass in Spanish at 'A' Level G.C.E. or the Higher grade of the Scottish Certificate of Education or in the Scottish Universities Preliminary examination, Higher standard.

To proceed to Intermediate Honours, second year, a merit certificate in the First Ordinary course and a pass in Latin (Lower standard) is essential. All Final Honours students must have passed an Intermediate Honours examination in Spanish, and in their second language where applicable.

Spanish can be started at the University. The Elementary class prepares students for the Preliminary examination as a qualification for the Ordinary degree courses. An Honours student starting Spanish at the University will be required to take five years instead of four.

2. SELECTION OF STUDENTS

Students are admitted by the Dean of the Faculty of Arts without any reference to the departments concerned.

3. TRANSFER

Students are not selected for Honours courses on entrance. The decision whether a student will finally take an Honours or Ordinary degree is deferred until the beginning of the second or, in some cases, the third year of study.

5. NUMBERS

The First Ordinary class has up to 40 students, the Second Ordinary and Intermediate Honours from 10 to 20. The Final Honours class (i.e. those students taking Spanish as a primary language) does not usually exceed 5.

Information supplied by Professor A. A. Parker

UNIVERSITY OF GLASGOW
Department of Hispanic Studies

I. COURSES OF STUDY

1. TYPES OF COURSES

Spanish is taught in the following courses:

(*a*) *Ordinary* (or first-year Pass) class: language, literature, history of Spain (with due reference to Catalonia and Portugal) from the beginning to 1625, phonetics and prosody.

(*b*) *Higher Ordinary* (or second-year Pass) class: language, literature, history from 1625 to the present day, with the outlines of Latin-American history and literature.

(*c*) *Honours* course (junior and senior years), either A. Peninsular (Spanish and Portuguese) or B. Latin-American (Spanish-American and Brazilian) Studies, including—in each year in each—a special subject studied in seminar; or A. plus B. The Portuguese language is studied throughout both years. Catalan (outlines of languages, literature and history) may be taken as an optional extra course.

2. CHARACTERISTICS OF COURSES

Ordinary and Higher Ordinary years are planned to offer a comprehensive survey of the evolution of language, literature and history down the centuries which, while complete in itself, will lay a broad foundation for the more specialized studies of the Honours years.

The Higher Ordinary course has sufficient Latin-American content to guide the intending Honours student in his choice between A., B., and A. plus B. (Considerable stress is laid in A. on medieval philology and in B. on thought.) There is also in this year a qualifying class in Portuguese for students intending Honours.

Ordinary and Higher Ordinary students receive lecture courses on history, history of language, history of literature, plus *lecture expliquée*, and small conversation group meetings with a Spaniard.

Honours classes, consisting of some six to ten students, are, in effect, all tutorial or discussion groups. Native Catalan and Portuguese speakers are on the staff. The Language and Literature of the Moors in Spain is another Honours option with (as for Catalan) a three-hour paper in the final degree examination.

3. COMBINATION OF SUBJECTS

Hispanic Studies as a subject for an Ordinary (or Pass) degree is one of five subjects combined according to certain broad Faculty requirements and may be offered on the first-year level or on both first- and second-year levels. For Honours, A. and B. combine to form a group, *or* either may be combined with any one of French,

German, Italian, Russian, Arabic, History, taken to the same level over the same four years. In addition the Honours student must have taken two outside subjects, one to be chosen from among Logic, Moral Philosophy, English, Political Economy History (for A. plus B. from among Modern History, Political Economy, Politics, Geography); both are taken at the Ordinary level.

4. RESIDENCE ABROAD

There is no residential requirement for Ordinary degree students. Students admitted to Honours normally, if combining A. or B. with another language, spend their third session in Spain or the other country, returning to enter Junior Honours, and spend the third term of that year in the other country or Spain. They will commonly have travelled already in both countries during one or more long vacations. Students taking A. normally go to Madrid University, those taking B. to the School of Spanish-American Studies in Seville. Students combining A. with B. normally spend the session preceding Honours in Spain and the third term of the Junior Honours year in Portugal. Specific tasks for the Department are not set them while abroad; they may be working on the dissertation which, for A. or B. students, can be offered in lieu of one paper in the Final degree examination, but which for A. plus B. students is compulsory.

II. ADMISSION TO COURSES

1. QUALIFICATIONS REQUIRED

Admission to the Ordinary class requires a pass in Spanish at the Higher level in the Preliminary examination (or the Higher grade of the Scottish Certificate of Education) or its equivalent. A pass in Latin (or Greek) at the Ordinary (or Higher) grade is required for admission to the Higher Ordinary class (plus, of course, a pass in Hispanic Studies on the Ordinary class level).

Admission to Honours requires a pass in Hispanic Studies on the Higher Ordinary class level and in the qualifying examination in Portuguese, and the approval of the Professor.

Spanish cannot be started from scratch in this University.

2. SELECTION OF STUDENTS

All students admitted to the Faculty and qualified in terms of II.1 above are admissible to the Ordinary class and in due course to the Higher Ordinary class.

3. TRANSFER

Students are considered for admission to Honours at the end of the Higher Ordinary year (see II.1 above). A student in Honours may fall back on an Ordinary degree. The time factor—not regulations—would normally rule out transfer to another Honours group.

4. NUMBERS

Some 6 to 10 students on average are admitted annually to the Honours school. *Information supplied by Professor William C. Atkinson*

UNIVERSITY OF ST. ANDREWS

Department of Spanish

I. COURSES OF STUDY

1. TYPES OF COURSES

Spanish may be read:

(*a*) for an *Ordinary degree* (three years) in combination with other modern languages;

(*b*) for an *Honours degree* (four years) in combination with other modern languages.

Note.—It is hoped to institute shortly an Honours degree in Spanish Language and Literature. This would include papers in Catalan and Portuguese.

2. CHARACTERISTICS OF COURSES

The first year is a general introduction to Spanish literature. This is based securely on the study of very few typical texts. No attempt is made at an overall view or 'historical survey'. The course is restricted to the 16th and 17th centuries.

In the second year prose literature of the 15th to 17th centuries is studied and an introduction to the period since 1898 is given.

In the first, third and fourth years medieval, *Siglo de Oro*, and post-1898 literature is studied in selected texts. No attempt is made to deal with 18th and 19th centuries. Main emphasis is laid not on literary 'history' but on critical evaluation of the works. Texts are relatively few in number, but some attempt is made to study them in depth.

Philology is studied concurrently from the first year onwards, with emphasis on dialectology. Catalan is taught, and some knowledge of Portuguese is expected.

The main attraction of the Department is its smallness and high staff–student ratio, which means that students get individual tuition from the beginning. Lectures are not compulsory. Provision is made for many special interests, both in courses and examinations, e.g. Spanish art or music.

3. COMBINATION OF SUBJECTS

Spanish is studied in combination with one of German, French, English, Russian or Arabic. The combination of Spanish and Arabic is increasingly popular.

All Honours students must read Philosophy and History for

one year. Ordinary students must read Philosophy, but after that their choice is almost unlimited.

4. RESIDENCE ABROAD

Students *must* spend the third term of their third year abroad· Many go to Salamanca. Those reading Arabic often go to Beirut or Khartoum. (The residential rule applies to Honours students only.)

5. METHODS OF STUDY

All students are allotted to tutors within the Department, and all receive weekly tutorial instruction, singly or in groups of two. Weekly essays are written.

6. OTHER ACTIVITIES

A choir studies Spanish Renaissance music and makes regular concert tours of Britain and Western Europe in alternate years.

II. ADMISSION TO COURSES

1. QUALIFICATIONS REQUIRED

Students can enter the Department only if they have a pass in Spanish at 'A' Level G.C.E. or at the Higher grade (Scottish Certificate). Without these qualifications they must attend the *Junior Class* for one year. In the case of the latter who wish to read for an Honours degree this need not lead to the lengthening of their course.

Students must have Higher or Advanced passes in Latin, or two modern foreign languages. These rules apply to all students. About 50 per cent of Spanish students start from scratch.

2. SELECTION OF STUDENTS

'A' Level results, or in exceptional cases, an internal departmental test of the same standard, are used for selection. Interviews have, unfortunately, been found impracticable.

3. TRANSFER

All students take the first-year course. They are then recommended for, or discouraged from, embarking on an Honours course. Transfer 'upwards' is possible but difficult after the beginning of the second year. Transfer from Honours to an Ordinary course is easy.

4. NUMBERS

Between 10 and 14 students are admitted annually to the Honours course.

Information supplied by Mr. L. J. Woodward, Senior Lecturer in Spanish

THE QUEEN'S UNIVERSITY
OF BELFAST

Department of Spanish

I. COURSES OF STUDY

1. TYPES OF COURSES

Spanish may be studied:

(*a*) as an *elementary course* for beginners;

(*b*) as a subject for the *First Examination in Arts*;

(*c*) for the *General B.A. degree*;

(*d*) as a *Subsidiary Honours* subject for the B.A. degree;

(*e*) as a *Joint Honours* subject for the B.A. degree;

(*f*) as a *Single Honours* subject for the B.A. degree.

2. CHARACTERISTICS OF COURSES

Work for the *First Examination in Arts* occupies one year and includes classes in the written and spoken language and a course on Spanish history and civilization. All students study two modern texts in detail. Intending Honours students take a further text of the 16th–17th centuries.

General degree. This is a two-year course, taken after the First Arts Examination, and includes classes in written and spoken Spanish, detailed study of six texts chosen from the period 1500 to the present day, a course in Descriptive Grammar and another in History of the Language.

The *Subsidiary* course corresponds to the first year of the General degree course. Three 16th–17th-century works are studied in detail. Students take the course in Descriptive Grammar, but not that in History of the Language.

Joint Honours students must take four basic papers in each language which they offer at their Final Examination. In Spanish these are:

(*i*) Translation from and into Spanish;

(*ii*) History of the Language;

(*iii*) Medieval Literature and History;

(*iv*) Literature and History from 1500 to the present day.

They also take two optional papers, either or both of which may be chosen from the list of options available in Spanish. This list always includes Catalan and Portuguese literature; the other optional subjects are varied in order to coincide as far as possible with the particular interests of students.

Single Honours students must take the four basic papers in Spanish. They also have to take: two optional papers; an essay paper in Spanish; an additional paper on Renaissance and modern literature; papers in either Catalan *or* Portuguese language and literature. Catalan and Portuguese for Single Honours are two-year courses; all optional courses take one year. All Honours courses occupy three years.

3. COMBINATION OF SUBJECTS

First Arts and *General degree* Spanish are taken in combination with two other Arts subjects.

Subsidiary Spanish is taken by students in other Honours Schools.

Joint Honours Spanish is taken in combination with French or German.

4. RESIDENCE ABROAD

Single Honours students in their second Honours year are required to spend a minimum of three months studying at a Spanish university.

Honours students who wish to spend a year in teaching and/or studying at a Spanish university are encouraged to do so. This is normally done between the first and second Honours years.

II. ADMISSION TO COURSES

1. QUALIFICATIONS REQUIRED

Students can enter the Department with 'A' Level passes in G.C.E. Spanish *or* French. About half our students begin Spanish at the University and are allowed to take the Elementary and First Arts courses concurrently.

All Honours candidates must have passed 'O' Level Latin and must take or have taken a one-year course in Medieval French.

2 and 3. SELECTION OF STUDENTS AND TRANSFER

Selection of students is entrusted to the Faculty's Advisers of Studies, who interview and recommend students to heads of departments. Admission to Honours courses depends on candidates' performance in the First Arts Examination. It is quite possible for a beginner to proceed to Honours, provided he has reached a sufficiently high standard by the end of his first year in the University.

4. NUMBERS

At present the number of students in a normal Honours year varies between 6 and 10, but no upper limit is fixed.

Information supplied by Professor Arthur Terry

RUSSIAN STUDIES

UNIVERSITY OF BIRMINGHAM

Department of Russian Language and Literature

I. COURSES OF STUDY

1. TYPES OF COURSES

Russian may be studied in the following courses:

(a) *Special Honours degree course:* Russian as principal subject studied for three years by students with 'A' Level Russian and for four years by students with no knowledge of Russian. Students also study a Subsidiary subject for two years.

(b) *Combined Honours degree:* Russian taken as one of two main subjects by candidates beginning the study of Russian. Both subjects will be taken to equal level. The fourth year will be devoted entirely to the study of Russian.

(c) *Russian as a Subsidiary subject* can be studied for two years.

(d) Special courses are provided for both undergraduate and post-graduate scientists.

(e) A one-year course leading to the degree of M.A. by examination is now available.

2. CHARACTERISTICS OF COURSES

The Special Honours course covers the modern Russian language, 18th-, 19th- and 20th-century literature, Russian history, Soviet history and institutions and the history of the language. Options include Russian social and political thought, medieval history, Old Russian, Old Church Slavonic and Serbian. In the preparatory year intensive work is done on the modern language exclusively. Comparatively little time is devoted to philology in the Special Honours course, and still less in the Combined Honours course. All first-year Honours students are required to attend a week's residential course in the Easter vacation with the members of staff of the Department. Activities include informal tuition, discussion groups on contemporary Russian topics, poetry and play-reading, Russian conversation, and a visit to the Shakespeare theatre at Stratford.

3. COMBINATION OF SUBJECTS

No compulsory combinations are demanded. In theory any Arts combination is possible but in practice students choose mainly a language (French or German), English or History.

4. RESIDENCE ABROAD

Residence in a Russian-speaking environment is required. In practice this normally means that second-year Honours students are obliged during the summer vacation of their second year (a) to attend a month's intensive Russian language course whether in England, France, Germany, Austria or elsewhere, and (*b*) to visit the Soviet Union for three weeks, usually with a student delegation. It is impossible yet for students to attend formal courses in the Soviet Union.

5. METHODS OF STUDY

Formal lectures are kept to a minimum. Most of the teaching is done on an informal tutorial basis, which up to now has been easy to organize because of relatively small numbers. A language laboratory is in use.

6. OTHER ACTIVITIES

There is a Russian Club which meets fortnightly, and also a Russian choir.

II. ADMISSION TO COURSES

1. QUALIFICATIONS REQUIRED

Three 'A' Level passes are required. No Latin requirement is laid down. Russian can be started from scratch (see I.1 above).

2. SELECTION OF STUDENTS

There is no entrance examination or test. Selection is based on 'A' Level marks, plus interview and school report. Almost all candidates are interviewed except obvious rejects or people whose marks are so good that an unconditional acceptance can be given immediately.

I personally attach importance to general spread rather than high marks in any one subject (Russian or otherwise). I would rather have three C's than one B and two D's.

General reading outside one's subject I rate higher than intensive reading in it. I am not keen on people who, after getting three poor passes, concentrate on two subjects only to improve their marks.

3. TRANSFER

Admission to the Honours course is on entrance, except that students who start from scratch do a year as Preparatory Honours students. We have no General courses here. All courses are either Special Honours or Combined Honours. Transfer from one to the other is possible but rare.

4. NUMBERS

The number admitted to the Special Honours course in Russian varies from 10 to 15 annually. The number admitted to Combined Honours varies from 5 to 12. Recent numbers (1963) were: Postgraduates, 5; Special Honours, 34; Combined Honours, 26; Subsidiary, 29; Science Faculty students, 60.

Information supplied by Professor R. F. Christian

UNIVERSITY OF BRISTOL

Russian Courses
(attached to the Department of English)

I. COURSES OF STUDY

1. TYPES OF COURSES

Russian may be studied:

(*a*) as one of the subjects in the three-year *General Honours* course;

(*b*) as a two-year *Subsidiary subject* to another modern language;

(*c*) as a one-year *Additional subject* to English.

2. CHARACTERISTICS OF COURSES

The course for the first part of the curriculum for the General degree of B.A. and first-year Subsidiary students consists of:

(1) Grammar; translation from and into Russian and free composition;

(2) the study of Russian texts;

(3) an outline in Russian civilization.

In the second and final years three courses are taken leading to three papers in the final examination. One course is devoted to the study of Russian texts from 1800 to the present day, one augments the outline course in Russian civilization and centres on five major novels read in English, and there is a course in grammar, translation and composition. An oral examination is held.

4. RESIDENCE ABROAD

Before presenting himself for his final examinations a student will be required to have spent one month (in the case of a General degree student) or not less than three weeks (in the case of a student who offers Russian as a Subsidiary subject) in a Russian environment approved by the Head of the Department.

II. ADMISSION TO COURSES

1. QUALIFICATIONS REQUIRED

Permission to take any of these courses is not normally granted to any student who has not first reached 'O' Level standard in Russian.

Information supplied by Mr. R. A. Peace, Lecturer in Russian

UNIVERSITY OF DURHAM

Russian Courses
(Department of German and Russian)

I. COURSES OF STUDY

1. TYPES OF COURSES

Russian may be studied:

(*a*) as a subject for the B.A. *General* degree;

(*b*) as a *Subsidiary* subject to Honours in some other subject.

Honours courses in Russian were started in October 1964.

2. CHARACTERISTICS OF COURSES

The first year of the B.A. General course is devoted almost exclusively to language study and at present may be taken by beginners. In the second and third years the course includes, besides linguistic work, the study of Russian literature and history of the 19th and 20th centuries.

Students reading Russian as a Subsidiary subject normally take two years of the General degree course.

3. COMBINATION OF SUBJECTS

Almost any combination of subjects is possible within the framework of the General degree.

4. RESIDENCE ABROAD

There is no residential requirement.

5. METHODS OF STUDY

In addition to lectures and language classes students are given as many tutorials as time will allow.

II. ADMISSION TO COURSES

1. QUALIFICATIONS REQUIRED

It is possible to accept beginners at the present time.

2. SELECTION OF STUDENTS

Students are selected for the General course by the individual colleges and for Honours courses in other subjects by the colleges and departments concerned: students wishing to take Russian as a General or Subsidiary subject are interviewed at the beginning of the academic year by the Russian teaching staff.

Information supplied by Mr. W. Harrison, Lecturer in Russian

UNIVERSITY OF ESSEX

School of Comparative Studies
(Departments of Government and Literature)
Schemes of Study with Russian

I. COURSES OF STUDY

1. TYPES OF COURSES

Russian can be studied in connection with the following schemes of study:

(*i*) *Government*
(*ii*) *Literature*

However, Russian is not studied as a discipline in itself, but is considered rather as being complementary to the study and understanding of other disciplines.

Both schemes are of three years' duration and lead to the award of the B.A. degree with Honours. Students who do not already have a good knowledge of Russian will be required to spend an additional year following an intensive course of language study at the University Language Centre. Previous knowledge of Russian is not essential for entry to the Centre.

(*i*) *Government*. The scheme will be based on the comparative study of Russian and British political institutions. It will include a general study of government in the world today with special emphasis on the action of social and economic forces in the structure of institutions, as well as in the conduct of politics. The scheme will also include a course on the history of political thought in Western Europe.

(*ii*) *Literature*. The scheme of study in Literature will include courses in modern history and in the development and structure of political and social institutions in Western Europe.

Emphasis will be placed on the literature of the last three centuries. Though literary study will be conducted with strict attention to chronology and in combination with political and social history, as much attention will be paid to critical elucidation and evaluation of specific works of literature as to literary history.

2. CHARACTERISTICS OF COURSES

In the first year, all students in the School will follow a common closely integrated group of courses. Students will not be required to decide upon their particular scheme of study until the end of the first year.

3. COMBINATION OF SUBJECTS

After the common first year, students will be required to follow either one or the other of the specialist schemes of study. There will be no ancillary or subsidiary subjects.

4. RESIDENCE ABROAD

Residence abroad will be encouraged.

II. ADMISSION TO COURSES

1. QUALIFICATIONS REQUIRED

Apart from the general entrance requirements of the University, applicants for admission to the School of Comparative Studies are required to have passed two subjects at Advanced Level. Applicants whose area of specialization is the Soviet Union would normally be expected to have passed a language other than English at Advanced Level. This need not necessarily be Russian, though in this case, a preliminary year of intensive language study at the University Language Centre would be necessary.

2. SELECTION OF STUDENTS

Selection is made on the basis of an applicant's performance both at Ordinary Level and Advanced Level, and careful attention is paid to reports obtained from the headmaster or headmistress. In most cases, applicants are invited to attend an informal interview with the professor of the Department.

3. TRANSFER

Special attention will, at all stages, be paid to the problems of students who wish to transfer from one scheme of study to another, although, in the case of transfer between two unlike subjects, a student's total period of study at the University may be extended beyond the normal three years.

Information supplied by the Registrar, University of Essex

UNIVERSITY OF EXETER

Russian Courses
(under the Department of German)

I. COURSES OF STUDY

1. TYPES OF COURSES

(*a*) *Combined Honours:* a three-year course, in which Russian is combined as an equal subject of study with either French or German.

(*b*) *General:* Russian is one of the subjects which may be taken for three years in a three-subject course leading to the General degree in Arts.

(*c*) *Additional* subject: a two-year course with either French Honours or German Honours.

Note.—Single Honours courses in Russian are planned for the near future.

2. CHARACTERISTICS OF COURSES

All courses in Russian aim chiefly at equipping the student with a sound practical knowledge of written and spoken Russian and at providing him with a broad view of Russian civilization and literature, especially since 1800.

3. COMBINATION OF SUBJECTS

See I.1 above.

4. RESIDENCE ABROAD

At present there is no residential requirement, but Combined Honours students will be encouraged to spend some time during a vacation with a Russian-speaking family.

5. METHODS OF STUDY

There are some general lectures, but the bulk of the teaching is conducted in small groups. There is weekly oral practice with a native Russian speaker.

II. ADMISSION TO COURSES

1. QUALIFICATIONS REQUIRED

For Combined Honours a good 'A' Level pass in Russian is necessary unless other qualifications are exceptionally good. For General or Additional subject courses a good 'O' Level pass is desirable.

2. SELECTION OF STUDENTS

Students are selected largely on the basis of G.C.E. results and reports from the applicants' schools. The majority of applicants for Combined Honours in Russian may expect to be invited for interview.

3. TRANSFER

Students are admitted to Combined Honours courses on entrance, but transfer is possible.

4. NUMBERS

At present numbers are small and no upper limit has been laid down.

Information supplied by Mr. D. J. Richards, Lecturer in Russian

UNIVERSITY OF HULL
Department of Russian Studies

I. COURSES OF STUDY

1. TYPES OF COURSES

Russian can be taken as from 1963 in courses leading
(a) to the *Ancillary* level (three terms), or
(b) to the *Subsidiary* level (five terms).

As from 1965 Russian will be taken up to Joint Honours degree level.

2. CHARACTERISTICS OF COURSES

In both Ancillary and Subsidiary courses the emphasis is on the study of the modern Russian language, but the Subsidiary course includes an introduction to Russian literature and a number of works are read in the original.

3. COMBINATION OF COURSES

Russian can be combined with a great number of subjects, but it is most usefully taken as part of a degree whose principal subjects are an ancient or modern language, Economics, History or Political Studies. The Ancillary course can also be taken by students reading for the degree of B.Sc.

4. RESIDENCE ABROAD

Unless exempted by the Head of the Department, students reading Subsidiary Russian are required to attend a Russian vacation course in this country or abroad (when possible, in the Soviet Union). Under certain circumstances a study tour to the Soviet Union may be substituted.

II. ADMISSION TO COURSES

Russian may in certain conditions be started at the University. Normally applicants for the Ancillary and Subsidiary courses will be expected to have passed in Russian at 'O' Level of the G.C.E., but consideration is given to those who have no qualifications in Russian, but have passed at 'O' Level in at least one foreign language, preferably Greek, Latin or German.

Information supplied by Mr. P. Henry, Lecturer in Russian

UNIVERSITY OF KEELE
Department of Modern Languages

RUSSIAN COURSE

At present Russian is available only in a one-year Subsidiary course for students reading Honours in other subjects.

As in Subsidiary German emphasis is laid on *reading* knowledge, some introduction to representative literature (in translation) and history of institutions.

This is a course for starters from scratch and there are no requirements for admission. Some Foundation Year students take introductory tutorials.

Honours Russian may begin by about 1965–66 if there are sufficient students with 'A' Level qualifications or who can be 'nursed' by intensive tuition.[1]

Information supplied by Professor K. Brooke

[1] For further information on language courses in the University of Keele, see Department of Modern Languages, French (p. 31) or German (p. 135) above.

UNIVERSITY OF LEEDS

Department of Russian Language and Literature

I. COURSES OF STUDY

1. TYPES OF COURSES

Russian can be studied to the following levels:

(*a*) *Special Honours*;

(*b*) *Joint Honours* (with another Modern Language);

(*c*) *General Honours* (Russian as one of three subjects).

2. CHARACTERISTICS OF COURSES

The *Special Honours* course includes:

(1) Study of the language (three papers);

(2) Literature, comprising three literary papers, including one on Tolstoy and Dostoevsky;

(3) The period of history 1856–1905 (one paper);

(4) Students choose two out of the following (one paper each):

(*i*) History 1905–1941;

(*ii*) History of the language;

(*iii*) Medieval Russian literature;

(*iv*) Russian Radical Thought.

We concentrate very much on the 19th and 20th centuries.

Joint Honours students do (1) and (2).

3. COMBINATION OF SUBJECTS

Russian as an Honours subject is normally studied with another modern language as a Subsidiary subject; but any subject within the Faculty of Arts may be taken.

4. RESIDENCE ABROAD

For political reasons there is no compulsory residence demanded.

5. METHODS OF STUDY

All teaching is by tutorial.

II. ADMISSION TO COURSES

1. QUALIFICATIONS REQUIRED

Honours or Joint Honours students with no previous knowledge of Russian are expected to have at least grade B in two 'A' Level subjects. Considerable importance is attached to good marks in Latin or Greek but there is no Latin requirement. Such students follow a four-year course.

Students who have Russian at 'A' Level are expected to have attained a mark of at least B in Russian and B in one other subject. Such students follow a three-year course.

2. SELECTION OF STUDENTS

Selection is based on 'A' Level results (see II.1 above) and interviews. All candidates are interviewed. In the interviews which last half to three-quarters of an hour, an attempt is made to assess general culture and intelligence as distinct from examination results.

Considerable importance is attached to head teachers' reports, especially from those who are known to us.

3. TRANSFER

Students are admitted to Special or Joint Honours courses on entrance.

It is possible to transfer from General to Special courses, if a student shows exceptional promise.

4. NUMBERS

Between 15 and 20 students are annually admitted to take the Special and Joint courses and about the same number to the General course.

Information supplied by Mr. F. M. Borras, Head of the Department of Russian

UNIVERSITY OF LIVERPOOL

Department of Russian

I. COURSES OF STUDY

1. TYPES OF COURSES

Russian can be taken in the following courses:

(a) *B.A. in General Studies* (with or without Honours);

(b) *B.A. Honours School of Russian*;

(c) *B.A. in Joint Honours.*

2. CHARACTERISTICS OF COURSES

All types of courses comprise:

(*i*) Modern Russian throughout the whole period of study. The language courses include, in addition to the normal exercises, phonetics and practical language work; also tape recordings of students' speech and the audio/visual method. A language laboratory is to be installed in the new Modern Languages building now under construction.

(*ii*) Literature: for those in General Studies 19th century with prescribed authors. For those in the Honours School three periods are studied: the early (up to 1800), 19th century, 20th century. Major writers in each period are dealt with in detail.

(*iii*) An outline of Russian history, with emphasis on the 19th century.

For *B.A. in General Studies*, an approved combination of three subjects, at least one of them studied throughout the course.

For the Honours School:

(*i*) In the preliminary year, an introductory course on comparative philology. Another subject which is normally an ancient or modern language and literature.

(*ii*) Outlines of historical grammar.

(*iii*) Options in the final year: a special paper on either Social Thought, Special Authors, Institutions, Philology, Old Slavonic, or, for approved students, a dissertation.

Joint Honours is a four-year course, both subjects being studied throughout that period (i.e. Russian and German, or French, or History, etc.) After the Preliminary Examination one of these is studied as the main subject.

3. COMBINATION OF SUBJECTS

See I.2 above.

4. RESIDENCE ABROAD

All students are required to attend an approved course, either in the U.S.S.R. or in another Slavonic country, or in a Western country where well-established Russian courses exist. Only in special cases would a student be granted exemption from this requirement. For those reading Joint Honours residence abroad is to be determined by the respective Heads of Departments.

5. METHODS OF STUDY

In addition to lectures and language classes much of the teaching is done in seminars and tutorials.

6. OTHER ACTIVITIES

Play readings, poetry readings, films and film strips, singing Russian songs, and talks, often given by the students themselves, under the auspices of the University Russian Society.

II. ADMISSION TO COURSES

1. QUALIFICATIONS REQUIRED

The matriculation requirements and Latin at 'O' Level.

Russian may be started from scratch; this involves a four-year course. In the first year a beginner studies Russian intensively and takes one more subject on the level of a first-year General course. If the results are satisfactory, he is allowed to enter the Preliminary course for the Honours Russian School or for Joint Honours.

2. SELECTION OF STUDENTS

As for other modern languages there is no written entrance examination. Selection to the Department of Russian is based mainly on references from schools, on interview, a good general aggregate of marks in the G.C.E. and, for the Honours School, Russian at 'A' Level. For those with no knowledge of Russian, see II.1; for transfer see II.3.

3. TRANSFER

Students may be transferred to Russian Honours:

(*i*) from a General B.A. course;

(*ii*) after one year on another Special Studies course, if they have done a Russian first-year course such as B.A. General or the equivalent (see I.2 above).

(*iii*) after the Preliminary examination for Joint Honours (or else he may enter the Honours School of his other subject).

Information supplied by Professor Nadejda Gorodetzky

UNIVERSITY OF LONDON
School of Slavonic
and East European Studies

I. COURSES OF STUDY

1. TYPES OF COURSES

(*i*) Russian is studied at this School:

(*a*) for an *Honours degree in Russian Language and Literature* or in *Russian Regional Studies*;

(*b*) as one of the subjects taken for a *General degree*;

(*c*) as a *Subsidiary subject*, by a student reading for an Honours degree in another subject.

(*ii*) Other Slavonic or East European languages are studied:

(*a*) for an *Honours degree* in *Czech and Slovak Language and Literature*, in *Hungarian Language and Literature*, in *Polish Language and Literature*, in *Rumanian Language and Literature*, in *Serbo-Croat Language and Literature*; in *Central European Regional Studies* (for which the student must read Czech or Hungarian or Polish or Slovak) and in *South East European Regional Studies* (for which the student must read Bulgarian or Hungarian or Rumanian or Serbo-Croat or Slovene);

(*b*) as one of the subjects taken for a *General degree*: Bulgarian, Czech and Slovak, Hungarian, Polish, Rumanian, Serbo-Croat;

(*c*) as a *Subsidiary subject*: Bulgarian, Czech and Slovak, Hungarian, Polish, Rumanian, Serbo-Croat;

(*d*) as a *required language*, by students of History Branch VI.

2. CHARACTERISTICS OF COURSES

Students who read for *Honours in Russian Language and Literature* must also read a Subsidiary subject, in which they are normally examined at the end of their second year. The final examination, which is taken at the end of the third year, consists of eight papers: translation, composition, essay in Russian, the history of the Russian language, two papers on the history of Russian literature and two papers on a Special Subject. The Special Subject is either the work of a Russian author, chosen from a list of authors, or Comparative Slavonic Philology. There is also an oral examination.

Students who read for *Honours in Russian Regional Studies* do not read a Subsidiary subject. The final examination, taken at the end of the third year, consists of ten papers: translation, composition, and the history of Russian literature from A.D. 1800; two papers on European history, three on the history of Russia, one on the history of political ideas and two on a special subject in Russian history. There is an oral examination.

Students who read Russian as a subject for a *General degree* take the examination at the end of the third year. It consists of three papers: one in translation and composition or essay; and two chosen from the history of the Russian language; the history of Russian literature since A.D. 1800; the history of Russia to A.D. 1725; the history of Russia from A.D. 1725 to A.D. 1941. There is an oral examination.

Students who read Russian as a *Subsidiary subject* normally take the examination at the end of their second year. It consists of two papers: one in translation and composition or essay; the second is chosen from those four papers from which the student for the General degree must choose two. There is an oral examination.

Examinations in *the Language and Literature of other Slavonic or East European languages*, in *Central European Regional Studies*, and in *South East European Regional Studies*, or in these languages for a *General degree* or as a *Subsidiary subject*, are formed on the same pattern as the corresponding examinations in Russian.

3. COMBINATION OF SUBJECTS

Those who read for Honours in Language and Literature must offer a Subsidiary subject chosen from the subjects which may be offered for a General degree.

4. RESIDENCE ABROAD

Students are not required to reside abroad as part of the course, though many of them travel to, or attend vacation courses in, the countries of Eastern Europe.

II. ADMISSION TO COURSES

1. QUALIFICATIONS REQUIRED

All students must meet the entrance requirements for admission to the Faculty of Arts. Students who are to read Russian must have passed in Russian at 'A' Level in the G.C.E. examination; students who are to read any of the other languages taught at the School must either have passed in the language at 'A' Level in the G.C.E. examination, or must be prepared to spend a preliminary year at the School before they begin the three-year course for a degree.

2. SELECTION OF STUDENTS

Candidates apply for admission through the Universities Central Council on Admissions. Those who live in this country are required to attend an interview.

3. TRANSFER

No transfer is possible.

4. NUMBERS

About 50 students are admitted each year to the various courses.

Information supplied by Mr. R. G. H. Whitworth, Secretary/Registrar, School of
Slavonic and East European Studies

UNIVERSITY OF MANCHESTER
Department of Russian Studies

I. COURSES OF STUDY

1. TYPES OF COURSES

The following courses may be taken in Russian:

(*a*) The *Honours course in Russian* lasts three years. Since, however, most students of Russian start the language at the University, the Honours course is in most cases preceded by a one-year course ('Intermediate'), which provides a first introduction to the language. Thus students taking Russian Honours, unless they have achieved 'A' Level G.C.E. in Russian before coming up, must spend four years at the University.

The Honours Russian course is divided into Part I (taken at the end of the second year of the Honours course) and Part II (taken at the end of the third). The Part I examination comprises six papers: two on set books (of which there are normally six), one on translation into Russian, one on unseen translation from Russian, one on Russian literature and one on Russian history. The lectures on which these last-named papers are set cover in outline respectively modern Russian literature from the middle of the 18th century and the salient features of Russian history from Rurik to 1917. The Part I examination does not call for any knowledge of Old Russian or Old Church Slavonic, but students are required in their second Honours year to attend an outline course of Old Church Slavonic grammar to prepare them for their work on the history of the Russian language in Part II.

The Part II examination comprises seven papers: translations into Russian, translation from Russian, Russian essay, the Russian novel, history of Russian language, the Soviet Union since 1917 and *either* Soviet Russian literature *or* comparative Slavonic philology *or* Russian history from 1762 to 1917.

(*b*) Some students prefer to take the *Honours Modern Languages* course in preference to Honours Russian as a single subject. This is in any case a four-year course. Usually the student starts on the other language (French or German, more rarely Spanish or Italian) and does his Intermediate (beginners') Russian simultaneously with his first year of Honours French (or whatever the other language may be). In his second year he takes second-year Honours French and first-year Honours Russian. He finishes with his other language by the end of his third year and has only Russian in his fourth year. For most students, therefore, Honours Modern Languages does not take more time than Honours Russian.

The course in Honours Modern Languages is the same as the separate courses in the two languages, except that (*i*) the student is entitled to drop one of the papers in Part II of both languages, (*ii*) he does not take the Part I examination in his second language (in the vast majority of cases, where Russian is taken it is as second language).

The market value of the Honours Modern Languages degree is greater than that of the degree in Russian Honours as a single subject.

(*c*) Russian may be taken as one of the subjects in the *General* (alias Ordinary) *degree*. The first year of the course is known as Intermediate and is also taken by most students intending to proceed to Russian Honours (see above). The second year course is known as General and the third as Special. The purpose of the course is to give students a good knowledge of the contemporary language.

2. CHARACTERISTICS OF COURSES

The principal stress throughout the Honours course is laid on the *modern* language. There is no medieval bias. Another feature of the course is that Russian (including Soviet) history is treated as an essential subject and is built into the course at the level both of Part I and of Part II.

3. COMBINATION OF SUBJECTS

Students who have not attained category B in Greek or Latin at 'A' Level G.C.E. are obliged to pass the Intermediate examination in Greek or Latin. They must also take another subject at Intermediate level and this can be practically any subject in the Faculty of Arts.

Students are also obliged to take one subject to General (second year of General degree course) level. They usually take one of the two subjects in which they passed Intermediate the year before.

4. RESIDENCE ABROAD

No rules concerning residence abroad are in operation.

5. METHODS OF STUDY

Because of the favourable staff-student ratio, it has been found possible to employ something like the tutorial system, particularly in the final year. Students' proses and essays are gone over individually with each student; the history and literature classes are small enough to make discussion between teacher and student possible.

II. ADMISSION TO COURSES

1. QUALIFICATIONS REQUIRED

Apart from the general requirements of candidates for admission to the Faculty of Arts, candidates for admission to the Russian

Honours course, whether as a separate subject or as part of Honours Modern Languages, are expected to have attained category B in any two Arts subjects (other than Art and Music) at 'A' Level G.C.E. This requirement is not rigid but will serve as an indication of the standard of attainment expected (see also II.3 below).

2. SELECTION OF STUDENTS

Selection is on the basis of 'A' Level results, supplemented by Intermediate results (since the student has in most cases been in the University for a year before he starts Honours Russian).

3. TRANSFER

Students who have done Russian G.C.E. 'A' Level may be admitted at once to the Honours course. Those who have not are sorted out at the end of the Intermediate course. Transfer is possible but becomes increasingly difficult the longer the student has been at the University.

4. NUMBERS

Over the five years 1958–62 the number of admissions to the Honours School (including both Russian Honours and Honours Modern Languages with Russian) has averaged 9.

Information supplied by the late Professor D. P. Costello

UNIVERSITY OF NOTTINGHAM

Department of Slavonic Studies

I. COURSES OF STUDY

1. TYPES OF COURSES

Russian can be studied:

(*a*) as an *Honours* course;

(*b*) in a *Joint Honours* course with *either* French *or* Spanish *or* German;

(*c*) as a *Subsidiary* subject.

2. CHARACTERISTICS OF COURSES

The *Honours* course is divided into Part I (first and second years) and Part II (third year).

Part I (with examination at the end of the second year) comprises an oral examination and five papers:

A. (*i*) Translation into Russian;

    (*ii*) Translation from Russian;

    (*iii*) Outlines of Russian literature from Peter the Great to the present day;

B. (*i*) Russian life and thought 1725 to 1881;

    (*ii*) History of the Russian language and outlines of pre-Petrine literature, together with a Subsidiary subject (see I.3 below);

Part II consists of an oral examination and six papers:

    (*i*) English essay *or* Practical criticism;

    (*ii*) Advanced Russian prose *or* Russian essay;

    (*iii*) Serbo-Croat: translation from and into English;

    (*iv*) Soviet history and politics;

    (*v*), (*vi*) Two of the following: (*a*) Pushkin and Lermontov; (*b*) poetry after 1841; (*c*) the 19th-century novel; (*d*) the 19th-century theatre; (*e*) selected 19th-century thinkers; (*f*) the Soviet novel.

By arrangement with the Head of the Department a dissertation may be substituted for papers (*i*) and either (*v*) or (*vi*).

The *Joint Honours* course comprises for Part I an oral examination in each of the two languages, three papers in the second language and three in Russian:

    (*i*) Translation from and into Russian;

    (*ii*) Outlines of literature from Peter the Great to the present day;

    (*iii*) Russian life and thought 1725–1881.

Part II consists of a *viva voce* examination in each of the two languages, four papers in the second language and four in Russian:

(*i*) Essay in English *or* Practical criticism;

(*ii*) Advanced Russian prose *or* Russian essay;

(*iii*) (*iv*) Any two of the subjects listed in the single Honours course under (*iv*), (*v*) and (*vi*).

Russian as a Subsidiary course. Students reading for an Honours degree in other departments may take Russian as their Subsidiary subject in Part I, provided they already have an adequate knowledge of the language. This involves taking papers A (*i*), A (*ii*) and A (*iii*).

3. COMBINATION OF SUBJECTS

Part I Russian is combined with one of the following: English, an ancient or modern foreign language, History, Philosophy, Biblical Studies, American Studies.

Other combinations, i.e. cross-faculty, e.g. Psychology and Geography, are possible, but tend to create serious time-table difficulties. No other regular combinations are in operation.

4. RESIDENCE ABROAD

Students are required to spend four weeks of the sixth term in an approved Russian milieu abroad. For Joint Honours the four weeks abroad will be spent in the long vacation.

5. METHODS OF STUDY

The tutorial system (weekly tutorials in small groups) is in operation in the third year; there are less frequent and less regular tutorials for the second year, and occasional supplementary tutorials for first-year students.

6. OTHER ACTIVITIES

Our students join with those of the other modern language departments in an evening of one-act plays (produced in their respective language department) once per session. The Slavonic Society holds meetings with outside speakers, etc.

II. ADMISSION TO COURSES

1. QUALIFICATIONS REQUIRED

Given a sufficient number of applicants of acceptable intellectual and personal calibre, preference in admission is given to applicants with knowledge of Russian; 'A' Level (or in borderline cases 'O' Level) Russian will be an advantage. But beginners will be accepted whenever the number of acceptable applicants knowing Russian falls short of the departmental intake quota by more than two or three places.

M.L.—K 2

2. SELECTION OF STUDENTS

Students are required to apply through the UCCA and the most promising applicants are interviewed.

3. TRANSFER

Students are admitted to their course on entrance. Transfer to other courses is possible but not encouraged.

4. NUMBERS

Up to 21 students are admitted annually.

Information supplied by Mr. F. F. Seeley, Head of the Department of Slavonic
Studies

UNIVERSITY OF OXFORD

Faculty of Medieval and Modern Languages
(Russian) [1]

I. COURSES OF STUDY

1. TYPES OF COURSES

Russian may be studied

(a) as the subject for an *Honours degree in only one language*;

(b) as a subject for an *Honours degree in two languages*, of which Russian may be either the first or the second language.

2. CHARACTERISTICS OF COURSES

Preliminary Examination for Modern Languages (First Public Examination). In the first two terms of study undergraduates must work for the First Public Examination (normally the Preliminary Examination for Modern Languages). The subjects in Russian are: one paper involving the close textual study of selected works of two authors; one paper of prescribed texts to be studied in relation to general trends in literature or thought or to historical background— the subject at present prescribed in Russian for this paper is 'Literature and Society, 1840–1900'.

Honour School of Modern Languages (Second Public Examination). Candidates offering Russian must offer some or all of the following papers according to whether they offer Russian as sole (10 papers), first (7 papers) or second language (4 papers).

(1) Translation into Russian;

(2) Translation from Russian;

(3) Essay in Russian;

(4) History of the Russian language to 1680 (with prescribed texts);

(5) History of the Russian language with special reference to its present state (with prescribed texts);

(6) Period of literature: one or two of the following periods may be offered: (*a*) to 1725, (*b*) 1820–1939;

(7) Medieval texts prescribed for study as examples of literature;

(8) Prescribed authors: (*a*) Pushkin and Gogol and/or two of (*b*) Dostoevski, Tolstoy, Chekhov, Gorki.

[1] For general information concerning courses, admissions, residence abroad, etc., for undergraduates reading modern languages at Oxford, and the Diploma in Slavonic Studies, see p. 348.

A candidate offering Russian as sole language must offer papers 1-5 inclusive; two periods from 6; paper 7; and two authors from each group in 8. A candidate offering Russian as a first language must offer papers 1-3; paper 5; one of the periods listed in 6; paper 7; and two authors (both selected from the same group) in 8. A candidate offering Russian as a second language must offer papers 1 and 2; one of the periods listed in 6; and two authors (both selected from the same group) in 8.

There are also 54 Optional Subjects in the Final Honours School of Modern Languages. A candidate aiming at a place in the First Class must take one of these. A candidate's choice of Optional Subject is not restricted to one concerned with the language or languages offered in the compulsory papers.

II. ADMISSION TO COURSES

1. QUALIFICATIONS REQUIRED

Generally speaking, Colleges are unwilling to offer places to candidates for admission wishing to read Russian unless they already have a good grounding in the language. However, candidates of proved linguistic ability who do not know the language are sometimes admitted to read Russian provided they take steps to obtain a knowledge of it between the time they are accepted for admission and the time they come into residence.

4. NUMBERS

The number of candidates offering Russian in the Final Honours Examination has varied in recent years between 25 and 45.

Information supplied by Professor S. Konovalov

UNIVERSITY OF WALES: UNIVERSITY COLLEGE OF NORTH WALES, BANGOR

Russian Courses
(in the Department of German)

I. COURSES OF STUDY

1. TYPES OF COURSES

(*a*) Students accepted into the Faculty of Arts may offer Russian as one of the subjects for *Part I of a degree course*. Part I consists of three subjects and occupies the first year.

(*b*) In the second year, students working for a Pass degree may offer Russian as an *Auxiliary subject*; students taking certain Honours courses may offer Russian as an *Accessory subject*.

(*c*) A one-year or two-year course without examination is available for science students who wish to learn to read Russian.

2. CHARACTERISTICS OF COURSES

Students with no previous knowledge of the language are mainly occupied with language study during the first year. They are expected, however, to read and study certain set texts taken from Russian literature of the 19th century. In the second year, lectures are given on the general outlines of Russian literature of the 19th and early 20th centuries and a detailed study is made of certain works from this period.

The aim of the present courses in Russian is to give students a good working knowledge of the language, both written and spoken, and an introduction to Russian literature.

3. COMBINATION OF SUBJECTS

Russian may be combined with a large number of other subjects. Reference should be made to the current prospectus.

4. RESIDENCE ABROAD

No rules concerning residence abroad are in operation for students of Russian.

5. METHODS OF STUDY

Use is made of records and tape recordings, and a language laboratory is available for intensive language practice.

II. ADMISSION TO COURSES

1. QUALIFICATIONS REQUIRED

In Part I, courses are provided for those who have no previous knowledge of the language as well as for those who have passed the 'O' Level or 'A' Level G.C.E. examination in Russian.

2. SELECTION OF STUDENTS

The selection of students is in accordance with the qualifications mentioned above, but the inclusion of Russian as part of a degree course is subject to the approval of the Dean of the Faculty.

Information supplied by Mr. K. H. Whibley, Lecturer in Russian

UNIVERSITY OF WALES:
UNIVERSITY COLLEGE, CARDIFF

Russian Course

I. COURSES OF STUDY

1. TYPES OF COURSES

A special two-year course in Russian (Elementary first year and Art-Science second year) was started in 1958–59 and has continued since for the staff (including Library) and for a few postgraduate students only.

2. CHARACTERISTICS OF COURSES

(*a*) First year: elementary Russian, grammar (complete course), reading. Approximate vocabulary assimilation about 2,000 words.

(*b*) Second year; advanced grammar and a combined

(*i*) short historical literature course with passages (all in Russian),

(*ii*) scientific translations.

Approximate vocabulary assimilation about 5,000 (these 5,000 frequency count words are said to constitute 95 per cent of the Russian spoken and literary word count (Wayne) and some 300 scientific terms are added for the science section in the second year). Practical home translations, if desired by anyone taking the course, receive individual attention.

There are no final examinations.

II. ADMISSION TO COURSES

1. QUALIFICATIONS REQUIRED

This course is at present open to the teaching staff of the University (including the Library staff) and to postgraduate students. Those attending can start from the beginning.

Information supplied by Mr. V. Shibayev, in charge of the course

UNIVERSITY OF WALES: UNIVERSITY COLLEGE OF SWANSEA

Russian Courses
(attached to the Department of German)

I. COURSES OF STUDY

1. TYPES OF COURSES

Students who have been admitted to the Faculty of Arts may take Russian as one of three subjects to be studied for the first-year course, *Part I*.

It is hoped that after the *Part I* stage, Russian may continue to be studied:

(*a*) as one of three subjects in the second year of the Pass degree (*Auxiliary*);

(*b*) as an *Accessory subject* accompanying an Honours course.

At a subsequent stage it is the intention to offer Russian as an Honours subject.

2. CHARACTERISTICS OF COURSES

Although much of the emphasis during the *Part I* course will be on language work, students are expected to study some literary texts and to obtain some knowledge of the literary background.

3. COMBINATIONS OF SUBJECTS

In the first-year course Russian may be combined with a varied number of Arts subjects.

4. RESIDENCE ABROAD

There are at present no requirements concerning residence abroad.

II. ADMISSION TO COURSES

1. QUALIFICATIONS REQUIRED

Normally some knowledge of Russian will be required, but candidates who have shown exceptional promise as linguists may also be accepted.

2. SELECTION OF STUDENTS

It is normally expected that students wishing to offer Russian in Part I will have 'A' Level qualifications in at least one foreign language, such as French or German or in Classics.

Information supplied by Mr. A. B. Murphy, Lecturer in Russian Language and Literature

UNIVERSITY OF EDINBURGH
Department of Russian

I. COURSES OF STUDY

1. TYPES OF COURSES

Russian may be taken for *Honours* or as part of an *Ordinary degree* course. When taken for Honours, it may be the principal language (studied for four years) or the secondary language (studied for two years).

The following courses are provided:

(*a*) *First Ordinary* and *Second Ordinary* (one year each);
(*b*) *Junior Honours* and *Final Honours* (one year each);
(*c*) *Elementary* (one year; non-graduating class);
(*d*) *Scientific Russian* (one year; non-graduating class).

The Intermediate Honours course, taken in the second year by those reading for Honours in Languages, is identical with the Second Ordinary course, but a higher standard of performance is required. Honours students whose principal language is not Russian take only the First Ordinary and Intermediate Honours courses in Russian. Those whose principal language is Russian continue into the Junior and Final Honours classes.

The subjects of the Final Honours examinations are:

(1) Essay in Russian;
(2) Prose composition;
(3) Translation;
(4) Russian literature I (exclusive of the authors on paper 5);
(5) Russian literature II (Pushkin, Gogol, Dostoevsky, Tolstoy);
(6) History and institutions of Russia;
(7) History of the Russian language;
(8) Special Subject.

2. CHARACTERISTICS OF COURSES

In the first term of the First Ordinary course the work is entirely linguistic, since it is necessary to bring students up to a common level for further degree work. Apart from classes and conversation groups, use is also made of the language laboratory. After the first term some literature is studied.

In the second year more literature is studied and a course of lectures on Russian Institutions to the middle of the 19th century is provided by the Department of History.

In the final two years the standard of language is high and the amount of literature studied is extensive. The period of literature studied is principally the 19th century and the early 20th century. The history course covers the last hundred years and is given in the Department itself.

A course in the history of the Russian language is given, having been introduced by a short outline in the second year.

Each Honours student chooses a Special Subject. The choices offered at present are: Early History of the Slavs, Pushkin, Comparative Slavonic Philology, 20th century Literature, and Western Influences on Russian Literature.

At present there is a general tendency towards modern studies in the Department, and this may become more pronounced in the future.

3. COMBINATION OF SUBJECTS

Honours students combine Russian with any other language (including English Language or English Literature), which is studied for the first two years of the Honours course, and in which students must reach the Intermediate Honours level.

For the Ordinary degree a variety of combinations is possible: the two-year course of Russian may be combined with any other two-year language course plus several non-linguistic subjects; a one-year course of Russian (First Ordinary) may be combined with almost any subject in the Arts Faculty. Nearly all Ordinary degrees must include at least one course in a foreign language.

4. RESIDENCE ABROAD

Honours students are required to attend a reputable summer school in Russian (which must have the approval of the Head of the Department) during at least two vacations.

Ordinary degree students are strongly recommended to attend at least one such summer school.

Residence in a Russian family may, with the approval of the Head of the Department, be substituted for attendance at a summer school. Many students now manage to take part in short visits by student groups to the Soviet Union during their period of study.

5. METHODS OF STUDY

Language is studied largely in practical classes but there are also lectures on grammar. Some tutorial meetings in the first two years are also devoted to linguistic work.

Literature and history are studied partly by way of lectures and partly by way of tutorial work. In the final two years there are also seminars on these subjects.

In the advanced courses, where groups are small, lectures are conducted informally—questions may be put and discussions initiated during the lecture.

6. OTHER ACTIVITIES

There is a University Russian Society, which meets two or three times a term. The Society also organizes football, hockey, etc., teams.

II. ADMISSION TO COURSES

1. QUALIFICATIONS REQUIRED

The requirement for all students is a pass on the Higher grade in the Scottish Certificate of Education, or the Scottish Universities Preliminary Examination. A pass at the 'A' Level in the G.C.E. is accepted as an equivalent to this requirement.

Students who begin in the Elementary class and wish to enter the First Ordinary class the following year may be allowed to do so if they obtain at least 70 per cent in the Elementary class examination (which is *not* a degree examination).

No Latin is required for entrance to any Russian courses.

2. SELECTION OF STUDENTS

Selection is the responsibility of the Dean of the Faculty of Arts, not of the Department. Selection is based on the performance of candidates in the Scottish Certificate of Education or the G.C.E.

3. TRANSFER

Students may declare themselves as Honours or Ordinary students on entrance, but those who at the end of the second year do not satisfy the Intermediate Honours requirements become Ordinary students.

Conversely, transfer from the category of Ordinary to Honours student is permissible if the necessary requirements are satisfied.

Candidates properly qualified may enter Honours in the third or even fourth year and it is possible to take Honours in Russian in a further two years after graduating in another subject, again provided that the candidate is properly qualified.

4. NUMBERS

There are no limits laid down. The number of students in Honours classes is small.

Information supplied by Professor D. Ward

UNIVERSITY OF GLASGOW
Department of Russian

I. COURSES OF STUDY

1. TYPES OF COURSES

The following courses in Russian are available:

(*a*) *Elementary* course in the first year at University for students who have not an adequate qualification in Russian (see II.1).

(*b*) *Ordinary:* this course may be taken in the first university year and corresponds to first-year courses in the commoner languages. Students have to take it in the second year if they come to the University as beginners in Russian. This is the lowest course which qualifies for a degree examination and must be successfully completed by candidates for an Ordinary or an Honours degree that includes Russian.

(*c*) *Higher Ordinary:* second or third university year. This course may be taken by Ordinary and must be taken by Honours students.

(*d*) *Honours:* third and fourth (or fourth and fifth) years. Honours in Russian is half the full course for a M.A. degree with Honours (six papers out of, generally, 12). The other half may be another modern or an ancient language or Music or History.

2. CHARACTERISTICS OF COURSES

Ordinary: language, history of literature with prescribed texts.

Higher Ordinary: language, history of literature with prescribed texts, outlines of Russian history.

Honours: language, including history of language and medieval texts, literature (medieval to 20th century) with prescribed texts, study of one of the following special subjects: modern Russian political and social institutions, special literary topic, comparative Slavonic philology, or (for students who do not offer these as independent degree subjects) Czech or Polish language and literature or Russian history 1801–1945.

3. COMBINATION OF SUBJECTS

A large number of subjects can be combined with Russian for the M.A. Ordinary degree, which normally requires three years. Candidates must take at least five subjects, of which three are studied in one-year (Ordinary) courses whilst two must be continued for a second year (Higher Ordinary). Many students who offer Russian as a subject for the Ordinary M.A. continue to the Higher Ordinary level. Ordinary degree students must offer Moral Philosophy or

Logic. Further details as to choice of subjects are contained in the University Regulations.

Honours students must pass in two subjects at Ordinary level besides the two of their Honours group (see Regulations). For combinations of Honours subjects see I.1(*d*) above.

4. RESIDENCE ABROAD

In view of the difficulties of arranging a stay in U.S.S.R. there is no residential requirement for students of Russian, but Honours students are encouraged to spend some time during vacation in a Russian environment in U.S.S.R. or elsewhere.

II. ADMISSION TO COURSES

1. QUALIFICATIONS REQUIRED

All students offering Russian for a degree must pass through the Ordinary class, for admission to which a pass in Russian is required at Higher Level in the Scottish Certificate of Education or Scottish Universities Preliminary Examination or at 'A' Level in the English G.C.E. or in some equivalent examination. Latin is not needed for entry into Russian classes.

Russian can be started from scratch in the Elementary class (see I.1(*a*) above).

2. SELECTION OF STUDENTS

The Dean of the Faculty of Arts, not the Department, admits students. Any student so accepted, who has the necessary qualification in Russian, may enter the Ordinary class.

3. TRANSFER

Students are not admitted to Honours courses on entry. All have to pass through the Ordinary class and normally the Higher Ordinary before entering the Junior Honours course. By the end of the Higher Ordinary year, students hoping to proceed to Honours will know whether they are recommended to do this or whether they would be better advised to complete their curricula for an Ordinary M.A. degree.

4. NUMBERS

Hitherto there have rarely been more than 12 students in either of the Ordinary or Higher Ordinary class and 6 in the combined Honours classes. The largest classes are often the Elementary ones.

Information supplied by Mr. V. E. J. Holttum, Senior Lecturer in Russian

UNIVERSITY OF ST. ANDREWS

Department of Russian

I. COURSES OF STUDY

1. TYPES OF COURSES

From session 1963–64 Russian has been introduced as a subject qualifying for graduation in Arts. In subsequent sessions it is intended to institute classes qualifying for the Special and Honours M.A. Examinations. As from 1963–64 the following courses are available:

(*a*) *General class*, qualifying for the General M.A. Examination;

(*b*) *Junior class*, for those with little or no knowledge of the language who wish to qualify for the General class;

(*c*) *Introductory class*, for students who wish to obtain a reading knowledge of Russian auxiliary to their main study.

2. CHARACTERISTICS OF COURSES

In the General class, language and literature will be studied.

In language, emphasis will be placed on the written and spoken language of the present day. Literature will be confined to the 19th and 20th centuries, with emphasis on set texts and individual authors rather than on the history of literature.

II. ADMISSION TO COURSES

1. QUALIFICATIONS REQUIRED

For admission to the General class, a pass in Russian in 'A' Level G.C.E., the Higher grade of the Scottish Certificate of Education, or the Scottish Universities Preliminary Examination (Higher Level) is required. Students in the Junior class are expected to take the Scottish Universities Preliminary Examination (Higher Level) to qualify for the General class.

Information supplied by Mr. H. J. Pitcher, Lecturer in Russian

THE QUEEN'S UNIVERSITY OF BELFAST

RUSSIAN STUDIES

There is at present no degree course at Queen's University, though it is hoped to introduce one in a few years' time. Russian has for some time been studied by scientists wishing to offer it instead of German, and a course for students in the humanities has recently been developed. The Extra-Mural Department arranges elementary and advanced courses for evening classes in Belfast and elsewhere, and holds series of lectures and weekend courses on Soviet affairs.

Information supplied by Mr. P. H. Waddington, Lecturer in Russian Studies in the
Extra-Mural Department

ITALIAN STUDIES

UNIVERSITY OF BIRMINGHAM
Department of Italian

I. COURSES OF STUDY
1. TYPES OF COURSES

(*a*) *Honours:* Italian studied for four years with usually one Subsidiary subject studied for two years.

(*b*) *Combined subjects:* Italian as one of the ingredients of the Combined Subjects course. The usual pattern is for students to read two subjects, each for three years.

(*c*) *Subsidiary subject:* Italian as Subsidiary in other Honours Schools. Usually a two-year course.

(*d*) *Supplementary subject:* This is a new experiment introduced by certain Honours Schools (e.g. English and Latin). Instead of a conventional Subsidiary subject, which is jettisoned after two years, students read a Supplementary subject for the whole of their four-year course, and papers in that subject form part of their final examination at the end of the third year.

(*e*) *Italian Renascence Studies:* This new B.A. degree course, straddling eight departments and based on Latin and Italian, is being instituted. It will include Italian language, *Renascence* literature and Italian criticism of the *Renascence*. Italian art and architecture, which will form a substantial part of the course, will be the responsibility of the Barber Institute of Fine Arts. 'A' Level Latin will be required for admission to this course.

2. CHARACTERISTICS OF COURSES

Very many students begin Italian from scratch. The first year is largely devoted to language work and modern texts (Pirandello and Tomasi di Lampedusa), though of course Honours students with perhaps 'A' Level Italian behind them will be doing more advanced work. As the Department is small in numbers we can keep our teaching arrangements fairly flexible and under our tutorial system students get a lot of individual attention.

Combined Honours students study a period of literature (the *Renascence*) and various combinations of set authors.

Italian Honours students study two periods of literature, set authors, philology, and take a paper also in modern Italian history. The Department now has a staff of five, consisting of the Serena Professor of Italian, two Lecturers, one Assistant Lecturer and a Colloquial Assistant.

3. COMBINATION OF SUBJECTS

Usually other modern languages are combined with Italian, though in the Combined Subjects course virtually any combination is possible. In addition there are special arrangements for Italian as Supplementary subject to English Honours and Latin Honours (see I.1 above).

4. RESIDENCE ABROAD

The third year of the Honours course is (from 1965) spent at an Italian university. Combined Honours students, who have to go to Italy for three months, also spend part of their time at a university.

All students have detailed reading lists to cover, in preparation for the work of their final year.

5. METHODS OF STUDY

See I.2 above.

II. ADMISSION TO COURSES

1. QUALIFICATIONS REQUIRED

Italian is very often started from scratch.

2. SELECTION OF STUDENTS

Selection is based on 'A' Level results and interview. Candidates for the Honours course are all interviewed. Combined Subjects students are admitted by a special Admissions Tutor.

3. TRANSFER

Students are admitted to the Honours course on entrance and transfer is possible.

4. NUMBERS

The number of students entering for Honours Italian remains small, though it shows a tendency to rise slightly (5 in 1963); the number of Combined Subjects students varies from year to year. In 1963–64 there were 11 in the first year.

Information supplied by Professor J. H. Whitfield

UNIVERSITY OF BRISTOL

Italian Studies

I. COURSES OF STUDY

1. TYPES OF COURSES

The University does not have a separate Department of Italian, but since 1963 a Lecturer in Italian who for administrative purposes is attached to the Department of French. An Assistant Lecturer in Italian joined the staff in August 1964. Italian instruction has latterly been provided over a number of years for students in Modern Languages, English and Classics, by a Junior Fellow who held the post in the Department of Latin; but Italian can henceforth be studied (beginning October 1964) as a full graduating subject in the *General* (*Honours*) *degree* and as a *Subsidiary* subject to other Special Schools (see (*a*) and (*b*) below).

(*a*) Italian can be chosen as one of a number of subjects for the *General degree of B.A.* Four subjects have to be taken during the first year, and a choice is allowed, subject to time-table limitations. Three of these four subjects are studied in the second and third years.

(*b*) Italian can be taken as a two-year *Subsidiary* subject to the Special B.A. degree in French, German, Spanish, Philology, Music or Geography.

The General degree (see (*a*) above) can be of either Honours or Pass standard according to the results obtained in the final examinations, the classification being: first class, second class (first and second division), third class and pass; and a Special Mention in Oral Italian may also be awarded.

A Commendation on the results of the whole of the final examination may be awarded to a candidate in his Subsidiary subject.

(*c*) It can also be taken as a one-year *Additional* subject in the Special School of English, and by students in the Faculties of Medicine or Veterinary Science.

(*d*) Not only has Italian long been an Additional subject to the Special School of English (see (*c*) above) and a prerequisite, in which instruction is given, for two special subjects of the Final Special School of French (viz. 'Romance Philology' and 'France and the Italian Renaissance'); it is since 1960 part of a two-year *Subsidiary* subject, 'Art History with Italian', to the Special Schools of French and Spanish;[1] in 1962 it became an *Optional* subject in the Final Part

---

[1] This subject will be replaced for the session 1964–65 by a full two-year Subsidiary subject 'History of European Art'. Students in the Special School of French who choose it will be expected to pass a qualifying examination in Italian before they enter their second year of study.

of the new four-year Joint Special School of French and Spanish; and from 1964–65 an optional Dante paper has been included for suitably qualified students in the Special School of English.

It is hoped that Italian will in due course be admitted to the Special Joint Schools in conjunction with other modern foreign languages (four-year course) and Drama (three-year course).

2. CHARACTERISTICS OF COURSES

All full courses (General, Subsidiary and Additional) provide lectures and tutorials in language and literature and include provision for oral work.

The other classes provide an introduction to the language with some reading of selected poetry as well as prose. Second-year classes include one for reading Dante; other texts are read with selected second- and third-year students; and *ad hoc* lectures and tutorials are given to those whose Special subjects require it.

4. RESIDENCE ABROAD

General degree students taking Italian for three years, must, unless exempted by the Arts Board, spend one month in Italy following an authorized course of study; and students taking the two-year Subsidiary course in Italian are required to produce evidence of having spent a minimum period of four weeks of supervised study in Italy.

All students who do any Italian at all are encouraged to travel in Italy and to attend holiday courses there.

II. ADMISSION TO COURSES

The matriculation requirements of the University must be met. A pass at 'O' Level in a classical language is normally required of candidates in the Faculty of Arts.

Selections for the General B.A. degree are not made by the Department; but Mrs. Miller, Lecturer in Italian, is prepared to accept candidates well qualified in other languages who have only taken and passed Italian at 'O' Level.

Those applying for admission to Italian as a Subsidiary subject will also be expected to have 'O' Level Italian; those who lack this qualification may be admitted following a special test to be passed at the opening of the session.

Information supplied by Professor W. McC. Stewart

UNIVERSITY OF CAMBRIDGE

Department of Italian

I. COURSES OF STUDY

1. TYPES OF COURSES

For details of the regulations of the Modern and Medieval Languages Tripos see the notes provided by the Board of the Faculty of Modern and Medieval Languages (p. 340 below).

2. CHARACTERISTICS OF COURSES

(*a*) *Part I.*

It is quite common for students without any previous knowledge of the language to begin Italian at Cambridge, and in such cases two years are normally required to complete Part I. However, most students who have not been taking Italian at school attend a course arranged by one of the Italian universities during the spring or summer preceding their entry into the University and are often then able to complete Part I in one year.

For Part I a sound knowledge of the contemporary language is required and the student is tested in writing an essay in Italian, in translating into modern Italian and in translating Italian from the year 1500 onwards. An oral examination is also compulsory. Students taking Part I in one year are also required to offer one of the following literary papers:

(*i*) Introduction to Dante and his Age and the Literature of the *Risorgimento.*

(*ii*) Introduction to Dante and his Age.

(*iii*) Italian Literature, Thought and History since 1880.

(*b*) *Part II.*

There is a wide range of Italian papers for Part II embracing both literary and philological subjects. Candidates are required to offer a total of four or five such papers together with an essay in one of their languages and a paper in translation and composition.

3. COMBINATION OF SUBJECTS

Students are required to offer two languages for Part I of the Tripos; they may offer Italian together with *either* another modern language *or* a classical language. For Part II one or more languages may be offered, and students may take a selection of Italian papers or a combination of Italian and papers from other languages.

4. RESIDENCE ABROAD

No residence abroad is required, but the great majority of students make good use of vacations for this purpose.

5. METHODS OF STUDY

Lectures and classes are provided for both parts of the Tripos and there are opportunities for conversational practice with the Italian lectors as well as with the numerous Italian students in Cambridge. Weekly supervision arranged by the Colleges is normal.

6. OTHER ACTIVITIES

There is an active Italian Society which arranges talks, readings, musical evenings, films, etc. A number of lectures are given in the Department each year by visiting Italian professors.

II. ADMISSION TO COURSES

1 and 2. QUALIFICATIONS REQUIRED AND SELECTION OF STUDENTS

Admission is in the hands of the Colleges. There are no Faculty requirements. Most Colleges require either a competent knowledge of Italian or of two other modern languages or of one other modern language and Latin, before admitting a student to read Italian. Courses are designed to cater both for beginners and for more advanced students.

3. NUMBERS

Numbers vary, but in recent years approximately 12 to 15 students have begun the Honours course each year.

Information supplied by Dr. C. P. Brand, Lecturer in Italian

UNIVERSITY OF HULL

Department of Italian

I. COURSES OF STUDY

1. TYPES OF COURSES

(*a*) *Joint Honours degree:* a three-year course; one other subject is studied for three years.

(*b*) *Subsidiary* subject: Italian as subsidiary to another Special Honours subject. A five-term course.

(*c*) *Ancillary* subject: Italian taken with certain specified Special Honours subjects (e.g. English). A one-year course.

There is no General degree in Arts in this University. The Pass degree course is one to which students may be relegated from the Honours degree courses after one or two years. It is hoped to introduce a Special Honours degree in Italian in the near future.

2. CHARACTERISTICS OF COURSES

In the first year, the study of literature is restricted to the contemporary period, in such a way that the course is valuable both to the student of the modern language and also as an introduction to Italian culture. Honours students also take a course in modern Italian history and institutions.

In their second and third years, Honours students continue their language work and also study the literature and culture of the Middle Ages, Renaissance and 19th and 20th centuries. In addition to this, students reading Joint French and Italian take a course on the Renaissance in Italy and France.

Subsidiary students in their second year continue their language work and also study in detail selected texts from different periods.

3. COMBINATION OF SUBJECTS

(1) The commonest Joint Honours combination is with French.

(2) Combination with all other subjects is possible in the Faculty of Arts, but Spanish, Swedish and Italian is not possible for time-table reasons.

4. RESIDENCE ABROAD

Honours students spend at least one month in Italy at the end of their first year. They may also spend a year in Italy between their second and third years.

5. METHODS OF STUDY

Since Italian is often begun from scratch, language courses are rapid and intense, and are taken by a native Italian. A language teaching laboratory is to be installed in the new Arts Faculty building. Great attention is paid, in all courses, to the modern language, both written and spoken; all students have weekly prose and conversation classes. Honours students have regular tutorials. Since classes tend to be small, students have a good deal of individual attention, and it is possible to have both formal lectures and discussions.

II. ADMISSION TO COURSES

1. QUALIFICATIONS REQUIRED

All students must matriculate in the University. In addition, students reading Joint Honours Italian must have a pass in Latin at 'O' Level. Students reading Subsidiary or Ancillary Italian must have a pass at 'A' Level in a modern or classical foreign language.

Italian can be started from scratch in this University, and in the first year courses are provided both for beginners and for students with a pass at 'A' Level. Both courses come together into one class in the second year.

2. SELECTION OF STUDENTS

(1) There is no separate entrance examination.

(2) 'A' Level results are an important basis for selection and are used to provide 'conditional marks', on the attainment of which a place is awarded. For students taking 'A' Level Italian, a good pass, usually at about grade B, is required. Students who wish to begin Italian from scratch must show evidence of linguistic ability in the form of a good pass with at least grade B in a modern foreign language.

(3) Most candidates for Honours Italian are interviewed. Interviews last for 30 minutes and are conducted by two members of the Department. In these interviews one looks mainly for intellectual curiosity and independence of mind.

(4) References from head teachers and language teachers are also important, although unfortunately varying in reliability.

3. TRANSFERS

Students are admitted to Honours Schools on entrance.

4. NUMBERS

Numbers are small, but increasing. In 1963, 5 students were admitted to the Joint Honours course, 10 in 1964.

Information supplied by Dr. B. Moloney, Lecturer in charge, Department of Italian

M.L.—L

UNIVERSITY OF LIVERPOOL

Department of Italian

I. COURSES OF STUDY

1. TYPES OF COURSES

Courses in Italian leading to the following qualifications are offered:

(*a*) *Honours* course in Italian only (lasting three or four years);

(*b*) a *Joint Honours* course in two languages, one Main and one Subsidiary; Italian may be taken jointly with certain other subjects, either as a Main or as a Subsidiary subject, lasting four years.

(*c*) *Italian as part of a General degree course:* a three-year Pass degree with several subjects in various combinations. For General Honours the minimum marks needed to qualify are roughly B-plus in three subjects.

2. CHARACTERISTICS OF COURSES

Unless a student on entrance has adequate preparation in Italian, four years are required for the Honours degree in Italian (first year: Preliminary Honours; second and third years: Part I; fourth year: Part II).

3. COMBINATION OF SUBJECTS

No compulsory combination of examinable subjects exists but students must study a second language during the second year (without examination).

4. RESIDENCE ABROAD

The final year must be spent in Italy at an approved university or other institution.

II. ADMISSION TO COURSES

1. QUALIFICATIONS REQUIRED

In addition to the entrance requirements laid down by the Joint Matriculation Board for entry into the Department the requirements are:

(*i*) 'O' Level Latin and

(*ii*) two subjects at 'A' Level of the G.C.E.

Italian can be started either at beginners' or intermediate level.

2. SELECTION OF STUDENTS

Selection is based on (*i*) 'A' Level results; (*ii*) interview (General students are interviewed if Liverpool is their first choice); (*iii*) head teacher's report.

There is no entrance examination or test.

3. TRANSFER

Admission to Preliminary Honours is in the first year normally leading to Part I examination in Italian Honours.

Transfer from General courses to Honours after the first-year General is possible.

Information supplied by Miss L. A. Zaina, Head of the Department of Italian

UNIVERSITY OF LONDON:
BEDFORD COLLEGE

Department of Italian

I. COURSES OF STUDY

Bedford College at present admits only women as under-graduates.

1. TYPES OF COURSES

(*a*) *Honours in Italian:* a comprehensive three-year series of courses in Italian language and literature.

(*b*) *General:* a three-year course to prepare students for an examination in Italian as one of the three subjects at the General examination. The course covers a study of Italian literature during two periods: (*i*) 1265–1599; (*ii*) 1816 to the present day. Also translation and composition work in Italian.

(*c*) *Subsidiary:* a two-year course in Italian as subsidiary to some other Honours subject. Similar to the General course, but with a study of only one (at choice) of the periods of literature (*i*) and (*ii*).

(*d*) The Department also provides a beginners' language course for first-year students from other departments, and a text-reading class for second-year students. This last is chiefly attended by students from the Departments of English and History.

2. CHARACTERISTICS OF COURSES

The courses for students reading for B.A. Honours in Italian are held intercollegiately with University College, an average of eight courses per year being given at each College. The courses cover the whole field of Italian literature, as well as the history of the Italian language and practice in its modern use. The content of each course naturally varies in accordance with the texts prescribed for special study during that year. All courses must be attended at some time in each student's three-year period of study, the only option being in the Special Subject (literary), where there is a choice of one out of two.

3. COMBINATION OF SUBJECTS

The majority of Honours students take French Subsidiary, but other languages are sometimes selected. The combinations of subjects chosen by General students of Italian vary widely, but languages tend to predominate.

4. RESIDENCE ABROAD

No rules concerning residence abroad are laid down, but students reading for an Honours degree are strongly recommended to spend a considerable part of each long vacation in Italy. General and Subsidiary students are given every encouragement to go to Italy whenever possible.

Students frequently follow vacation courses at the Universities of Florence or Perugia, but this is not obligatory. Practice in the language is regarded as the most important thing while abroad.

5. METHODS OF STUDY

Each Honours student has an individual weekly tutorial, and conversation classes are given to small groups by the Italian student-assistant.

General and Subsidiary students do not usually have individual tutorials, but a seminar class is held for General students in their third year. All students in the Department must attend a weekly conversation class.

II. ADMISSION TO COURSES

1. QUALIFICATIONS REQUIRED

Honours. Some knowledge of the Italian language is required—preferably, but not necessarily, to G.C.E. 'A' Level, Latin to 'O' Level at least. The College Entrance Examination must be taken with Italian as principal subject. This tests linguistic ability only, not literary knowledge.

General and Subsidiary. Candidates for these courses usually take Italian as subsidiary subject in the College Entrance Examination, but in both cases the language can be started from scratch when the candidate shows evidence of some linguistic ability (e.g. 'O' Level in another language). Latin is not obligatory.

2. SELECTION OF STUDENTS

Honours in Italian. All candidates who reach a satisfactory standard in the written part of the Entrance Examination are interviewed before admission to the College.

General and Subsidiary. These candidates are not as a rule interviewed before admission.

No personal reference is required other than that given by the head of the candidate's school on the application form.

3. TRANSFER

Students are admitted to the Honours course in Italian on entrance.

Transfer to other courses is possible in suitable cases, provided that it is effected within the student's first term in College.

4. NUMBERS

Between 2 and 6 students start Italian Honours each year.

Information supplied by Mrs. E. H. Thorne, Senior Lecturer in the Department of Italian

UNIVERSITY OF LONDON:
BIRKBECK COLLEGE

Department of Italian

Students are normally admitted to Birkbeck College only if they are in full-time employment.[1]

I. COURSES OF STUDY

1. TYPES OF COURSES

This Department does not, as yet, offer Honours courses in Italian. It is, however, the intention of Birkbeck College to introduce such courses within the next few years. At present, therefore, only the following courses in Italian are available:

(a) Italian as a subject in the *B.A. General degree*;

(b) Italian as a *Subsidiary subject to B.A. Honours* in another principal subject;

(c) There is also a one- or two-year *Elementary* course for beginners in Italian (see II.1 below).

2. CHARACTERISTICS OF COURSES

See I.5 below.

3. COMBINATION OF SUBJECTS

Italian can be studied with Classics, English, French, German, Spanish, History of Art, History, Philosophy, Geography, Psychology. Of these, the first six are the most popular combinations, but any Arts subject is permissible. There is no compulsory combination of subjects—only time-table difficulties may tend to limit the choice.

4. RESIDENCE ABROAD

This being a General department, no rules of residence are in operation but students are nevertheless encouraged to spend some weeks at an Italian university vacation course for foreign students.

5. METHODS OF STUDY

Since classes are small we try to conduct them on an active quasi-seminar basis. Little value is attributed to the formal lecture; active participation of the student in the work we do is strongly encouraged. Thus literature is dealt with largely on the basis of discussion of texts

[1] Many of our students come on an intercollegiate basis from other day colleges of London University, either because Italian is not available in their own college, or because of time-table difficulties, or for other reasons.

in class, with intervention by the lecturer when appropriate, and periodic summing up. It is regarded as important to encourage the student to work out a balanced judgment of his own and not to tell him what to think. At the same time, since the student reads aloud the passage of Italian poetry before offering his version, errors of pronunciation and intonation can be corrected; and the ensuing discussion, while mainly literary, permits of brief comment on points of vocabulary, grammar and syntax. Thus each literature class is to some extent also a class in language and phonetics.

While we still conform to weekly prose composition, we place much greater emphasis on extempore translation and composition in class: the teacher reads to the class a passage in one language, the students simultaneously write down their version in the other, at the end results are discussed. Increasing use is being made of our recently acquired tape recorder; and we are currently engaged in preparing an Italian programme for the language laboratory which Birkbeck is setting up.

II. ADMISSION TO COURSES

1. QUALIFICATIONS REQUIRED

Entrance to this Department is based on minimum entrance requirements of London University, which include Latin at 'O' Level and one language other than English.

As Italian is little taught in schools we accept students from scratch; but they must first follow a course in elementary Italian provided by us, until they reach a level suitable for admission to the first-year General class. This course normally lasts one year, sometimes two years. Students with G.C.E. qualifications in Italian—and their number is steadily growing—can be admitted directly to the first-year course.

2. SELECTION OF STUDENTS

No student is admitted unless he has been interviewed either by the Head of the Department or his assistant. We try to find out what we can about his character, the reasons for his wanting to study Italian, etc. We try to disabuse some students of the idea that Italian is an easy option, something that can be 'got out of the way' without much effort.

Information supplied by Mr. D. S. Duncan, Head of the Department of Italian

UNIVERSITY OF LONDON:
UNIVERSITY COLLEGE
Department of Italian

I. COURSES OF STUDY

1. TYPES OF COURSES

Italian can be taken in the following courses:

(*a*) *Honours*

(*b*) *Subsidiary*

(*c*) *Elementary Italian* for students in other departments.

No General degree course is provided at this College.

2. CHARACTERISTICS OF COURSES

The main Honours courses consist of

(1) History of the language (a three-year course);

(2) Courses on the various set books;

(3) Courses on history of Italian literature at various periods;

(4) Translation classes for first-, second- and third-year Honours students. There is no possibility of options.

3. COMBINATION OF SUBJECTS

Honours students take one Subsidiary subject; this is generally French or Latin. Other combinations are possible, e.g. Greek, German, Spanish or History of Art.

4. RESIDENCE ABROAD

We encourage students to spend their summer vacations at the end of their first and second years in Italy. While abroad they are expected to attend a summer course at an Italian university.

5. METHODS OF STUDY

All Honours students have one tutorial and one conversation class every week. They are taken in groups of three or four.

II. ADMISSION TO COURSES

1. QUALIFICATIONS REQUIRED

Besides the matriculation requirements of the University of London, Latin at 'A' Level G.C.E. is desirable for Honours students. Applicants with a pass in Latin at 'O' Level G.C.E. only may be accepted, but will be required in their first year to take a course in Latin in order to give them an adequate knowledge of the language. Italian can be started from scratch at this College.

2. SELECTION OF STUDENTS

Students are selected on 'A' Level results and interview. The interview lasts about 15 to 20 minutes and is conducted by all the teaching members of the Department. Our aim is to ascertain whether the candidate has the interests and ability to secure at least a second-class Honours degree.

3. TRANSFER

Students are selected for Honours Italian on entrance.

4. NUMBERS

About 6 to 10 students are admitted annually to the Honours School.

Information supplied by Professor R. Weiss

UNIVERSITY OF LONDON: WESTFIELD COLLEGE

Department of Italian

I. COURSES OF STUDY

1. TYPES OF COURSES

Italian cannot be studied as an Honours subject in this College.

There are two courses available here:

(*a*) For language students who choose Italian as their second language a two-year course subsidiary to their studies for an Honours degree;

(*b*) For History students who require knowledge of Italian for their Special Subject and work mainly on Renaissance texts. This course lasts two terms.

2. CHARACTERISTICS OF COURSES

Italian as a Subsidiary subject consists of the following classes: First year: grammar, prose and translation classes, a class in Italian phonetics; a lecture course in general Italian literature from Dante to Tasso. Second year: prose and translation classes, the study of prescribed texts, classes in Italian on 16th- to 20th-century literature, conversation classes.

In addition, students are admitted to courses at the Warburg Institute on the civilization of the Renaissance in Italy.

The examination consists of:

(1) translation from and into Italian;

(2) outlines of the history of Italian literature from Dante to Tasso with special reference to the *Divina Commedia*;

(3) an oral examination.

3. COMBINATION OF SUBJECTS

Italian as a Subsidiary subject is taken by students reading for French, Spanish or German Honours.

4. RESIDENCE ABROAD

Residence abroad is not obligatory but most students seem able to arrange a visit or visits to Italy during vacations.

II. ADMISSION TO COURSES

1. QUALIFICATIONS REQUIRED

Acceptance is dependent on satisfying the normal requirements of the University of London.

Satisfactory knowledge of a classical language is required.

No 'General' students are accepted.

2. SELECTION OF STUDENTS

Only students who have passed in Italian at least at 'O' Level are accepted for the Subsidiary course.

Information supplied by Mrs. P. Waley, Lecturer in Italian

UNIVERSITY OF MANCHESTER

Department of Italian Studies

I. COURSES OF STUDY

1. TYPES OF COURSES

Italian can be studied for *Honours* or *General Arts* degrees:

(*a*) *Honours School of Italian Studies;*

(*b*) *Honours School of Modern Languages;*

(*c*) *Honours School of English and Italian;*

(*d*) *General degree of B.A.*

2. CHARACTERISTICS OF COURSES

(*a*) The *Honours School of Italian Studies* offers a three-year course, divided into (1) Preliminary and (2) Final. The Preliminary examination is taken at the end of the first session.

Subjects studied for (1):

(*i*) Translation from English into Italian and from Italian into English;

(*ii*) Specified aspects of the history of Italian literature in the 19th century;

(*iii*) Specified aspects of the history of Italian literature from 1870 to the present day;

(*iv*) Specified aspects of the history of Italian art and architecture in the Middle Ages and Renaissance.

Subjects studied for (2):

(*i*) Translation from English into Italian;

(*ii*) The history of the Italian language;

(*iii*) The writing of an essay in Italian on a subject relating to Italian literature, art, history or thought;

(*iv*) Specified aspects of the history of Italian literature from 1600 to 1800;

(*v*) Specified aspects of the history of Italian literature from 1400 to 1600;

(*vi*) Specified aspects of the history of Italian literature in the Middle Ages;

(*vii*) Dante:

(*viii*) A special subject chosen from a group to be prescribed from year to year.

Students are required to complete a course in a specified period of Italian history.

(*b*) The *Honours School of Modern Languages* offers four-year courses in which Italian is combined with French or Spanish or German or Russian, both languages being studied at Honours level. Italian may be chosen either (1) as the first or (2) as the second language.

(1) The subjects studied are the same as for the *Honours School of Italian Studies* minus one subject in the Final. The courses in Italian are completed in the first three years, while the courses in the second language (Final courses only) begin in the second year and are completed in the fourth.

(2) The subjects studied are the same as for the Final part only of the *Honours School of Italian Studies*, minus one subject. Intermediate and General Italian must also be taken, together with the Honours courses in the first modern language. Honours courses in Italian begin in the second year and are completed in the fourth.

(*c*) The *Honours School of English and Italian* offers a four-year course which is a genuine amalgam of the two subjects. The course is designed to accommodate not only candidates who enter the University intending to combine English with Italian, but also those who during the first year of the Honours course in English develop an interest in Italian and wish to transfer to the joint course. The examination is divided into a Preliminary, a Part I and a Part II examination. The Preliminary examination consists entirely of English papers and is taken in the summer term of the first session of the Honours course. Part I is taken not later than the end of the session before the Final year of the Honours course. Part II is taken at the end of the fourth session.

Subjects studied for the Preliminary examination:

(*i*) translation from specified Old English Texts with literary and linguistic questions arising out of them;

(*ii*) prescribed English authors, 1550–1700.

Subjects studied for Part I:

(*i*) translation from English into Italian and from Italian into English;

(*ii*) Petrarch and Boccaccio and the literature of the 13th and 14th centuries, with specified texts;

(*iii*) Chaucer and the literature of the 14th and 15th centuries with specified texts;

(*iv*) prescribed Italian authors, 1400–1600;

(*v*) Spenser and Milton;

(*vi*) prescribed English authors, 1700–1830.

Subjects studied for Part II:

(*i*) translation from English into Italian;

(*ii*) the writing of an essay in Italian on an Italian subject;

(*iii*) Dante;

(*iv*) Shakespeare;

(*v*) prescribed Italian authors, 1600–1800;

(*vi*) three English Romantic poets;

(*vii*) aspects of the history of Italian literature in the Romantic period;

(*viii*) history of criticism and literary theory; *or*

a Special Subject to be chosen from the group of subjects prescribed from year to year in the Honours School of English or Italian Studies.

(*d*) Italian may be taken as first- (*Intermediate*), second- (*General*) and third-year (*Special*) course for the *General degree of B.A.* These include the study of the language (grammar, composition, etc.), translation and reading from specified books: for the first year modern and contemporary texts, for the second year Dante, Petrarch and Boccaccio, and in the third year the *Ottocento*.

3. COMBINATION OF SUBJECTS

See above, I.2 (*b*), (*c*), for the main combinations offered by the *Honours School of Modern Languages* and the *Honours School of English and Italian*. In order to satisfy Subsidiary requirements, students in the single *Honours School of Italian Studies* combine Italian with the following subjects:

(1) Intermediate (first-year) Latin;

(2) Intermediate (first-year) English or another modern language or subject approved;

(3) a General (second-year) course in any subject taken at Intermediate.

Students in the *Honours School of Modern Languages* complete, in their first year, courses of at least Intermediate grade in Latin *or* Greek (where the other language offered for Honours is a Romance language, Latin *must* be taken).

Students in the *Honours School of English and Italian* complete a course of at least Intermediate grade in Latin and a course of at least General grade in the History of Italian Art.

4. RESIDENCE ABROAD

Students in the *Honours School of Italian Studies* and students in the *Honours School of Modern Languages* who have chosen Italian as their first language are expected to spend the third term of their second year at an Italian university. The Department supports their application for grants from local or Italian authorities. Students in the *Honours School of Modern Languages* who have chosen Italian as their second language are encouraged to spend some time in Italy when they go to the country of their first language.

5. METHODS OF STUDY

The teaching includes formal lectures, seminars and tutorials. The staff includes some native Italian-speaking teachers and the instruction is conducted in Italian as well as in English (usually an English lecturer lectures in English, the Italian in Italian). Italian is taught from scratch for *General degree* students, for students of *Modern Languages Honours* taking Italian as a second language, and for *English and Italian Honours* students.

6. OTHER ACTIVITIES

Students normally join the Manchester Dante Society and British-Italian League, of which the members of the staff are active members. The Society meets fortnightly for lectures, socials, discussions, etc.

II. ADMISSION TO COURSES

1. QUALIFICATIONS REQUIRED

For the *Honours School of Italian Studies* and the *Honours School of Modern Languages* with Italian as the first language, in addition to the general entrance requirements laid down by the Joint Matriculation Board, the Faculty of Arts requires a pass in Latin at 'O' Level and the Italian Department requires marks of at least B grade in at least two 'A' Level subjects, one of which must be Italian, and good supporting marks.

For the *Honours School of Modern Languages* with Italian as the second language and the *Honours School of English and Italian*, admission to the Italian part of the course depends on the students' performance in Italian at Intermediate Level at the end of their first year (normally a First Class is required).

2. SELECTION OF STUDENTS

For qualifications required, see II.1 above. Before being finally admitted, students are normally interviewed by members of the staff.

3. TRANSFER

In special cases, transfer is possible from the *Honours* to the *General degree* course or vice versa, and from the Single to the Double *Honours* course or vice versa.

4. NUMBERS

Normally no more than 10 students are admitted annually to the *Italian Honours Schools*.

Information supplied by Professor G. Aquilecchia

UNIVERSITY OF OXFORD
Faculty of Medieval and Modern Languages
(Italian) [1]

I. COURSES OF STUDY

1. TYPES OF COURSES

Italian may be studied

(a) as the subject for an *Honours degree in only one language*;

(b) as a subject for an *Honours degree in two languages*, of which Italian may be either the first or the second subject.

2. CHARACTERISTICS OF COURSES

Preliminary Examination for Modern Languages (First Public Examination). In the first two terms of study undergraduates must work for the First Public Examination (normally the Preliminary Examination for Modern Languages). The subjects in Italian are: translation from and into Italian; prescribed texts (two papers) chosen from the period 1880–1914.

Honour School of Modern Languages (Second Public Examination). Candidates offering Italian must take some or all of the following papers according to whether they offer it as sole (10 papers) first (7 papers), or second language (4 papers):

(1) Translation into Italian;

(2) Translation from Italian into English;

(3) Essay in Italian;

(4) History of the Italian language to 1220 (with prescribed texts);

(5) History of the Italian language with special reference to its present state (with prescribed texts);

(6) Period of literature: one or two of the following: (a) 1200–1375, (b) 1450–1600, (c) 1750–1870;

(7) Dante, with a special study of two *cantiche* of the *Divina Commedia*;

(8) Prescribed authors: two of (a) Petrarch, Boccaccio, Ariosto, Tasso, and/or two of (b) Alfieri, Foscolo, Manzoni, Leopardi.

Candidates offering Italian as sole language must take papers 1-5, papers 6 (two periods), 7, 8 (a) and (b); those offering it as first language papers 1-3, 5, 6 (one period), 7, 8 (a) or (b); and those

[1] For general information concerning courses, admissions, residence abroad, etc., for undergraduates reading modern languages at Oxford, see p. 348.

offering it as the second language, papers 1, 2, 6 (one period) and 7. A candidate aiming at a place in the First Class must also offer an Optional Subject, which may be taken in any language (there is a choice of 54 subjects in all, of which 8 are Italian subjects).

II. ADMISSION TO COURSES

1. QUALIFICATIONS REQUIRED

Candidates of proved linguistic ability, who have not been taught Italian in their schools, are sometimes admitted to read Italian, usually on the understanding that they take steps to obtain a know-ledge of the language between the time they are accepted for admission by a College and the time they come into residence.

4. NUMBERS

The numbers of candidates offering Italian in the Preliminary Examination and the Final Honour School have varied in recent years between 12 and 20.

Information supplied by Professor C. Grayson

UNIVERSITY OF READING
Department of Italian Studies

I. COURSES OF STUDY

1. TYPES OF COURSES

Italian studies are available:

(a) as a *Single* subject;

(b) as a *Combined* subject course with French, German or Latin;

(c) as a *Special* subject course by students following courses in Classics, English, French, German, History and Music.

2. CHARACTERISTICS OF COURSES

(a) The *Single* subject course extends over ten terms after the First University Examination, and includes a year of study at a university in Italy. The course includes:

(1) Language work; translation into and from Italian, essays and oral work in Italian.

(2) History of the language, and an introduction to Romance philology.

(3) Study of specified aspects of:
   (i) Italian Literary History.
   (ii) Renaissance Art and Thought.
   (iii) The Development of Modern Italy.

(4) A Special Subject which may be studied in another Department.

(b) The *Combined* subject courses.

Italian and French. The course extends over ten terms and includes a year's study abroad, divided between universities in France and Italy. There are six papers in Italian: three in language; Dante; the Italian Renaissance; and the Development of Modern Italy.

French and Italian. The course extends over ten terms and includes a year's study abroad, divided between universities in France and Italy. There are four papers in Italian: two language papers; Specified Aspects of Italian Literature and Art: 1200–1600; the Development of Modern Italy.

German and Italian. The course extends over ten terms and includes a year's study abroad, divided between universities in German-speaking countries and Italy. There are three papers in Italian: Language; Specified Aspects of Italian Literature and Art: 1200–1600; the Development of Modern Italy.

Latin and Italian. The course extends over ten terms. There are four papers in Italian: two language papers; Specified Aspects of Italian Literature and Art: 1200–1600; the Development of Modern Italy. The course includes a year of study at a university in Italy.

3. COMBINATION OF SUBJECTS

See I.1 and 2 above.

4. RESIDENCE ABROAD

One year at an Italian university is part of the Single Honours course in Italian and the course in Latin and Italian. Six months are required for Combined courses in Italian and French, French and Italian, German and Italian.

II. ADMISSION TO COURSES

1. QUALIFICATIONS REQUIRED

A two-term Italian beginners' course, which forms part of a three-subject first-year examination is designed to give access to all courses listed in I.1 and I.2 above.

2. SELECTION OF STUDENTS

Selection of students is based on consideration of both 'A' Level results and interviews. Entrance examinations are envisaged for adult candidates.

3. TRANSFER

Students are admitted to courses on the basis of the results attained in the First University Examination. A tentative selection is made on entrance. Transfers are permissible.

Information supplied by Mr. J. A. Scott, Acting Head of the Department of Italian Studies

UNIVERSITY OF WALES: UNIVERSITY COLLEGE OF NORTH WALES, BANGOR

Department of French and Romance Studies
(Italian)

I. COURSES OF STUDY

1 and 2. TYPES AND CHARACTERISTICS OF COURSES

The study of Italian is divided as follows:

(*a*) *Part I*, which in turn is divided into two groups: (A) Beginners, (B) students already possessing a pass in G.C.E. Italian at least to 'O' Level. In course (A) mainly language is taught; in (B) language and also literary texts of the *Risorgimento* period.

(*b*) *Part II Pass degree*. There is both a Main (two-year) course and an *Auxiliary* (one-year) course. The latter comprises, in addition to language work, the study of mainly 19th- and 20th-century Italian literature; the former also includes Dante and Renaissance authors.

(*c*) *Part II Honours degree*. There is no Honours School of Italian, but Italian may be taken as an *Accessory* (one year) to another Honours subject (usually French). The Accessory course, in addition to language, consists of the study of selected authors and texts of the period 1750 to 1960. Italian may also be taken as a Special Subject paper in the Final Honours examination in French. The course comprises language work and the study of Dante and Italian Renaissance literature.

4. RESIDENCE ABROAD

There is no requirement regarding residence in Italy, but students are encouraged to attend a recognized summer school in Italy during their period of study.

II. ADMISSION TO COURSES

1. QUALIFICATIONS REQUIRED

For entry into Part I (A) course, no requirement is laid down. For entry into Part I (B), 'O' or 'A' Level Italian is required. In both cases possession of 'O' Level Latin is considered desirable.

For other information on this course, see p. 91 above, University of Wales: University College of North Wales, Bangor; Department of French and Romance Studies.

Information supplied by Professor I. W. Alexander

UNIVERSITY OF WALES: UNIVERSITY COLLEGE OF SWANSEA

Italian Courses
(attached to the Department of Romance Studies)

I. COURSES OF STUDY

1. TYPES OF COURSES

Students who have been admitted to the Faculty of Arts may take Italian as one of three subjects to be studied for the first-year course (Part I), and thereafter

either (*a*) as one of two subjects in the General degree,

or (*b*) as an *Accessory* subject accompanying an Honours course.

A Joint Honours course in Italian and French, and an Honours course in Italian, will be added as soon as possible.

II. ADMISSION TO COURSES

1. QUALIFICATIONS REQUIRED

Previous knowledge of Italian will not be insisted on, but candidates must have shown some aptitude for languages.

Information supplied by Professor R. C. Knight

UNIVERSITY OF ABERDEEN

Department of Italian

I. COURSES OF STUDY

1. TYPES OF COURSES

Italian can be studied in this University as an element in (*a*) *Ordinary* and (*b*) *Joint Honours* degree courses; (*c*) an *Elementary* course is also available.

At present no single-language Honours course is contemplated in Italian.

(*a*) *Ordinary* (i.e. *General*) *degree*; a three-year course in which a student must complete *seven* 'degree-courses'. To study a subject for one year (Ordinary course) counts as *one* such course; to study it for two years (i.e. Ordinary and Advanced course) counts as *two* such courses. The language cannot be studied further than this in the Ordinary degree course.

Thus Italian can be studied by Ordinary degree students for one or two (consecutive or otherwise) years, *at any stage* in their three-year degree course. An examination is held at the end of each year consisting in both cases of one language and one literary paper and an oral examination.

(*b*) *Joint Honours:* there are Joint Honours groups in Italian with English, French, Latin and Spanish.

Italian (as also the other language in the course) is studied for four years, termed Ordinary, Advanced, Junior Honours and Senior Honours years. In the first two years the courses are those taken by students for the Ordinary degree, and the examinations are as above. The final examination after the fourth year (there is no examination after the third year) consists of six papers in language, literature and history of the language.

An Honours student also studies, each for one year, two outside subjects of his own choice, one at least of which must be chosen from outside his own department of study. These are normally studied, and the examinations taken, in the first and second years.

(*c*) *Elementary course:* a preparation (language only) for entrance to the Ordinary course, open also to students not intending to proceed to a degree in Italian.

2. CHARACTERISTICS OF COURSES

Lectures. In this University the basis of instruction in all years is the formal lecture.

Classes. All years have weekly prose and conversation classes.

Tutorials. Ordinary and Advanced classes are divided into groups of four for weekly tutorial groups on some aspect of the literature under study.

Honours students also have individual weekly tutorials, and whenever it is considered desirable, discussions, with prepared papers, are substituted for set lectures.

Essays. All students submit written essays on literary topics.

Literature for the first year will in the future be restricted to post-1800 literature, in such a way that the maximum link is maintained between the language of the texts and the language as the students are learning it, without any diminution in the overall value of the course as an introduction to Italian culture and civilization.

3. COMBINATION OF SUBJECTS

Ordinary. Italian can be taken in any combination of subjects available to Ordinary degree students.

Honours. There are Honours groups with English, French, Latin and Spanish.

4. RESIDENCE ABROAD

There is no compulsory residence qualification in this Department for Ordinary degree students, though, of course, if the student wishes to qualify as a teacher of the language in Scotland he has to fulfil the residence requirements of the Scottish educational system.

The Department specifies a minimum of six months as the qualifying residence in Italy for Honours students, but in practice the aim is that students should spend a year—preferably between the Advanced and Junior Honours years—in Italy. Students spending a year abroad are expected to do a good deal of advance reading for their Honours years, and to follow available university courses relevant to their Honours syllabus.

5. METHODS OF STUDY

See I.2 above.

II. ADMISSION TO COURSES

1. QUALIFICATIONS REQUIRED

(*a*) *Ordinary degree.* A student will normally be expected to have attended the Elementary class or to have equivalent qualifications in Italian language. In rare cases students with high general linguistic qualifications may attend Ordinary and Elementary courses concurrently.

(*b*) *Honours degree.* No Latin or other specific qualification is required. The student is not officially an 'Honours' student until he has entered the Junior Honours (3rd) year, which normally means that he has completed his first and second (Ordinary and Advanced) years, for which the entrance qualifications are given in (*a*) above. (Intending Honours students with no knowledge of Italian will normally qualify to attend Ordinary and Elementary classes concurrently in their first year.)

2. SELECTION OF STUDENTS

There is rarely the possibility of using past performance in the language as a guide.

(*i*) *Intending Ordinary degree students.* Students are selected only in accordance with the above qualification requirements. In normal circumstances any student with no previous knowledge of Italian whose programme allows him or her to attend the Elementary class prior to joining the Ordinary class will be expected to do so.

(*ii*) *Intending Honours degree students.* As the intending Honours student enters the Ordinary class in his first year at University, proof of linguistic aptitude, or an elementary knowledge of Italian, in accordance with entrance requirements outlined above, is normally required before a student is encouraged to embark on an Honours degree in Italian. The final decision as to whether or not a student may proceed to an Honours degree is made at the end of the second (Advanced) year, and depends on the candidate's performance up to that point.

3. TRANSFER

A student is never really an *Honours* student until he enters the Junior Honours year—normally after completing the first year (Ordinary) and the second year (Advanced). Any student, on entrance, can plan his curriculum in such a way as to make the first two years suitable for inclusion in *either* an Ordinary *or* an Honours degree.

4. NUMBERS

Honours Italian students number 2 to 3 a year; the average number of Ordinary degree students is about 15.

Information supplied by Mr. P. M. Brown, Lecturer in Italian

UNIVERSITY OF EDINBURGH

Department of Italian

I. COURSES OF STUDY

1. TYPES OF COURSES

The following Italian courses are available:

(*a*) An *Elementary language course* (one year);

(*b*) The *Ordinary M.A.* courses, I and II;

(*c*) *Honours M.A.* with French or Spanish or Latin or English Language or Literature;

(*d*) *Honours* in Italian only; this is a Second Honours degree, i.e. only students who have already graduated with Honours in some other language are entitled to read for this degree in Italian Honours only;

(*e*) Italian literature for English Honours students;

(*f*) Italian language for History Honours students;

(*g*) A Dante tutorial open to all Honours students.

2. CHARACTERISTICS OF COURSES

The *Elementary language course* usually starts with 30 to 45 students but ends with 20 to 35. Half of these intend to take First Ordinary Italian.

The *Ordinary course* includes a full history of Italian literature with texts and two special subjects (Dante and ten *cantos*; one of the major classics).

Intermediate Honours. The studies include two special subjects usually taken from different centuries and of widely different interest. The subjects are changed every year so as to enable Honours students to read in class on six different phases of Italian culture. (This course at a lower level is used also as the second Ordinary course.)

The *Final Honours* curriculum can be either Type 'A' with French or Spanish or English Literature as a secondary subject or Type 'B' with Latin as a secondary language.

Special courses: (*e*) to (*g*)

Honours English: two subjects are chosen every year dealing with Italian writers or periods which influenced English literature more than other writers or periods.

Honours History: a course in practical Italian is provided, meant to enable students to read historical documents.

For *Honours students:* reading of the *Divina Commedia* at the highest possible level of philological criticism.

3. COMBINATION OF SUBJECTS

For combining Honours Italian with French, Spanish or Latin or English Language or Literature see I.2 above.

For the Ordinary M.A. Italian can be included in a wide range of combinations of subjects, for which the calendar should be consulted.

4. RESIDENCE ABROAD

Residence abroad and two months attendance at a summer course at an Italian university are required by this Department as a help towards a better knowledge of the language. The Scottish Education Department makes a full year abroad a condition for certain teaching appointments and proper measures have been set down to satisfy this requirement for students intending to become teachers.

II. ADMISSION TO COURSES

1. QUALIFICATIONS REQUIRED

Ordinary grade ('O' Level) for Honours students is required.

Advanced Level Italian for all students taking graduating courses, but Italian can be started from scratch in our Elementary Italian non-graduating classes (see I.1 above).

2. SELECTION OF STUDENTS

No selection is made for entrance to the Italian Department. Students 'select' themselves when they abandon the Department finding Italian too hard going, or when the staff fail them at the end of their first year, or ask them to stop attending during their first year if unsatisfactory.

3. TRANSFER

Students are admitted to the Honours course if they fulfil the entrance qualifications gained in the Ordinary class. Within limits transfer between Ordinary and Honours courses is possible in both directions.

4. NUMBERS

From one to four students annually enter the Honours class.

Information supplied by Professor M. M. Rossi

UNIVERSITY OF GLASGOW

Department of Italian Language and Literature[1]

I. COURSES OF STUDY

1. TYPES OF COURSES

Italian can be taken in the following courses:

(*a*) *Ordinary* and (*b*) *Higher Ordinary:* these qualify for graduation in the Ordinary M.A. degree;

(*c*) *Honours:* a two-year course. It is necessary to have passed Higher Ordinary first.

2. CHARACTERISTICS OF COURSES

The courses are more or less traditional.

(*a*) *Ordinary:*
   (1) translation into and from Italian and elementary history of the language;
   (2) prescribed books and general history of 19th-century literature.

(*b*) *Higher Ordinary:*
   (1) translation into and from Italian;
   (2) essay and special period (at present the 13th century as introduction to Dante);
   (3) prescribed books.

(*c*) *Honours:*
   (1) translation into and from Italian;
   (2) Italian literature up to 1550;
   (3) Italian literature after 1550;
   (4) essay;
   (5) history of the Italian language and old texts;
   (6) special subject (social, art or linguistics): a dissertation may be written in lieu of this.

All classes have an oral examination.

3. COMBINATION OF SUBJECTS

French is the subject most commonly taken in Honours with Italian, but cases of German and Spanish occur. Two languages are compulsory.

---

[1] This entry is an unrevised copy of the entry submitted by this Department to the 1961 edition. Applicants are strongly advised to check the information by reference to the current prospectus.

4. RESIDENCE ABROAD

Residence abroad is desirable; all Honours students spend at least one long vacation (three months) in Italy and usually one Easter vacation.

5. METHODS OF STUDY

The Department has an Italian lecturer for conversational classes and reading. Since the Honours classes are small, it is possible to run them mostly as tutorials.

6. OTHER ACTIVITIES

There is an Italian Society run by the students themselves, which meets once a fortnight. Students also pay a reduced subscription to the Dante Alighieri Society.

II. ADMISSION TO COURSES

1. QUALIFICATIONS REQUIRED

Knowledge of Latin to at least Ordinary grade of the Scottish Certificate of Education is required.

Italian must be at the Higher grade, but students are admitted to the Ordinary Class if they have passed the Ordinary grade, but are not permitted to sit the degree examination, unless they pass the Higher in March.

We run an elementary class starting from scratch, but this does not count towards the degree; it is only to enable students to pass their Higher grade of the Scottish Certificate of Education.

2. SELECTION OF STUDENTS

Any student who has passed the necessary preliminary examination is admitted to the Ordinary class.

3. TRANSFER

Honours students are expected to have reached a good standard in the Higher Ordinary examination.

4. NUMBERS

In Italian, there are usually one, two or three Honours students per annum.

Information supplied by Professor M. F. M. Meiklejohn

GENERAL SCHEMES OF STUDIES
WITH MODERN LANGUAGES

UNIVERSITY OF CAMBRIDGE

Faculty of Modern and Medieval Languages [1]

I. COURSES OF STUDY

The qualifications for B.A. Honours are:

 (*i*) nine terms' residence;

 (*ii*) reaching Honours standard in any two of the examinations known as 'Tripos' examinations.

1. TYPES OF COURSES

In Modern and Medieval Languages there are courses of study for

 (*a*) the *Modern and Medieval Languages Tripos*, which is divided into two parts. The first part (Tripos Part I) is taken after a one-year or a two-year course of study and the second (Tripos Part II) after two years or one year of more specialized study;

 (*b*) the *Preliminary Examination* for each part of the Tripos;

 (*c*) an *Oral Examination in Modern Languages*;

 (*d*) a *Certificate of Competent Knowledge in Foreign Languages*;

 (*e*) *Special Examination* in certain modern languages for the Ordinary B.A. degree;

 (*f*) the *Diploma in Slavonic Studies*.

2. CHARACTERISTICS OF COURSES

Two languages must be offered for Part I of the Modern and Medieval Languages Tripos, and in Part II any combination of subjects from a specified schedule.

Tripos Part I consists of composition, translation, essay and literary papers in each language.

Tripos Part II consists of a large choice of literary, historical and philological papers, from which a certain number must be chosen. An essay, and a composition and translation paper in a language appertaining to the candidate's choice of other papers must be offered. The Oral Examination in Modern Languages includes dictation, reading, exposition by the candidate of one or several subjects, proposed by the examiners, and conversation. The subjects for conversation and exposition are taken mainly from books prescribed by the Faculty Board of Modern and Medieval Languages.

The Certificate of Competent Knowledge in Foreign Languages is a slightly modified version of the Part I syllabus.

[1] For further information on German see p. 125 and on Italian p. 308.

The Diploma of Slavonic Studies is a shortened course of studies intended for graduates in other subjects. This Diploma is likely to be modified in the near future.

3. COMBINATION OF SUBJECTS

Many combinations of subjects are possible, for which the *Students' Handbook of the University and Colleges of Cambridge* should be consulted.

It should be pointed out that candidates who have taken Part I in another Tripos may take Part I or Part II of the Modern and Medieval Languages Tripos in order to qualify for a degree, and candidates who have taken Part I of the Modern and Medieval Languages Tripos may take Part I or Part II of another tripos in order to qualify for a degree. These combinations are subject to the requirements of the various Triposes allowing the examinations to be taken within the terms available to the candidate.

4. RESIDENCE ABROAD

Residence abroad is desirable in the vacations, but cannot be required in term because of the University's regulations concerning residence of undergraduates.

5. METHODS OF STUDY

The tutorial system (i.e. teaching by supervisors in each subject) is in force, but the University also provides formal lectures and classes.

II. ADMISSION TO COURSES

1. QUALIFICATIONS REQUIRED

Admission to a College, which is competitive, secures at the same time admission to the University. University entrance requirement is the Previous Examination, or an equivalent (see *Commonwealth Universities Yearbook* 1964, p. 1648, but the requirements for Previous and Exemption are likely to be changed).

Languages taught in the Department of Slavonic Studies, Scandinavian, Italian, Spanish, and Other Languages (Dutch, Hungarian, Modern Greek, Portuguese, Provençal and Vulgar Latin) can be started after the undergraduate has arrived in residence.

2. SELECTION OF STUDENTS

Colleges select all the students. Details of College entrance and scholarship examinations are given in a special number of the *Cambridge University Reporter* published annually in May and obtainable (price 6d.) from the University Press.

3. TRANSFER

Students are admitted to their courses on entrance.

4. NUMBERS

Approximately 180 Honours students are annually admitted to the Modern and Medieval Languages Tripos.

Information supplied by Dr. R. G. Popperwell, Secretary of the Board of the Faculty of Modern and Medieval Languages

UNIVERSITY OF EAST ANGLIA
School of European Studies

I. COURSES OF STUDY

1. TYPES OF COURSES

(*a*) *B.A. with Honours in European Studies.* The School of European Studies offers courses designed to introduce students to the civilization of Europe through the study of history, literature and philosophy. The study of a foreign European language or languages is also an essential part of the work of all students in the School, irrespective of the kind of specialization they ultimately choose. The main languages of the School in 1964 are German and Russian.

(*b*) *M.A. in European Studies.* It is proposed to institute in 1967 a one-year programme of studies leading to the degree of M.A. in European Studies.

2. CHARACTERISTICS OF COURSES

In the early years of the School's development, attention will be directed in the main to two areas of Europe: Germany and her Northern neighbours; and Eastern Europe. For the present the emphasis is on modern rather than medieval or ancient times.

The course is basically one of three years and leads to an Honours degree in Arts. All undergraduates in their first two terms in the School take a largely common course, which includes some literary, some historical and some philosophical study; they also do intensive work in the language or languages of their choice. A Preliminary Examination is held at the end of an undergraduate's second term; marks obtained in the Examination are combined with marks during the two terms of course work, the latter accounting for up to half the final assessment. The Preliminary Examination must be passed before the student can proceed; any student who fails the Examination at the first attempt repeats it at the end of the third term. Students who pass the Examination then decide whether their subsequent studies are to have an historical, a literary, a philosophical or a regional emphasis, and their work becomes progressively more specialized, though never narrowly so. Throughout the course they will continue to make a study of their language or languages.

3. COMBINATION OF SUBJECTS

The structure of the courses is designed to encourage a student not only to choose freely from among a number of different options taught within the School itself, but also to include in his work, if he so wishes and if it can be arranged, subjects taught in other Schools of

M.L.—M

the University, particularly the School of English Studies and the School of Social Studies.

4. RESIDENCE ABROAD

All students of the School who include the study of German in their course will be required, as an integral and essential part of their work for their degree, to spend a year abroad in a country in which German is normally spoken; this they can generally do under the official scheme as paid assistants in a grammar school. Students who include Russian in their course are urged wherever possible to attend an approved course either in the U.S.S.R. or elsewhere, and to make what vacation visits to the U.S.S.R. are possible. Students who include both German and Russian in their course may choose between these two alternatives, or do both.

5. METHODS OF STUDY

While provision is made for lecture courses of the traditional type, the emphasis throughout the University of East Anglia is upon teaching in small groups, from the individual tutorial on the one hand to the seminar (in groups of 8 to 20) and the discussion class (in groups of 12 to 30) on the other.

II. ADMISSION TO COURSES

1. QUALIFICATIONS REQUIRED

Passes in two approved subjects at Advanced Level are required, one of which must be in a modern foreign language. This need not necessarily be in German or Russian, though for certain of the courses in the School (e.g. those including the specialist study of literature) it might be inadvisable to start without an Advanced Level qualification in the relevant language. A working knowledge of French, sufficient to allow works of French literature and scholarship to be read with reasonable understanding in the original, is also normally looked for in every student on entry.

2. NUMBERS

A total of about 50 students will be admitted annually to the School in its early years.

Information supplied by Professor J. W. McFarlane

UNIVERSITY OF ESSEX

School of Comparative Studies
(Departments of Government and Literature) [1]

I. COURSES OF STUDY

1. TYPES OF COURSES

In 1965 the School of Comparative Studies will offer (*a*) *a scheme of study in Government* and (*b*) *a scheme of study in Literature*. These will provide parallel chronological courses comparing aspects of the development and life of a country or region (such as its political institutions or its literature) with the same aspects of British life: for example, schemes will be based on the development and present state of British and American political institutions and on 19th- and 20th-century Russian and English literature. The regions for comparative study with Britain will initially be:

(*i*) The United States of America and Canada;
(*ii*) The Soviet Union;
(*iii*) Latin America.

In order to appreciate fully the literary or political culture of a society, a very deep knowledge of the language of that society is required. Students who do not have a good knowledge of the language of their area of specialization (Russian or Spanish or Portuguese) will need to spend a preliminary year following a course of intensive language study at the University Language Centre, which was opened in October 1964. No previous knowledge of the language is required to enter the Centre.

The schemes of study in both Literature and Government are of three years' duration and lead to the award of the B.A. degree with Honours. For those students required to spend a preliminary year at the Language Centre, the duration of the course will be four years.

2. CHARACTERISTICS OF COURSES

(*i*) *Common first year*. In the first year all students in the School will follow a common closely integrated group of courses. These will include the study of some of the problems of contemporary society by means of selected English and foreign texts, as well as an examination of the cultural, social and political crisis of the period 1688–1815 in England. Students will not be committed to a particular scheme of study until the end of their first year.

(*ii*) *Government*. The second year of the scheme will provide

[1] For further information on Spanish see p. 211 and on Russian p. 270.

students with the historical background to their area of specialization. The problems of government in the world today will be studied with regard to the part played by social and economic forces in the structure of institutions as well as in the conduct of politics. There will also be a course on the history of political thought, mainly devoted to the development of political ideas in Western Europe up to the middle of the 19th century.

The third year of the scheme will then concentrate on the comparative study of politics in the two selected areas. Students will be encouraged to undertake longer studies in the nature of a short thesis and these will be taken into account in the awarding of the final degree.

(*iii*) *Literature.* The study of literature in the School of Comparative Studies will include courses in modern history and in the development and structure of political and social institutions, and students will be required to study, along with English literature, one foreign literature. Initially, courses will be offered in three such literatures, viz. Russian, North American and Latin American. But it is intended that students with qualifications in languages other than Spanish and Russian (e.g. Advanced Level passes in French, German, Italian, Latin or Greek) will be enabled to profit from the work they have done.

Though certain 17th-century authors will be studied (e.g. in the case of English, Shakespeare), the emphasis will be on literature of the last three centuries; and this will be studied over the whole three years of the scheme in chronological order, beginning at 1700 or 1660.

In the second year, literature of the 19th century in Great Britain and in one of the other three selected cultures will be studied. Students will be invited to select, from a fairly wide range of alternatives, certain themes to be studied intensively, rather than attempting a general survey.

In the last year, however, when students will concern themselves with literature of the present century, the courses will be designed on the assumption that this literature is homogeneous and international. Such broad themes as 'naturalism' and 'symbolism' will be pursued so as to show how they are equally meaningful in each of the four literatures particularly studied, as well as in others.

Though literary study will be conducted with strict attention to chronology and in combination with political and social history, as much attention will be paid to critical elucidation and evaluation of specific works of literature as to literary history. Some of the tasks assigned for written work may go beyond the scope of the essay and demand something in the nature of a thesis or monograph, or a small research project undertaken either singly or in small teams. In certain cases, work of this nature will be taken into account, along with performances in written examinations at the end of the second and third years, in assessing the class of degree to be awarded.

(*iv*) *Examinations*. Progress examinations will normally be held in June at the end of the first year. A degree examination will be held in the summer at the end of a three year scheme of study, although some parts of the examination may take place earlier in the scheme (but not before June at the end of the second year).

3. COMBINATIONS OF SUBJECTS

After the common first year, students will be required to follow either one or the other of the specialist schemes of study. There will be no ancillary or subsidiary subjects.

4. RESIDENCES ABROAD

Residence abroad will be encouraged.

5. METHODS OF STUDY

The dominant form of teaching will be discussion classes of up to ten students, though lecture classes will play an important part, particularly in the student's first year. Instruction will be given on methods of study at individual tutorials.

II. ADMISSION TO COURSES

1. QUALIFICATIONS REQUIRED

Apart from the general entrance requirements of the University, applicants for admission to the School of Comparative Studies are required to have passed two subjects at Advanced Level. Applicants intending to specialize in Russian or South American studies would normally be expected to have passed a language at Advanced Level, though this need not necessarily be Russian or Spanish or Portuguese.

2. SELECTION OF STUDENTS

Selection is made on the basis of an applicant's performance both at Ordinary Level and Advanced Level, and careful attention is paid to reports obtained from the headmaster or headmistress. In most cases, applicants are invited to attend an informal interview with the professor of the Department.

3. TRANSFER

Special attention will, at all stages, be paid to the problems of students who wish to transfer from one scheme of study to another, although in the case of transfer between two unlike subjects, a student's total period of study at the University may be extended beyond the normal three years.

Information supplied by the Registrar, University of Essex

UNIVERSITY OF OXFORD

Faculty of Medieval and Modern European Languages and Literature (other than English)[1]

I. COURSES OF STUDY

1. TYPES OF COURSES

The following European languages can be offered for examination at Honours level: French, German, Italian, Spanish, Russian, Medieval and Modern Greek, and Portuguese.

Students may read for:

(*a*) an *Honours degree* in only one of these languages;

(*b*) an *Honours degree in two languages*, choosing one as their first and the other as their second language.

Before being able to opt for any Final Honours course, however, the student must pass the qualifying First Public Examination. For students who propose to read languages, this is usually the Preliminary Examination for Modern Languages, but the statutory qualification for admission to the Final Honour School can be obtained by passing any one of the various examinations which constitute the First Public Examination.

(*c*) French, German, Italian and Spanish may also be offered in the *Final Pass School*; but undergraduates are now only rarely admitted to the University to read for the Pass School.

(*d*) There is also a postgraduate course in Russian in combination with one or two of the following languages: Bulgarian, Czech, Polish and Serbo-Croat. The course includes language, literature and history and leads to the *Diploma in Slavonic Studies*. The period of study may be spread over one or two academic years and the examination comprises five subjects which can be selected from some twenty options.

(*e*) Candidates may read for the postgraduate degrees of Bachelor of Letters and Doctor of Philosophy in modern languages and there has recently been introduced a postgraduate degree of Bachelor of Philosophy in General and Comparative Literature, in which it will be possible to offer English along with other European literatures.

2. CHARACTERISTICS OF COURSES

A Preliminary Examination for Modern Languages is held in March and in June. Candidates normally take it in March in their

[1] For further information on French, see p. 72; German, p. 168; Spanish, p. 241; Russian, p. 289; Italian, p. 326.

first year of residence. Two languages must be offered, either two modern languages (the same languages which may be offered in the Final Honour School), or one classical (Latin or Greek) and the other modern. Compulsory papers in each language are set in translation from and (except in Latin and Ancient Greek) into the language, with two papers on prescribed texts, one on texts to be studied as literature, the second on texts to be studied in relation to general trends in literature or thought or to historical background. In the classical languages there are two papers of prescribed books. There is an oral examination in modern languages.

Examinations at Honours level are held in the month of June in each year, and are normally taken by candidates in their third year. The required standard is the same in a sole, first or second language, but the history of the languages, texts illustrative of medieval literature and free composition in the language are required only in a candidate's sole or first language. Translation from and into the language, prescribed literary texts, and a period of literature, are required in any language offered and a candidate must show knowledge of so much of the thought and history of the country in question as is necessary for the understanding of the literature. An optional subject is required from candidates seeking a place in the first class. There is a compulsory oral examination in which distinction may be awarded.

3. COMBINATION OF SUBJECTS

No combination of subjects is possible, except those indicated in 1. (*b*).

4. RESIDENCE ABROAD

Residence abroad for one term may, on certain conditions, exempt an undergraduate from one of his nine terms of residence for the degree of Bachelor of Arts. Residence abroad for a longer period necessitates postponement of the final examination until the end of the fourth year. Undergraduates in fact go abroad rarely for one term, not infrequently for three terms, but only with the approval of their College, which is in all respects the relevant authority. Some Colleges encourage undergraduates to intercalate a year abroad as assistants.

5. METHODS OF STUDY

The tutorial system is in force in all Colleges.

II. ADMISSION TO COURSES

1. QUALIFICATIONS REQUIRED

Irrespective of proposed subjects of study, Latin or Greek at 'O' Level is required from all candidates who have not passed at 'A' Level in either mathematics or a scientific subject.

Languages taught in the Faculty cannot normally be started from scratch.

2. SELECTION OF STUDENTS

The selection of students is entirely in the hands of the Colleges. A new admissions procedure has recently come into effect and information about this may be obtained either from Colleges or from the Oxford Colleges Admissions Office, 58 Banbury Road, Oxford, and also from a supplement to the *Oxford University Gazette* published early in the summer of each year and available from the Oxford University Press Depository, 116 High Street, Oxford.

3. TRANSFER

Since the Honours course is not begun until after the First Public Examination, the final decision as to which subject will be read for Honours is not taken until this examination has been passed. Any transfer to other subjects is at the discretion of the College.

4. NUMBERS

The number of students normally admitted to read for Honours in Medieval and Modern European Languages is between 200 and 250 a year.

Information supplied by Mr. A. D. Crow, Chairman of the Board of the Faculty of Medieval and Modern European Languages and Literature

THE UNIVERSITY OF SUSSEX

The School of European Studies

I. COURSES OF STUDY

1. TYPES OF COURSES

The University of Sussex is organized not in departments but in Schools of Studies, within which undergraduates specialize in some particular discipline—their *major subject*—while sharing certain *common subjects* with undergraduates majoring in other fields. French, German and Russian are studied in the School of European Studies and may be pursued as either

(*a*) a *major subject* for an *Honours degree*, or

(*b*) a *common subject* by undergraduates whose major subject is English, History, Philosophy, Sociology, Economics, providing them with an opportunity to improve their knowledge of the language for translation purposes, but also to study some literature in that language.

N.B.—The formal study of *two* foreign languages is not possible.

The Honours course (where French, German or Russian is the major subject) lasts four years, of which the third year is spent either at a foreign university or as assistant in a foreign school. Admission to the Honours course is conditional upon satisfactory results in the B.A. Preliminary Examination (taken after two terms).

There are no General degree courses.

2. CHARACTERISTICS OF COURSES

A. *Preliminary course*

(*a*) Translation and prose composition in the language proposed for major study (one hour per week);

(*b*) Critical reading of set texts, including, for purposes of comparison, some major works of European literature to be studied by all language students regardless of their choice of language (and therefore in translation where necessary). (One tutorial hour per week);

(*c*) Tutorials and lectures in Philosophy and History: common courses taken by all undergraduates.

B. *B.A. Honours course.* Undergraduates are taught and examined in a total of ten subjects, as follows:

(*a*) *Common papers*

The following courses are taken in common with all undergraduates in the School of European Studies:

(*i*) The European Tradition (texts of Plato, Virgil, Dante, studied to illumine aspects of the civilization of Greece, Rome and medieval Christendom); or The Russian Foundations (for students of Russian; with study of Byzantine and early Russian texts).

(*ii*) The Modern European Mind (study of texts illuminating major intellectual and moral issues in modern Western society and culture: Marxism, Existentialism, Psychology, etc.).

(*iii*) A period of European history.

(*iv*) A paper in philosophy.

(*v*) A translation paper in French, German or Russian (to include a prose, in the case of candidates majoring in a modern language, for translation into the language of their choice).

A searching oral test forms part of the final degree examination.

(*b*) *Papers in major subjects*

either *French*

(*vi*) A topic in French history and literature (e.g. 'Politics and religion in the age of Pascal', or 'French Romanticism and the social question, 1830–48').

(*vii*) French Moralists (a study of the tradition of moral discourse in France centred on Montaigne, Pascal and Rousseau, but with the possibility of a further 'special interest' being offered within this general field).

(*viii*) French Poetry (both individual poets and poetic movements, with detailed study of some representative French poets from Villon to the present).

(*ix*) French Drama (representative plays by major French dramatists from Garnier to the present; some knowledge of the work of other European playwrights expected).

(*x*) French Fiction (representative French fiction from Madame de Lafayette to the present; some knowledge of the work of other European novelists expected).

or *German*

(*vi*) A topic in German history and literature (e.g. 'Naturalism and the industrialization of Germany', or 'Contemporary Germany').

(*vii*) Goethe.

(*viii*) German Poetry (representative poetry from Luther's hymns to the present day and detailed study of the complete work of one major poet).

(*ix*) German Drama (representative plays from Lessing to Brecht and detailed study of the complete work of one major dramatist).

(*x*) German Fiction (representative novels and *Novellen* from the 18th century to the present day; for purposes of comparison some knowledge will be expected of novels by other European writers).

or *Russian*

(*vi*) Russian History (a choice of one of three periods), or a topic in Russian history and literature (e.g. Literature and Revolution 1905–1930).

(*vii*) Pushkin and his Contemporaries (their work to be studied as a whole, and not piecemeal in other papers).

(*viii*) Russian Poetry (the major poets from the 17th century to the present).

(*ix*) 20th-century Russian Literature (the detailed study of any three from a list of important topics).

(*x*) Russian Fiction (the major works of the great Russian novelists and short-story writers of the 19th century, with a closer study of any one writer).

3. COMBINATION OF SUBJECTS

All undergraduates in the School of European Studies must study one language. If this language is not their major subject, they will be given opportunities of making use of their linguistic knowledge in studying other subjects, and of taking at least one course in the appropriate literature.

It is not possible to combine two *major* subjects of study. A limited choice is permitted within the framework of the five common papers. The five major papers must all be in the same major area of study.

4. RESIDENCE ABROAD

All students whose major subject is a language are required to spend their third year at an appropriate foreign university or in a foreign school as assistants. They are expected to prepare and send home a short dissertation in the foreign language while they are abroad.

5. METHODS OF STUDY

(*i*) All tuition is based on tutorials (at most two undergraduates attend each tutorial hour) for which weekly written work is expected. Normally one term is devoted to each paper.

(*ii*) In addition there are weekly language classes (where written translation exercises are corrected) and oral classes conducted, in the case of French and German, by a *lecteur* and *Lektor*.

(*iii*) Lectures are voluntary; but a full lecture list is offered, especially for guiding undergraduates through such new courses as The Modern European Mind.

6. OTHER ACTIVITIES

From the beginning of the University undergraduates studying modern languages have organized social, theatrical and musical occasions and regularly invited guest speakers.

II. ADMISSION TO COURSES

1. QUALIFICATIONS REQUIRED

Two G.C.E. passes at 'A' Level are required, one of which must be in the language in which a candidate intends to major. For 'O' Level requirements see the Prospectus of the University of Sussex; Latin is not required.

2. SELECTION OF STUDENTS

Candidates are selected on the basis of interview and in the light of their examination results and headmaster's report.

3. TRANSFER

Admission is granted to the Faculty of Arts and undergraduates are allowed to change their major subject of study, provided that:

(*a*) they gain the approval of the Dean of the Schools of Studies concerned;

(*b*) they have an adequate knowledge of the language they wish to study.

4. NUMBERS

At present (1963) approximately 30-40 undergraduates are admitted annually who intend to major in French, approximately 10-15 who intend to major in German, and approximately 5-10 who intend to major in Russian.

Information supplied by Professor Martin Wight, Dean of the School of European
Studies

UNIVERSITY OF YORK

Department of Language

I. COURSES OF STUDY

1 and 2. TYPES AND CHARACTERISTICS OF COURSES

No 'Language and Literature' departments are at present envisaged at the University of York, but the Department of Language will conduct teaching and research in the fields of general linguistics and the psychology and sociology of language (with special reference to the language problems of multilingual countries) and will also, in conjunction with the Department of Education, offer service courses in an increasing number of European, African and Asian languages. The Department of Education will pay special attention to the training of language teachers in modern methods based on contrastive descriptions of the languages involved.

Linguistics may be taken as a Subsidiary subject by candidates for the first degrees of the University, and M.A. and Ph.D. courses will also be offered, for entry to which the equivalent of a good first degree and command of an ancient, medieval or modern language in addition to modern English is required.

Information supplied by Professor Le Page

APPENDIX

Summary of Modern Language Studies at British Universities

The two tables below list the studies in modern languages and related subjects at universities in the United Kingdom. Table 1 names the universities in alphabetical order and shows which languages they offer. Table 2 is arranged according to languages and shows where these can be studied.[1] Courses of study described in this *Guide* are indicated by italics. *The inclusion of a language or related subject in these tables does not necessarily mean that the courses provided lead to a degree. For further details the interested reader must obtain the latest information from the calendar or prospectus of the university concerned.*

TABLE 1

Universities	Languages
BIRMINGHAM	*French*, French-Canadian Studies, *German*, Greek (Modern), *Italian*, Latin-American Studies, Linguistics, Old Provençal, Portuguese, *Russian*, *Spanish*.
BRISTOL	Catalan, *French*, *German*, *Italian*, Portuguese, *Russian*, *Spanish*.
CAMBRIDGE	Akkadian, Altaic, Arabic, Aramaic, Catalan, Chinese, Comparative Philology, Czech, Danish, Dutch, French, *German*, Greek (Modern), Hebrew, Hungarian, Indian Studies, Iranian Studies, *Italian*, Japanese, Linguistics, Norwegian, Oriental Studies, Pali, Persian, Phonetics, Polish, Portuguese, Prakrit, Provençal, Rumanian, Russian, Sanskrit, Serbo-Croat, Slovak, Spanish, Swedish, Tibetan, Turkish.
DURHAM	Arabic, Catalan, Chinese, Egyptian *French*, *German*, Hebrew, Linguistics, Oriental Studies, Persian, Portuguese, *Russian*, *Spanish*, Turkish.
EAST ANGLIA	*European Studies*, German, Russian, Norwegian.
ESSEX	French, German, Latin-American Studies, *Russian*, *Spanish*.

Although some ancient languages (e.g. Sanskrit) have been included in this list as 'related subjects', Latin and classical Greek, widely available at most universities, are not specifically mentioned. Students interested in modern Greek and modern Hebrew should make enquiries, wherever this is not expressly stated, whether these two languages are taught only in their classical or also in their modern form.

Universities	Languages
EXETER	*French, German,* Italian, *Russian, Spanish.*
HULL	*French, German, Italian,* Linguistics, *Russian, Spanish,* Swedish.
KEELE	*French, German, Russian.*
LANCASTER	*French.*
LEEDS	Arabic, Chinese, *French, German,* Hebrew, Icelandic (Modern), Italian, Linguistics, Phonetics, Portuguese, Provençal, *Russian,* Semitic Languages, *Spanish.*
LEICESTER	*French, German.*
LIVERPOOL	Arabic (Classical), Catalan, Celtic Studies, Dutch, Egyptian, Esperanto, *French, German, Italian,* Portuguese, *Russian, Spanish,* Spanish-American Studies.
LONDON: BEDFORD COLLEGE	Dutch, *French, German, Italian.*
BIRKBECK COLLEGE	Dutch, *French, German, Italian,* Spanish.
KING'S COLLEGE	*French, German,* Greek (Modern), Latin-American Literature, Portuguese, *Spanish.*
QUEEN MARY COLLEGE	*French, German,* Latin-American Literature, Portuguese, Russian, *Spanish.*
ROYAL HOLLOWAY COLLEGE	*French, German.*
SCHOOL OF ORIENTAL AND AFRICAN STUDIES (SOAS)	Languages of India, Pakistan and Ceylon, South East Asia, and the Far East (including Chinese and Japanese), the Near and Middle East (including Arabic, Modern Hebrew, Persian and Turkish), African Languages, Linguistics, Phonetics.
SCHOOL OF SLAVONIC AND EAST EUROPEAN STUDIES (Slavonic)	Albanian, Bulgarian, Czech, Hungarian, Polish, Rumanian, *Russian,* Serbo-Croat, Slovak, Slovene.
UNIVERSITY COLLEGE	Comparative Philology, *French, German,* Hebrew, *Italian,* Phonetics, Scandinavian Studies (including Danish, Icelandic, Norwegian and Swedish), Spanish.

Universities	Languages
LONDON (*cont.*) :	
WESTFIELD COLLEGE	Catalan, *French, German, Italian*, Portuguese, *Spanish*. Romance Philology, including the rudiments of Old Provençal and Rumanian.
MANCHESTER	Arabic, Celtic, *French, German*, Hebrew, Irish, *Italian*, Latin-American Studies, Linguistics, Oriental Studies (Eygptian, Persian, Turkish), Phonetics, Portuguese, *Russian, Spanish*, Swedish, Welsh.
NEWCASTLE	Dutch, *French, German*, Latin-American Studies, Linguistics, Phonetics, Portuguese, Scandinavian Studies (Danish, Norwegian, Swedish), *Spanish*.
NOTTINGHAM	Catalan, Danish, *French, German*, Italian, Old Provençal, Portuguese, Slavonic Studies (Polish, *Russian*, Serbo-Croat), *Spanish*, Swedish.
OXFORD	Arabic, Aramaic, Bulgarian, Celtic, Chinese, Czech, Egyptian, *French, German*, Greek (Medieval and Modern). Hebrew, *Italian*, Japanese, Latin-American Studies, Pali, Persian, Polish, Portuguese, *Russian*, Sanskrit, Serbo-Croat, Slavonic Studies, *Spanish*, Turkish.
READING	Danish, Dutch, *French, German, Italian*, Linguistics.
SHEFFIELD	Catalan, Danish, Dutch, *French, German*, Latin-American Studies, Portuguese, Provençal, *Spanish*.
SOUTHAMPTON	*French, German, Spanish*.
SUSSEX	African Studies, Asian Studies, *European Studies* (*French, German, Russian*).
WARWICK	*French*, Italian.
YORK	*Linguistics*.
WALES:	
ABERYSTWYTH	*French, German*, Irish, Italian, Phonetics, Russian, Spanish, Swedish, Welsh.
BANGOR	Arabic, *French, German*, Irish, *Italian*, Linguistics, Norwegian, Phonetics, Provençal, *Russian*, Welsh.

Universities	Languages
WALES (*cont.*) :	
CARDIFF	Catalan, *French, German*, Italian, Linguistics, Phonetics, Portuguese, *Russian, Spanish*, Swedish, Welsh.
SWANSEA	*French, German*, Linguistics, *Italian, Russian*, Welsh.
LAMPETER	*French*, German, Welsh.
ABERDEEN	Arabic, Celtic (Gaelic), *French. German*, Greek (Modern), Hebrew, *Italian*, Russian, *Spanish*, Swedish.
EDINBURGH	Arabic, Celtic, *French, German, Italian*, Latin-American Studies, Linguistics, Persian, Phonetics, Portuguese, Provençal, *Russian*, Sanskrit, *Spanish*, Turkish.
GLASGOW	African Studies, Arabic, Catalan, Celtic, Czech, *French, German*, Hebrew, *Italian*, Latin-American Studies, Linguistics, Norwegian, Polish, Portuguese, *Russian*, Scottish Language and Literature, *Spanish*, Slovak.
ST. ANDREWS	Arabic, Catalan, *French, German*, Hebrew, Polish, *Russian*, Scottish, Semitic Languages, *Spanish.*
BELFAST	Catalan, Celtic, *French, German*, Portuguese, *Russian, Spanish*, Swedish, Welsh.

TABLE 2

Languages	Universities
AFRICAN STUDIES	London (SOAS),[1] Sussex, Glasgow.
AKKADIAN	Cambridge.
ALBANIAN	London (SOAS, Slavonic).[2]
ALTAIC	Cambridge.
ARABIC (Classical and Modern)	Cambridge, Durham, Leeds, Liverpool, London (SOAS), Manchester, Oxford, Wales (Bangor), Aberdeen, Edinburgh, Glasgow, St. Andrews.
ARAMAIC	Cambridge, Oxford.

[1] SOAS: School of Oriental and African Studies.
[2] Slavonic: School of Slavonic and East European Studies.

Languages	Universities
ASIAN STUDIES	Cambridge, London (SOAS), Sussex.
BENGALI	London (SOAS).
BULGARIAN	*London (Slavonic)*, Oxford.
BURMESE	London (SOAS).
CATALAN	Bristol, Cambridge, Durham, Liverpool, London (Westfield), Nottingham, Sheffield, Wales (Cardiff), Glasgow, St. Andrews, Belfast.
CELTIC	Liverpool, Manchester, Oxford, Wales (Bangor), Aberdeen, Edinburgh, Glasgow, Belfast.
CENTRAL EUROPEAN STUDIES	*London (Slavonic)*.
CHINESE	Cambridge, Durham, Leeds, London (SOAS), Oxford.
COMPARATIVE LITERARY STUDIES	*Essex*, Manchester, *Oxford*.
COMPARATIVE PHILO-LOGY	Cambridge, London (University), Oxford.
CZECH	Cambridge, *London (Slavonic)*, Oxford, Glasgow.
DANISH	Cambridge, London (University), Newcastle, Nottingham, Reading, Sheffield.
DUTCH	Cambridge, Liverpool, London (Bedford, Birkbeck), Newcastle, Reading, Sheffield.
EGYPTIAN	Durham, Liverpool, Manchester, Oxford.
ESPERANTO	Liverpool.
EUROPEAN STUDIES	*East Anglia, Sussex*.
FRENCH	*Birmingham, Bristol,* Cambridge, *Durham,* Essex, *Exeter, Hull, Keele, Lancaster, Leeds, Leicester, Liverpool, London (Bedford, Birkbeck, King's, Queen Mary, Royal Holloway, University, Westfield), Manchester, Newcastle, Nottingham, Oxford, Reading, Sheffield, Southampton, Sussex, Warwick, Wales (Aberystwyth, Bangor, Cardiff, Swansea), Lampeter, Aberdeen, Edinburgh, Glasgow, St. Andrews, Belfast.*

Languages	Universities
FRENCH-CANADIAN STUDIES	Birmingham.
GERMAN	*Birmingham, Bristol, Cambridge, Durham, East Anglia,* Essex, *Exeter, Hull, Keele, Leeds, Leicester, Liverpool, London* (*Bedford, Birkbeck, King's, Queen Mary, Royal Holloway, University, Westfield*), *Manchester, Newcastle, Nottingham, Oxford, Reading, Sheffield, Southampton, Sussex, Wales* (*Aberystwyth, Bangor, Cardiff, Swansea*), Lampeter, *Aberdeen, Edinburgh, Glasgow, St. Andrews, Belfast.*
GREEK (Modern)	Birmingham, Cambridge, London (King's), Oxford, Aberdeen.
HEBREW (including Modern)	Cambridge, Durham, Leeds, London (SOAS, University), Manchester, Oxford, Aberdeen, Glasgow, St. Andrews.
HINDI	London (SOAS).
HISPANIC STUDIES	(See Spanish and Portuguese.)
HUNGARIAN	Cambridge, *London* (*Slavonic*).
ICELANDIC (Modern)	Leeds, London (University).
INDIAN STUDIES	Cambridge, London (SOAS).
IRANIAN STUDIES	Cambridge, London (SOAS).
IRISH	Manchester, Wales (Aberystwyth, Bangor).
ITALIAN	*Birmingham, Bristol, Cambridge,* Exeter, *Hull,* Leeds, *Liverpool, London* (*Bedford, Birkbeck, University, Westfield*), *Manchester,* Nottingham, *Oxford, Reading,* Warwick, *Wales* (Aberystwyth, *Bangor,* Cardiff, *Swansea*), *Aberdeen, Edinburgh, Glasgow.*
JAPANESE	Cambridge, London (SOAS), Oxford.
LATIN-AMERICAN STUDIES	*Birmingham, Bristol, Essex,* Leeds, Liverpool, London (King's, Queen Mary, Westfield), Manchester, *Newcastle,* Oxford, Sheffield, *Edinburgh, Glasgow.*
LINGUISTICS	Birmingham, Cambridge, Durham, Hull, Leeds, London (SOAS), Manchester, Newcastle, Reading, York, Wales (Bangor, Cardiff, Swansea), Edinburgh, Glasgow.

Languages	Universities
MALAY	London (SOAS).
MARATHI	London (SOAS).
NORWEGIAN	Cambridge, East Anglia, London: (University), Newcastle, Wales (Bangor), Glasgow.
ORIENTAL STUDIES	Cambridge, Durham, London (SOAS), Manchester, Oxford.
PALI	Cambridge, London (SOAS), Oxford.
PERSIAN	Cambridge, Durham, London (SOAS), Manchester, Oxford, Edinburgh.
PHONETICS	Cambridge, Leeds, London (SOAS, University), Manchester, Newcastle, Wales (Aberystwyth, Bangor, Cardiff), Edinburgh.
POLISH	Cambridge, *London* (*Slavonic*), Nottingham, Oxford, Glasgow, St. Andrews.
PORTUGUESE	Birmingham, Bristol, Cambridge, Durham, Leeds, Liverpool, London (King's, Queen Mary, Westfield), Manchester, Newcastle, Nottingham, Oxford, Sheffield, Wales (Cardiff), Glasgow, Belfast.
PRAKRIT	Cambridge.
PROVENÇAL	Birmingham, Cambridge, London (Westfield), Nottingham, Leeds, Sheffield, Wales (Bangor), Edinburgh.
RUMANIAN	Cambridge, *London* (*Slavonic, Westfield*).
RUSSIAN	*Birmingham, Bristol,* Cambridge, *Durham, East Anglia, Essex, Exeter, Hull, Keele, Leeds, Liverpool, London* (Queen Mary, *Slavonic*), *Manchester, Nottingham, Oxford, Sussex, Wales* (Aberystwyth, *Bangor, Cardiff, Swansea*), Aberdeen, *Edinburgh, Glasgow, St. Andrews, Belfast.*
RUSSIAN REGIONAL STUDIES	London (Slavonic), Glasgow.
SANSKRIT	Cambridge, London (SOAS), Oxford, Edinburgh.
SCANDINAVIAN STUDIES	London (University), Newcastle. (See also individual languages.)

Languages	Universities
SCOTTISH LANGUAGE	Glasgow, St. Andrews. (See also Celtic.)
SEMITIC LANGUAGES	Leeds, London (SOAS), Manchester, Oxford, St. Andrews.
SERBO-CROAT	Cambridge, *London (Slavonic)*, Nottingham, Oxford.
SINHALESE	London (SOAS).
SLAVONIC STUDIES	*Oxford, London (Slavonic), Nottingham.* (See also individual languages.)
SLOVAK	Cambridge, *London (Slavonic)*, Glasgow.
SLOVENE	*London (Slavonic).*
SOUTH-EAST EUROPEAN STUDIES	*London (Slavonic).*
SPANISH	*Birmingham, Bristol,* Cambridge, *Durham, Essex, Exeter, Hull, Leeds, Liverpool, London* (Birkbeck, *King's, Queen Mary,* University, *Westfield), Manchester, Newcastle, Nottingham, Oxford, Sheffield, Southampton, Wales* (Aberystwyth, *Cardiff), Aberdeen, Edinburgh, Glasgow, St. Andrews, Belfast.*
SWEDISH	Cambridge, Hull, London (University), Manchester, Newcastle, Nottingham, Wales (Aberystwyth, Cardiff), Aberdeen, Belfast.
TAMIL	London (SOAS).
TIBETAN	Cambridge.
TURKISH	Cambridge, Durham, London (SOAS), Manchester, Oxford, Edinburgh.
URDU	London (SOAS).
WELSH	Manchester, Wales (Aberystwyth, Bangor, Cardiff, Swansea), Lampeter, Belfast.

PRINTED BY R. & R. CLARK, LTD., EDINBURGH